KT-219-792

INTRODUCTION

PATTERNS OF SOIL DRYING IN THE PROXIMITY OF TREES ON CLAY SOILS

This Volume presents the accumulated results from three similar projects whose aim has been to determine the patterns of soil drying, both spatially and with time, which occur in the proximity of trees on clay soils. A total of 60 trees have been studied, covering a range of tree species and soil types (Figure 1). All of these studies have been in simple "open field" sites, mostly in parks and around playing fields, where there are none of the potential complications which occur in the urban situation, such as those produced by building foundations and trenches for underground services, or from the disturbance to water supply created by drainage systems and hard surfaces. The relevance and application of these results to these urban situations are considered in Volume 1.

The projects started in 1978 with instructions from Milton Keynes Development Corporation (MKDC). They were concerned about the potential effects of their extensive tree planting and landscape programme near many of the houses which were under construction at that time. A pilot project in 1978 looked at different methods for studying the effects of trees, particularly by the direct measurement of soil shrinkage using rod gauges and also using the neutron probe to measure moisture content, and concluded that the neutron probe provided the most useful information. In 1979 neutron probe access tubes were installed near 12 trees around Milton Keynes on the Oxford and Boulder Clay of that area, and on 3 trees in London on London Clay (funded by Tree Conservation Ltd (TCL)).

This work was greatly extended in 1981 under instructions from the National House-Building Council (NHBC) who wanted additional information on which to base a revision of the 1974 edition of their Practice Note 3 "Root damage by trees - siting of dwellings and special precautions", as it was then called. This involved an additional 24 trees (3 of which were those previously funded by TCL), which provided a wider range of species and clay types.

The projects were further extended in 1983 under instruction from the Department of Environment (DoE) by the addition of a further 24 trees. 12 of these extended the range of species, and 12 were plane trees on a single site on London Clay, which were used to investigate the effects of different pruning regimes on soil moisture deficits.

In 1985 the information from all of these projects was used as one of the main sources of data for the revision of NHBC Practice Note 3 "Building near Trees" (and in the subsequent revision of this guidance in 1992 as NHBC Standards Chapter 4.2).

The main projects went into abeyance after 1985, but with arrangements for them to be reactivated in the event of an extreme drought. Such conditions occurred in 1989, and readings were taken in that year and again in 1991 on a selection of the trees. These demonstrated the value of monitoring the long-term changes in soil moisture content, and so readings have continued on a regular bi-annual basis since 1992 on 21 of the trees, with this work funded by the Department of Environment.

Each of the 60 trees included in the projects usually have 5 neutron probe access tubes, giving a total of 292 tubes (some trees share a common control tube). During the course of the project a total of 3,203 profiles have been determined at varying times from these tubes. Each profile involves between 24 to 35 readings, dependent on the length of the tube. To date there have been 94,800 individual measurements of soil moisture content. This book presents all of the results of this unique mass of information.

Species	Clay type					Total
	London	Gault	Oxford	Boulder	Clay silt	
Horse chestnut	4	3	2	2	-	**11**
Lime	1	-	2	2	-	**5**
Norway maple	2	-	-	2	-	**4**
Oak	2	-	-	2	-	**4**
Plane	12	-	-	-	-	**12**
Poplar	3	2	2	2	1	**10**
Silver birch	2	1	-	1	-	**4**
Whitebeam	2	-	-	2	-	**4**
Leyland cypress	2	2	-	2	-	**6**
Total	**30**	**8**	**6**	**15**	**1**	**60**

Figure 1

Number of trees in projects, classified by species and soil type.

Number	Species	Clay	Location	Sponsor	Page
1	Horse chestnut	London	King Edward Park, Wembley	NHBC *	14
2	Horse chestnut	London	King Edward Park, Wembley	NHBC	22
3	Horse chestnut	London	Barham Park, Wembley	NHBC *	26
4	Horse chestnut	London	Woodside Park, N22	TCL/NHBC	30
5	Horse chestnut	Gault	St. John's College, Cambridge	NHBC *	34
6	Horse chestnut	Gault	St. John's College, Cambridge	NHBC *	42
7	Horse chestnut	Gault	Wimpole Hall, Nr Cambridge	NHBC	48
8	Horse chestnut	Oxford	College of F.E., Bletchley	MKDC *	52
9	Horse chestnut	Oxford	Willen Hospice, Willen	MKDC	58
10	Horse chestnut	Boulder	Church Green, Bletchley	MKDC	62
11	Horse chestnut	Boulder	Turnberry Close, Bletchley	MKDC	66
12	Lime	London	Woodside Park, N22	TCL/NHBC	70
13	Lime	Oxford	Willen Priory, Willen	MKDC	74
14	Lime	Oxford	Willen Priory, Willen	MKDC	78
15	Lime	Boulder	C of E School, Bletchley	MKDC *	82
16	Lime	Boulder	Stacey Hall, Wolverton	MKDC	88
17	Norway maple	London	Centenary Park, Stanmore	DoE	94
18	Norway maple	London	Centenary Park, Stanmore	DoE	98
19	Norway maple	Boulder	The Ridgeway, Welwyn	DoE	102
20	Norway maple	Boulder	Parkway Junior School, Welwyn	DoE	106
21	Oak	London	Roxeth Recreation Ground, Harrow	DoE *	110
22	Oak	London	Roxeth Recreation Ground, Harrow	DoE *	116
23	Oak	Boulder	Boxfield, Welwyn	DoE *	122
24	Oak	Boulder	Boxfield, Welwyn	DoE	126
25	Poplar	London	Woodcock Park, Brent	NHBC *	130
26	Poplar	London	Woodcock Park, Brent	NHBC *	138
27	Poplar	London	Downhills Park, N17	TCL/NHBC	146
28	Poplar	Gault	Pembroke College, Cambridge	NHBC	150
29	Poplar	Gault	Pembroke College, Cambridge	NHBC	156
30	Poplar	Oxford	Merlin Gardens, Bedford	MKDC *	160
31	Poplar	Oxford	Putnoe Green, Bedford	MKDC *	166
32	Poplar	Boulder	Rickley Park, Bletchley	MKDC	172
33	Poplar	Boulder	Rickley Park, Bletchley	MKDC	178
34	Poplar	Clay silt	Barn Elms Park, SW13	NHBC	184
35	Silver birch	London	Barham Park, Wembley	NHBC *	188
36	Silver birch	London	Fryent Way, NW9	NHBC	194
37	Silver birch	Gault	Emmanuel College, Cambridge	NHBC	198
38	Silver birch	Boulder	The Don, Bletchley	NHBC	202
39	Whitebeam	London	Preston Park, Wembley	DoE	206
40	Whitebeam	London	Canons Park, Edgeware	DoE	210
41	Whitebeam	Boulder	Chequers, Welwyn	DoE	214
42	Whitebeam	Boulder	Russellcroft, Welwyn	DoE	222
43	Leyland cypress	London	Eton Grove Open Space, NW9	NHBC *	226
44	Leyland cypress	London	Eton Grove Open Space, NW9	NHBC	230
45	Leyland cypress	Gault	Corpus Christi College, Cambridge	NHBC *	234
46	Leyland cypress	Gault	Corpus Christi College, Cambridge	NHBC *	240
47	Leyland cypress	Boulder	The Leys, Bletchley	NHBC *	246
48	Leyland cypress	Boulder	Rickley Park, Bletchley	NHBC	250
49 - 60	Plane	London	Cottenham Park, SW20	DoE *	256 - 299

(* Regular readings continued to 1995 under sponsorship of Department of Environment)

Figure 2

Summary of trees included in project

3520880949

TREE ROOT DAMAGE TO BUILDINGS

Volume 2
PATTERNS OF SOIL DRYING IN PROXIMITY TO TREES ON CLAY SOILS

P.G. BIDDLE

M.A., D.Phil., F.Arbor.A., M.A.E.

Cover design. Oak (Tree 22)
- see page 116.

First published 1998

by

Willowmead Publishing Ltd.
Ickleton Road, Wantage, OX12 9JA

© P.G.Biddle 1998

ISBN for complete set of 2 volumes: 0 9533086 0 X

ISBN Volume 2: 0 9533086 2 6

All rights reserved.

Except as noted below, no part of this book may be reprinted,
or reproduced or utilized in any form or by any electronic,
mechanical or other means, now known or hereafter invented,
including photocopying and recording,
or in any information storage and retrieval system,
without permission in writing from the Publisher.
Such permission need not be sought for the reproduction by any means
of short extracts, provided each extract is clearly acknowledged,
and is solely for research, personal study or legal purposes.

This publication contains Crown copyright material from research projects
which were undertaken for the Department of the Environment, Transport and the Regions
and is reproduced with the permission of the Controller of Her Majesty's Stationery Office.

Printed by Acorn Press Swindon Ltd.
Westmead Drive, Westmead Industrial Estate, Swindon, SN5 7UU

MATERIALS AND METHODS

The Neutron probe

All of the field readings of soil moisture content have been made using a Neutron Probe, or 'Neutron Soil Moisture Gauge' to give it its full title. The principle of measuring soil moisture in this way was first proposed in the 1940's, but the practical field development has only come as a result of subsequent advances in electronics. The two Probes which have been used in this study, like most probes in this country, are based on designs developed at the Institute of Hydrology [1] in Wallingford, and are known as Wallingford Neutron Probes. At the start of the project in 1978 a single probe was used, this being manufactured by D.A. Pitman Ltd. (type 225.D1). A second probe, manufactured by Didcot Instrument Company Ltd., was purchased in August 1983. Both probes have been used in all subsequent work; the probes are interchangeable with no detectable difference in the results, but for convenience the same probe is usually used at each access tube.

The main bulk of the instrument is in the carrying case and the transport shield for the radio-active source (Figure 3). Hinged at the top of the case is the ratescaler which calculates and displays the results on a digital display. The ratescaler is connected to the probe by a cable which is also used for lowering the probe, with a wheel measure on the cable to record the depth of the probe. The important parts of the instrument are in the probe, which is lowered into the soil down aluminium 'access tubes' which have been carefully inserted into the ground. These tubes allow repeated measurements of the moisture content of the surrounding soil to be made at any subsequent time. The probe contains a radioactive source consisting of a small encapsulated unit of Americium[241]/Beryllium (50mi/C) which emits fast neutrons. Such neutrons will be slowed down and reflected by certain atoms, in particular hydrogen, to generate a 'cloud' of slow neutrons around the source. The density of this cloud is determined by a boron trifluoride detector which is mounted in the probe close to the neutron source. The electrical pulses from the detector are amplified before passing up the cable to the ratescaler for calculation and display.

Most chemical elements within the soil have some ability to slow and scatter neutrons, but the most effective element is hydrogen which is, of course, a constituent of water (H_2O). The aluminium access tubes are virtually transparent to the neutrons. Apart from water, the other main source of hydrogen in soil is in organic matter (roots etc.), but this is much less abundant than water. Hydrogen is not a significant constituent of other soil molecules, except as bound water. The elements within the dry soil matrix have some neutron-absorbing ability, which for a given soil is proportional to its dry bulk density, and this produces a background contribution to the count rate. This background count will remain constant for any soil, but if there is any change

---

[1] Further details of the theory and practical application of the Neutron Probe are contained in "Neutron Probe Practice", J.P. Bell (1976). Report 19 of the Institute of Hydrology, Wallingford.

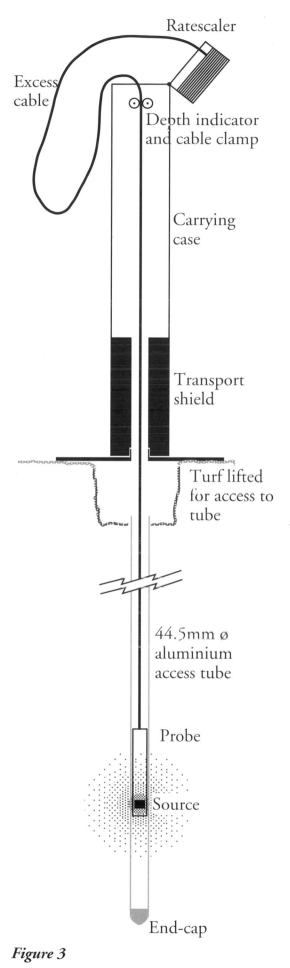

Figure 3
Diagram of Neutron probe

in the water content it will produce a change in the count rate in direct proportion to the water content. For this reason the neutron probe is particularly valuable in situations where non-destructive measurements of moisture change are required in the same location on successive occasions.

The sphere of influence of the probe is dependant on the probability of any fast neutron which is emitted eventually being scattered back to the detector. The greatest influence is in the immediate vicinity of the source, with this diminishing in accordance with the inverse square law. In practice the effective radius is about 150mm in wet soil, increasing to about 300mm in a very dry soil; the indicated moisture value is a mean for a sphere of the effective radius, centred at the measuring point. The optimum spacing for readings for defining the whole moisture profile will be slightly less than this radius, with no greater resolution gained by decreasing this figure. For this reason, and because it simplifies the calculation of moisture deficits, readings were routinely taken at 100mm intervals down the access tubes (except for a few sets of the early readings where they were taken at 200mm intervals in the lower parts of the tubes where there was no significant change occurring).

The reading which is obtained from the soil (R) is converted to its moisture content value by reference to a water standard (Rw). This water standard is the reading obtained from an access tube surrounded by water, in practice using a tube standing in a large butt of water. The value of the water standard differs for the two probes, and also slowly diminishes with the radio active decay of the source. However, as the half life of Americium [241] is 450 years, this rate of decay is very slow.

For accurate measurement of soil moisture content (θ) ideally one should calibrate the readings to the specific soil conditions of the site, and even to the changes of soil at different depths. This would be impractical, and it is quite sufficient to use standard calibration curves which are appropriate to the Wallingford Probe; these are for:

Clay: $\theta = (0.958\frac{R}{Rw} - 0.012) \times 100$

Loam: $\theta = (0.867\frac{R}{Rw} - 0.016) \times 100$

Silts, sands and gravels: $\theta = (0.790\frac{R}{Rw} - 0.024) \times 100$

All of the results have therefore been calculated using the first of these calibration curves, appropriate for clay. This may produce some inaccuracy in the absolute value of moisture content if there are localised bands of sand or loam within the clay. However, as the slopes of the curves are similar, it makes very little difference to the <u>changes</u> in moisture content, which is the prime interest of this study.

For instance, if the clay calibration curve is used, a neutron probe reading of 385 would indicate a moisture content of 40.0% (if Rw = 895):

$$\theta = (0.958 \frac{385}{895} - 0.012) \times 100 = 40.0$$

If the loam curve is applied to these same readings the moisture content would be 35.7%, and if the sand curve is used the result would be 31.6%, i.e. if the soil is sand rather than clay, the use of the clay curve would over-estimate the actual value by 40.0 - 31.6 = 8.4%. If the next set of readings gives a neutron probe reading of 478, application of the clay curve would indicate a 10% increase in moisture content to 50.0%, whereas application of the sand curve would indicate an increase in moisture content from 31.6% to 39.8%, which is an increase of 8.2%. Use of the incorrect curve therefore only gives an error of 10.0 - 8.2 = 1.8% in the value for the change of moisture content. In practice, as most measurements are in fairly uniform clay, the errors in determining changes in moisture content will be negligible.

The accuracy of the readings is also influenced by the duration of the count period, with readings averaged over a longer period obviously being more accurate than over a short period. Either 16 or 64 second periods are provided by the instrument; virtually all of the readings have used the longer and more accurate 64 second period. The random counting error with the 64 second count will be about $\pm0.7\%$ at the 95% probability level (the exact error varies slightly, dependant on the values).

The measurements of soil moisture content (θ) which is obtained with the probe is on a volumetric basis (θ = volume of water per unit volume of soil, x 100). This value of moisture volume % therefore differs from the more commonly used measurement of moisture content (w) which is on a gravimetric basis (mass of water expressed as a percentage of the dry soil mass). The relationship between these methods of defining moisture content, and the methods for converting between the values, are described in Volume 1 (page 57).

The use of volumetric moisture content greatly simplifies calculation of the soil moisture deficits, as it provides an immediate measure of the volume of water within the soil, without the need to determine the specific gravity. Thus, a 100mm layer thickness of soil with a moisture volume of 43.5% contains 43.5mm of water (see also Volume 1, page 51). If this soil dries to a moisture volume of 30% it would contain 30mm of water, indicating a moisture deficit of 13.5mm. With the readings taken at 100mm intervals there is therefore no need to include the layer thickness in this calculation of moisture deficit.

Access tube installation

The access tubes are 44.5mm O.D. aluminium tubes, of 1.6mm wall thickness. These are carefully installed into the soil to ensure as tight a fit as possible.

To achieve this a hole is first reamed out using a set of mild steel guide tubes of 44.25mm O.D. The lower end of the guide tube has a 45° internally bevelled cutting edge, and the top end is strengthened with a collar to receive the blows when it is rammed into the soil. A set of guide tubes is used, with lengths of 1, 2, 3, and 4m. These are used in combination with a set of augers, each of which are 0.15m longer than the corresponding tube, i.e. 1.15m auger is used with the 1.0m guide tube. The auger head which is used is a 30mm diameter Edelmann.

The hole is reamed out by first clearing a small patch of turf, and placing over this a thick steel plate with a central 45mm diameter hole. This provides a suitable working platform and helps to prevent any wobbling of the guide tube while it is being driven in or extracted. The 1m tube is placed vertically into position through the plate, and the auger is then inserted through the tube and used to remove the soil to its full length, i.e. to 15cm beyond the end of the guide tube. The auger is then withdrawn, and the tube is driven down by 10cm using an internal ram. The auger is then used to clear the soil which has been trimmed off by the cutting edge of the tube, and then to drill on down to 15cm below the base of the tube. In this way the auger is always working just ahead of the cutting edge of the guide tube. The process is repeated, lowering the tube by 10cm on each occasion, until the 1m tube is inserted. This tube is then withdrawn by gripping it with a ball cone clamp, and lifting this clamp with a rack jack supported on the steel plate. This process is then repeated successively with the 2m, 3m, and if appropriate 4m, guide tubes. The shorter tubes can usually be driven into the pre-augered holes using a hand-held internal ram, but the longer tubes usually require an Atlas Copco mechanical hammer with a specially modified head to fit the strengthened collar of the guide tube. Withdrawing the longer tubes, even with the aid of the rack jack, requires considerable force and winding.

As soon as the final ream is removed, the permanent aluminium access tube is driven down into the hole. The bottom of this tube has been shut off with a bullet-shaped moulded aluminium cap. The top end of the tube is trimmed off to about 15cm below the soil surface, and sealed with a rubber bung. This is then covered by the turf or other ambient surface material so as to hide the tube. A piece of metal is placed just below ground level in this covering material, and when readings are taken this metal is located with a metal detector (aided by careful measurements from surrounding features), and a small piece of turf is removed to expose the bung and the top of the access tube. Some of the initial access tubes which were installed were covered by a vandal-proof screw cap, mounted in a small piece of concrete and buried just below the surface of the soil. However, a simple rubber bung was found more convenient to use and caused less disturbance of the surrounding soil. Only one of the tubes was vandalised despite the work generating considerable interest from local children.

Installation of the access tubes was done in late summer, when the soil was as dry as possible. Any subsequent rehydration and swelling of the clay helps to ensure a tight fit. Inevitably further drying of the soil will cause it to shrink and potentially create a very slight gap between the tube and the soil, but such gaps are unlikely to be any greater than the naturally occurring cracks within the normal soil structure. Occasional problems were encountered with stones or gravel catching on the cutting edge and being carried down, possibly scoring the adjacent soil; any significant problem of this type caused the hole to be abandoned and relocated elsewhere.

Figure 4

Preparing for the installation of an access tube. The auger is ready to drill down until its handle is flush with the top of the guide tube. The internal ram is to the left, and the rack jack, ball cone clamp and other extracting equipment to the right.

Site selection

The remits from the sponsors for the projects required the inclusion of various tree species on different clay types. The types of clay which were selected were:-

i) Gault, from the Cambridge area where it tends to have a particularly high plasticity index.

ii) London Clay, primarily from the north west London area where again it tends to have a high plasticity index.

iii) Oxford Clay, from the Milton Keynes area (the Development Corporation being sponsors for this part of the work).

iv) Boulder Clay, from the Milton Keynes area, and other localities convenient for the other sites.

v) Clay silt, derived from Thames alluvium.

Areas where these soils outcrop in the appropriate localities were identified with the aid of the relevant Geological Survey maps (scale 1:50000 or 1:63360).

The following species of tree were included in the project:-

Horse chestnut	-	*Aesculus hippocastanum*
Lime	-	*Tilia x europaea*
Norway maple	-	*Acer platanoides*
Oak	-	*Quercus robur*
Poplar (hybrid black)	-	*Populus x euramericana*
Silver birch	-	*Betula pendula*
Whitebeam*	-	*Sorbus aria*
Leyland cypress	-	X *Cupressocyparis leylandii*
Plane	-	*Platanus x acerifolia*

* All of the whitebeam were grafted onto hawthorn (*Crataegus monogyna*) rootstock.

For a tree to be suitable for study, it needed to be growing in a reasonably isolated situation where the access tubes could be located clear of the influence of other trees. Some of the trees were individual specimens; others formed part of a row or group, provided adjacent trees were not likely to be having a dominating influence. Features such as ditches, drains, or roads were avoided, but other features such as natural slopes or proximity of paths and other small features were deemed acceptable. In practice the majority of suitable sites were found in public parks, playing fields, or other areas of public open space. Any tree past the stage of early maturity was deemed acceptable. Despite the comparatively broad parameters for suitability, it proved surprising difficult to locate suitable trees.

The species, clay type, and location of the 60 trees which were used in the various projects are listed in Figure 2.

Location of access tubes

The majority of trees had five access tubes located in their proximity. Four of these were close to the tree, at a distance usually defined as being a proportion of the height of the tree at the time of installation. For the majority of trees these proportions were 0.2, 0.4, 0.6, and 0.8 x tree height. However, for the poplar and oak these distances were increased to 0.25, 0.5, 1.0 and 1.5 x height. For the Leyland cypress the distances were reduced to 0.15, 0.3, 0.5, and 0.75 x height. The fifth tube was intended as a control, and is referred to as the "control tube". It was located in similar conditions but beyond any potential influence of the tree. This was usually at a distance of twice the height of the tree, increasing this to three times the height for the poplar and oak. The exact distances vary in some cases, particularly with the trees in the initial project. The proportions relative to the height of the trees have altered as the trees have grown.

The tubes are normally located along a single radius out from the tree, but in some cases there are minor deviations to avoid other features or the influence of other trees (particularly for the control tube). The direction relative to slopes and to the north point was determined solely by the most suitable alignment, and therefore produces a range of differing situations.

Timing of readings

A set of readings down a single access tube is a lengthy process, typically taking about 45 minutes. It involves recording for 64 seconds at 100mm intervals from a depth of 0.3m to the base of the access tube, usually a depth of about 3.7m. Even with two neutron probes working on adjacent access tubes it takes at least 2 hours to complete the readings at a single tree. These practical considerations limit the number of readings per year.

At the start of the project a complete set of readings was taken at all of the access tubes on all of the trees each spring and each autumn, as far as possible trying to get these readings to correspond to the time of year when the soil is at its wettest and driest respectively. They were also taken from one or two of the access tubes on a selection of the trees at more frequent intervals. These more frequent readings show the progressive changes in soil moisture content through the seasons, and helped to show when the soil was at its wettest and driest.

After about the first three years of each project the spring readings were discontinued as they were giving virtually identical results each year. The autumn readings were continued through until at least 1984 and in most cases also taken in autumn 1985. 1984 was a very dry year, and provided an indication of the soil drying occurring during such conditions. It was considered that the readings were becoming repetitious, and regular readings therefore ceased, with arrangements to recommence if there were extreme drought conditions in a future year. Such conditions were deemed to have developed during 1989, and a further set of autumn readings were taken that year. The results were generally very similar to those of 1984, and for this reason no readings were taken in 1990. With hindsight the lack of readings that year was an unfortunate omission.

No arrangements had been made for readings in 1991, but information in the late autumn of that year from the Building Research Establishment project at Chattenden indicated that considerable moisture deficits had developed. Hasty arrangements were made to take readings on most of the trees which still remained (a total of 26), with this work being completed during the period from 25th October to 12th November. Rain during October had certainly caused some recovery, but the underlying deficits were still present.

Since 1991 the readings have been continued on 21 of the trees. As many of these show evidence of significant changes in the spring readings compared with the start of the project, the readings in 1992, 1993 and 1994 were taken each spring and autumn.

Laboratory soil analyses

Soil samples were taken at various depths while some of the access tubes were being drilled. These were used for soil classification tests, in accordance with standard techniques defined in BS 1377:1975 "Method of Test for Soils for Civil Engineering Purposes". Liquid limit was determined by the 1 point method using the Cassegrande apparatus.

PRESENTATION OF RESULTS

The results for each of the 60 trees are presented from page 14 to 299; the page numbers for the individual trees are included in Figure 2. The information presented for each tree generally follows a similar format, and includes the following details:-

Site description

Location A brief description is given, together with the six figure Ordnance Survey map reference.

Size The height of the tree is given, as recorded at the start of the project and at the time of the most recent set of readings. In all cases heights have been estimated visually, using a convenient ranging rod (such as the 4m guide tube), as the basis for the estimation. For most trees the breast height diameter (bhd) is also given. This is calculated from the girth, measured at 1.5m above ground level, divided by π.

Current status It is noted whether readings are still in progress every spring and autumn; in all cases these readings are likely to continue for the foreseeable future.

Many of the sites have been destroyed, either because the trees have been felled or because of substantial disturbance to the access tubes.

Some of the trees were producing very similar and repetitious results so that routine readings have been discontinued; a brief reason for this is noted.

Site A brief description of the site, including details of other trees in the vicinity, the direction of the access tubes relative to the tree, any significant slope, the ground cover and any other significant feature.

Soil profile The soil types which were recorded at the time that the access tubes were installed are recorded by descriptive diagrams, using the symbols as recommended in Table 11 of BS 5930:1981, including combined symbols for composite soil types. The symbols used and their descriptive terms are shown in Figure 5.

Across the top of the soil profiles, details are given on the distance of the access tube from the tree (measured from the centre of the tree), and also this distance expressed as a fraction of the height of the tree at the start of the project.

Soil classification tests Results are given for the standard soil classification tests, including details on the depth of sampling, and the distance from the tree.

Photograph A photograph of the tree is presented for most of the trees. These are either black and white photographs taken at the start of the project, or subsequent colour photographs. If trees have changed significantly in appearance, before and after photographs are included. Some trees or sites had been destroyed before suitable photographs were taken.

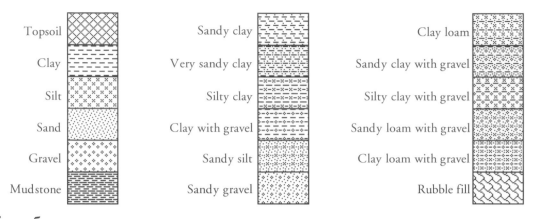

Figure 5

Symbols used for soil descriptions

Spring soil moisture content profiles

These graphs plot the moisture content against the depth for each of the access tubes (example at Figure 6). The profiles shown are the average moisture content of the readings in the spring, recorded over the first three years of the project (referred to as "**spring average**"). This use of the average of three sets of readings helps to eliminate random counting error, and also the variations which can occur near the surface as a result of the weather conditions immediately prior to the readings (in some cases, if readings were taken late in the spring, some drying may have occurred as a result of the effects of grass; conversely recent rain can produce higher than normal moisture content values).

If soil conditions are comparatively uniform across the site, the five profiles will be very similar (for instance tree 21, page 110). However, very few of the trees have such similar results at each of the access tubes. The variation can either be attributed to variation in the natural moisture content profiles as a result of variable soil conditions, or because of the existence of a persistent soil moisture deficit in the spring when these readings were being taken. Determining whether this variation is due to soil conditions or to a persistent deficit is discussed in further detail in Chapter 13, page 209 of Volume I.

For these graphs, and for other graphs which compare the conditions at the different access tubes, standard symbols and colours are used to denote each of the access tubes, as indicated in Figure 7.

The horizontal axis to these graphs covers a range of at least 25% moisture volume percentage (i.e. from 30 - 55% in the example in Figure 6). A greater range, at a smaller scale, is used where it is necessary to encompass the full range of values.

In all cases the readings start at a depth of 0.3m. The readings at shallower depth are of negligible relevance and would be affected by the removal of turf to expose the top of the buried tubes.

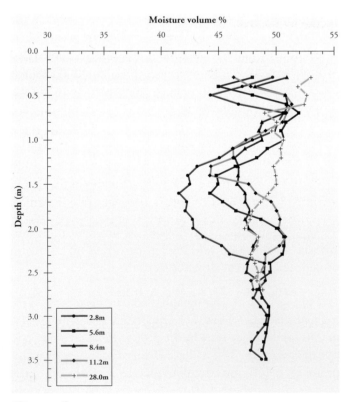

Figure 6

Example of spring soil moisture content profiles (tree 1) at the five access tubes at varying distance from the tree (m).

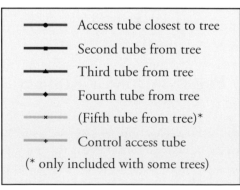

Figure 7

Symbols used for different access tubes

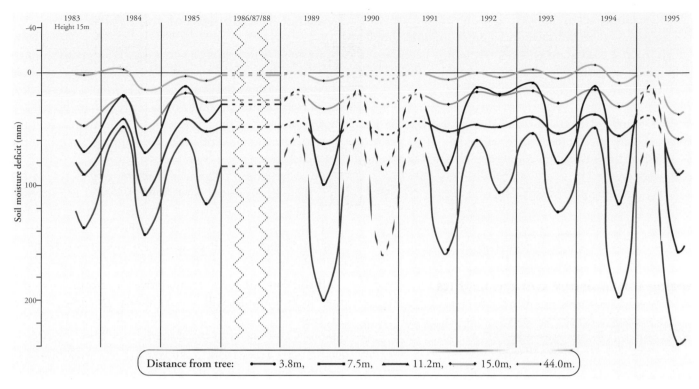

Figure 8

Example of seasonal fluctuation in soil moisture deficit (no readings from 1986 - 1988 and in 1990, and no readings in spring 1989, 1991 and 1995). (tree 23)

Seasonal fluctuations in soil moisture deficit at 1m depth

These diagrams summarise the seasonal changes in soil moisture deficit which have occurred between spring and autumn of each year for each of the access tubes (example at Figure 8). The calculations of soil moisture deficit (see Volume 1, page 51 for method of calculation) are all made by comparison to the **control profile** . The control profile is based on the spring average readings at the control access tube down to its base. If the other tubes go deeper than the control, the spring average readings from the most distant available tube are included. It is assumed that the control profile provides the most reliable indication of the equilibrium moisture content of the soil at field capacity in the absence of any drying effect from root activity either by trees or other vegetation. By definition, the soil moisture deficits in the spring at the control tube will average zero. The autumn values at the control tube usually show a slight fluctuation compared with the spring readings, reflecting soil drying by grass or other local vegetation. As all of the soil moisture deficits are calculated below a depth of 1m, the seasonal effects from grass are generally very small.

The other sets of lines show the results from the other access tubes, using the standard colours and symbols (Figure 7). As these are all calculated by comparison to the control profile, if they are displaced below the zero line it may imply the existence of a persistent moisture deficit (see Chapter 6, page 88 of Volume I).

Where the amplitude of seasonal fluctuation is similar to that of the control tube, it implies that root activity from the tree is not having any significant additional influence (at least below 1m depth). Where the amplitude of fluctuation is greater than that of the control, it implies an influence by the tree.

Readings were not taken in some years, particularly 1986/87/88, and also 1990. Spring readings were also omitted in some years. The lines are shown as intermittent dashes during these periods, in some cases indicating assumed values which appear appropriate to the readings recorded in adjacent years.

The height of the tree is shown at the top of the graph (just beneath the year). A note is also made of any significant changes in the size of the crown of the tree as a result of pruning or storm damage.

Maximum soil drying in various years

One, or more usually two, graphs are used to show the driest profile recorded in each year of the project, usually for the access tube closest to the tree. Where results have only been recorded for five or less years all of these profiles are combined on a single graph; where results have been recorded for five or more years they are divided between two graphs which are shown immediately adjacent to each other across the page.

These profiles all use a standard colour scheme and symbol for each year, as indicated in Figure 9. In other graphs which use these standard colours, where it is necessary to distinguish the spring from autumn readings, solid symbols have been used for the spring readings.

The graphs of maximum soil drying also include the spring average profile for the relevant tube. This is shown as a dashed line, using the colour appropriate for that access tube (Figure 7).

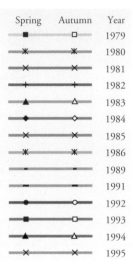

Spring	Autumn	Year
■	□	1979
✳	✳	1980
✕	✕	1981
+	+	1982
▲	△	1983
◆	◇	1984
✕	✕	1985
✳	✳	1986
▬	▬	1989
▬	▬	1991
●	○	1992
■	□	1993
▲	△	1994
✕	✕	1995

Figure 9

Colours and symbols for different years.

Seasonal development of soil drying

In some years readings were taken at intervals through the year at some of the access tubes. The profiles (example at Figure 10) show the progressive development of soil drying during the summer and, where readings have been taken during the winter, the subsequent rehydration during the winter. These graphs also include the spring average profile (as a dashed line) as a basis for comparison. Where these readings have been taken at the access tube closest to the tree, these lines are shown in varying shades of pink/red, with these colours increasing in density during the summer. The driest profile recorded for the year uses the standard colour and symbol (——●——) appropriate to the access tube closest to the tree. Different shades of red are used for profiles when the soil is rehydrating.

Likewise, shades of purple are used for the successive readings taken on the second access tube from the tree.

Adjacent to each of the graphs which present the profiles of the seasonal development of soil drying is a secondary graph which presents this information in terms of the development of soil moisture deficit during the season (example at Figure 11). These soil moisture deficits are all calculated by comparison with the spring average profile. The development of deficit during the season is shown for a depth of 0.3m below ground level, and also the depths of 1.0 and 2.0m below ground level. Different colours are used to distinguish these lines for the different access tubes.

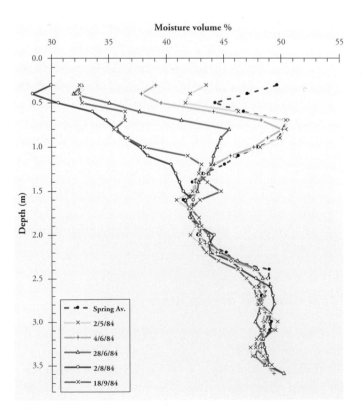

Figure 10

Example of profiles showing seasonal development of soil drying (2.8m from tree 1, 1984).

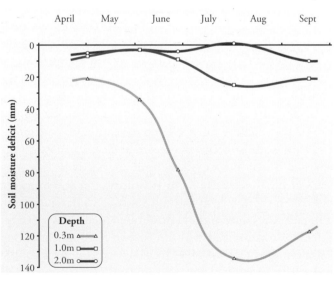

Figure 11

Example of seasonal development of soil moisture deficit at various depths, derived from moisture content profiles in Figure 10 (2.8m from tree 1, 1984).

Seasonal and persistent deficits

These graphs indicate, by appropriate shading, the relevant changes in moisture content which have occurred during the project (example at Figure 12). The results which are shown must inevitably depend on which profiles are selected for presenting this information. The graphs generally include some, or all, of the following profiles:-

i) control profile;

ii) a spring profile from near the start of the project;

iii) the driest autumn profile;

iv) one, or in some cases two, of the spring profiles from near the end of the project.

Shading is then used to indicate the following changes:-

i) Seasonal. [ ] The difference between the driest autumn profile and the spring profile at the start of the project;

ii) Semi-persistent. [ ] The difference between profiles in spring 1992 and spring 1994, to indicate the persistent deficit which developed during the dry period of 1989 to 1991, but which was not maintained in subsequent years;

iii) Persistent. [ ] The difference between the spring profile at the start of the project and at the end of the project where the soil has become drier during this period;

iv) Rehydration. [ ] The difference between the spring profile at the start of the project and at the end of the project where the soil has become wetter during this period;

v) Assumed persistent. [ ] The difference between the control profile and the next wettest set of readings (which will usually be the spring profile at the start or end of the project, depending on whether the soil has been getting drier or wetter during the period). The relevance and validity of the assumed persistent deficits is considered in further detail in Chapter 6 of Volume I (page 88).

Reduction in soil moisture content and soil moisture deficit.

Diagrams to show the spatial patterns of soil drying are always presented together on the same page. The method used for presenting these diagrams is shown in Figures 13 and 14 (overleaf). Suitable dates are selected, usually to show drying in a particularly dry year. For some trees additional pairs of diagrams are included to show development or rehydration of a persistent deficit, or other features.

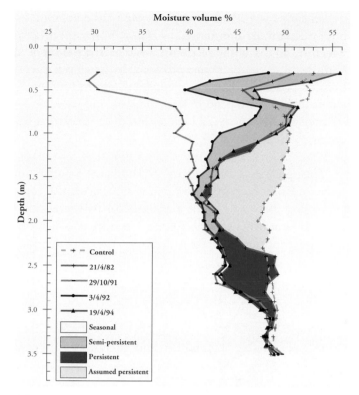

Figure 12

Example of seasonal and persistent deficits (no rehydration in this example). (Tree 1, 2.8m from tree).

The horizontal scale in these figures depicts the distance of the access tubes from the tree, with the centre of the tree being above the left hand axis (the tree is included in diagrammatic form in Figure 13). To allow comparison between trees of differing size (height), the scale for the horizontal axis is adjusted so that a distance equal to the tree height is always the same, this is shown by a marker on the underside of the axis line. The location of the access tubes is related to this distance, and is shown along the upper side of the horizontal axis. At this scale the control tube would usually be far off the page to the right; for this reason there is a discontinuity in the horizontal scale, with the results for the control tube shown to the right of this break.

The vertical scale on these diagrams shows the depth in metres. A symbol ($\perp$) is used to show the depth of each of the access tubes at the appropriate position; the access tube therefore extends from the mark on the horizontal scale to this symbol at the base. These diagrams also include a line showing the depth of foundations which would be advocated by the NHBC guidelines appropriate to the species of tree and soil conditions.

Figure 14 shows a typical set of results, but including the actual data on which they are based, to show how they are produced. The data is obtained from a computer spreadsheet, and is superimposed on a computer-based drawing programme with the decimal points aligned on the position of the access tube (a font (Geneva) with an appropriate line spacing is used to match the vertical scale). When the data from all five of the access tubes has been superimposed in this way, the diagrams are produced by visual interpretation of the data, linking the comparable results for the different tubes with the aid of bezier curves, and based on an assumption that there is a logical pattern of soil drying between adjacent tubes.

The upper diagram in Figure 14 shows the reduction in soil moisture content on the relevant date, usually compared with the spring average readings for that access tube (or with some other specified date). The difference in moisture content on these dates is shown by the colour and intensity of the shading. For this purpose the lower limit of accuracy below which the differences are non-significant is taken as 0.7%. As shown by the key to this diagram, the colours of shading correspond to non-significant (i.e. 0.7%) - 2.5%, 2.5 - 5.0%, 5.0 - 7.5%, 7.5 - 10%, 10 - 15%, 15 - 20% and greater than 20%. When interpreting the results, a single anomalous reading may be ignored, or considered as an average with adjacent values.

The lower diagram in Figure 14 shows the soil moisture deficits. These are calculated by summing the values of reduction in moisture content (as shown in the upper diagram), working progressively up from the base of the tube. Contours are then drawn to link the similar values in each of the access tubes. These contours are at intervals of 25mm for soil moisture deficit in excess of 25mm, and also at 15mm, 10mm, 5mm and 2.5mm. A moisture deficit of 2.5mm corresponds approximately to the lower limit of statistical significance, but as both this value and the 5mm contour are of dubious accuracy and relevance, they are shown as a dotted line.

In both diagrams the values for the control tube to the right of the discontinuity are shown by horizontal areas of shading or contours, although in practice they will merge with the rest of the diagram.

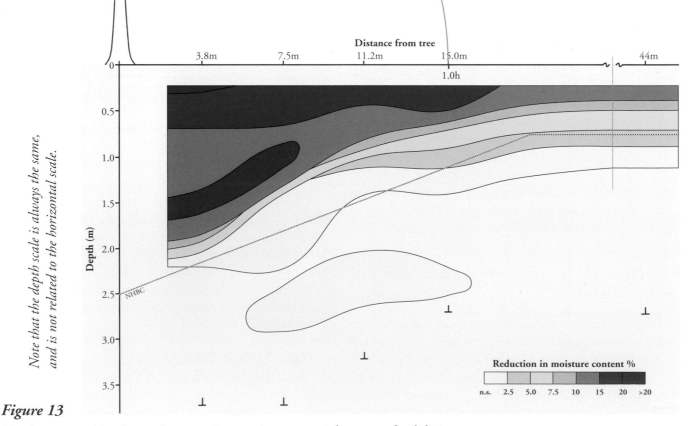

Figure 13

Tree location and height in relation to diagam showing spatial pattern of soil drying.

Reduction in soil moisture content on 21/9/89 compared with spring average

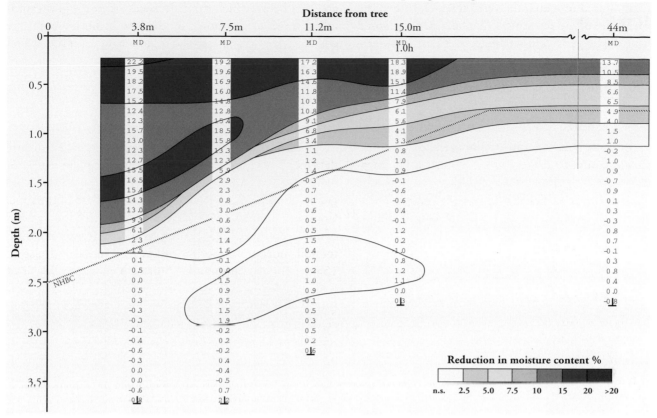

Soil moisture deficit on 21/9/89 compared with spring average

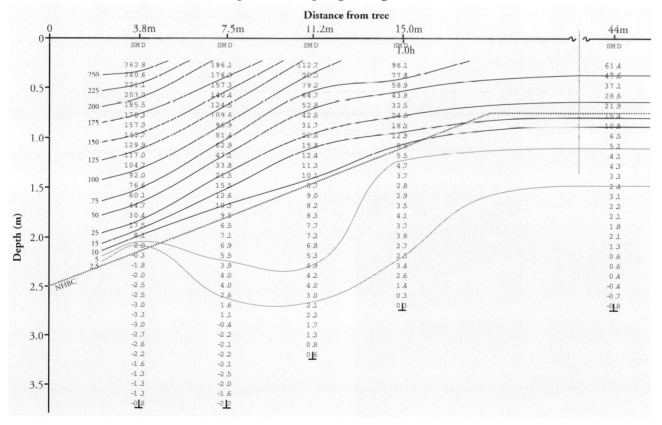

Figure 14

Method for deriving diagrams showing reduction in soil moisture content and soil moisture deficit (including data) (tree 23).

Horse chestnut
London Clay

Location: King Edward VII Park,   Tree height: 14m (1981); 15m (1994)
Wembley   Map. ref: TQ 184 856   b.h.d.: 67cm (1992).

Current status: Routine readings still in progress. Tube 8.4m from tree vandalised soon after insertion, but reinstated in April 1994.

Site: Ash tree 8m to the north. Access tubes in close mown grass to the west of the tree. Ground slopes gently down to the west.

Soil profile:	Distance from tree (m)	2.8	5.6	8.4	11.2	28.0
	x height (in 1981)	0.2	0.4	0.6	0.8	2.0

Soil classification tests:

Distance from tree (m)	2.8	5.6
Depth (m)	2.0	1.5
Plastic limit	28	30
Liquid limit	88	64
Plasticity index	60	34
% linear shrinkage	16.6	13.2

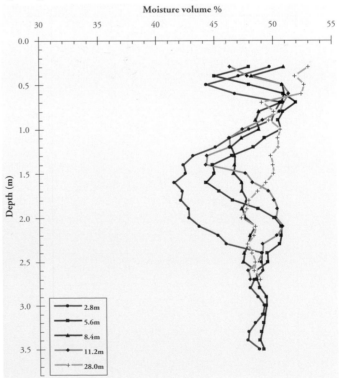

Spring soil moisture content profiles

Comments: The profiles suggest that a significant persistent deficit was present at the start of the project, at least at the two access holes closest to the tree.

Seasonal fluctuations in soil moisture deficit at 1.0m depth

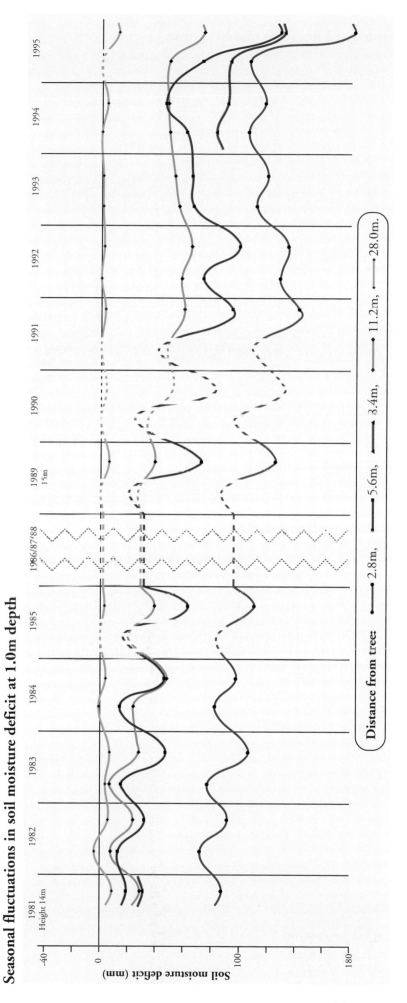

Distance from tree: — 2.8m, — 5.6m, — 11.2m, — 28.0m.

Comments: There was a gradual increase in the persistent deficit at the two access tubes closest to the tree throughout the period from 1981 to 1991 totalling 56mm and 60mm respectively during this period, and an increase at the access tube 11.2m from the tree during the dry period from 1989 - 1991. From 1991 to 1994 there was a slight reduction in the persistent deficit, but there was a considerable increase in drying in 1995. Vandalism of the access tube 8.4m from the tree prevented readings between September 1981 and April 1994, but a 50mm persistent deficit appeared to have developed during the intervening period.

Maximum soil drying recorded at 2.8m from tree in various years.

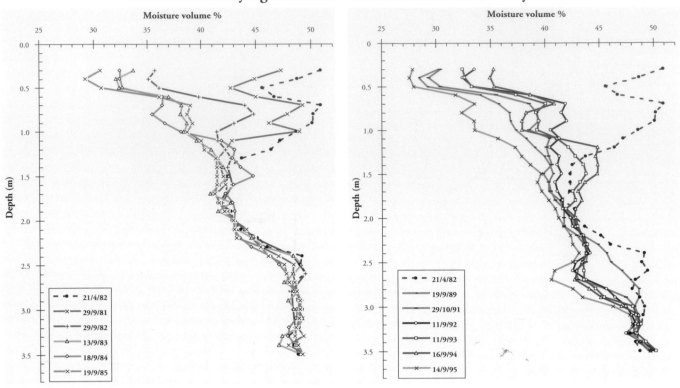

Comments: A gradual reduction in moisture content occurred, particularly below 2m, in 1991 and subsequent years. Increased drying in 1995 primarily above 2.0m is unlikely to be sustained in subsequent years.

Seasonal development of soil drying at 2.8m from tree during 1983

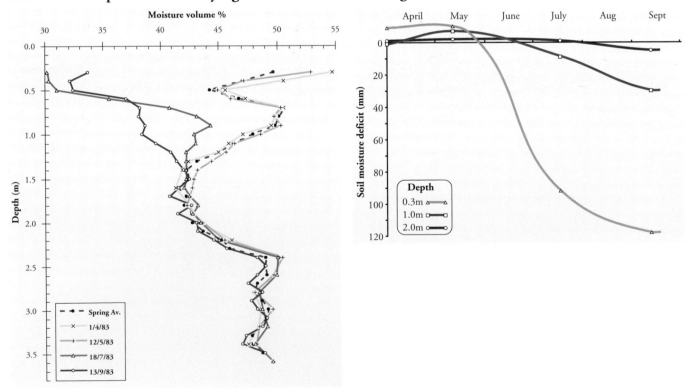

Comments: Most soil drying in 1993 was restricted to within 1.4m of the surface.

Seasonal development of soil drying at 2.8m from tree during 1984

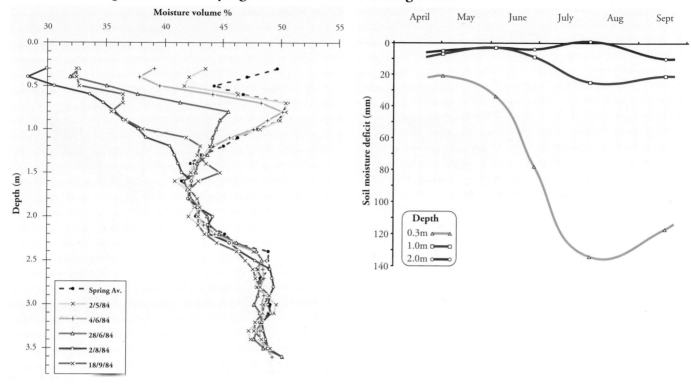

Comments: Soil drying extended to 1.6m, with early rainfall in September allowing some recovery.

Seasonal development of soil drying at 5.6m from tree during 1984

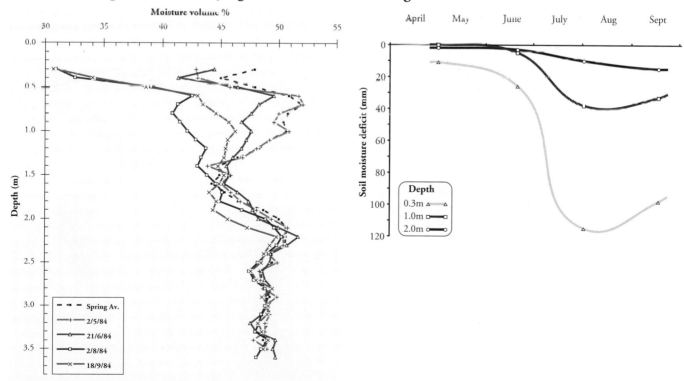

Comments: Although this access tube is further from the tree, drying extended to greater depth (2.3m).

Seasonal and Persistent deficits

2.8m from tree

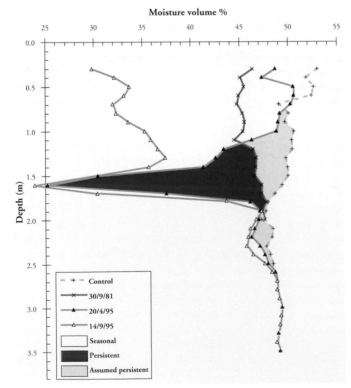

Comments: Persistent deficit of 33mm developed between April '82 and April '94 from 2.1 - 3.1m depth. Assumed persistent deficit of 72mm in April '82.

5.6m from tree

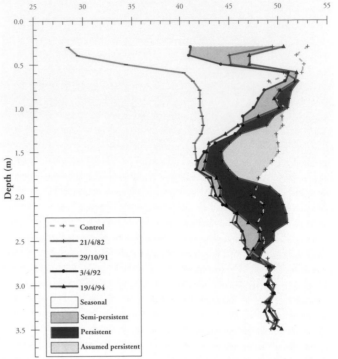

Comments: Persistent deficit of 48mm developed between April '82 and April '94 from 0.7 - 2.7m depth. Assumed persistent deficit of 13mm in April '82.

8.4m from tree

Comments: Vandalism at this hole prevents proper analysis, but available readings imply 50mm persistent deficit established between 1981 and April '94.

11.2m from tree

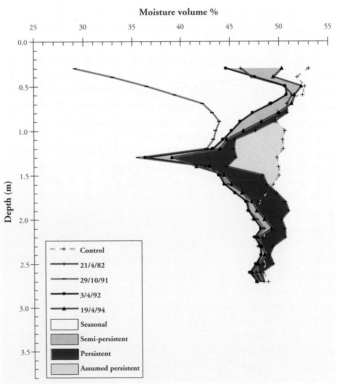

Comments: Persistent deficit of 41mm developed between April '82 and April '94 from 0.8 - 2.7m depth. Assumed persistent deficit of 8mm in April '82.

Reduction in soil moisture content on 18/9/84 compared with 21/4/82

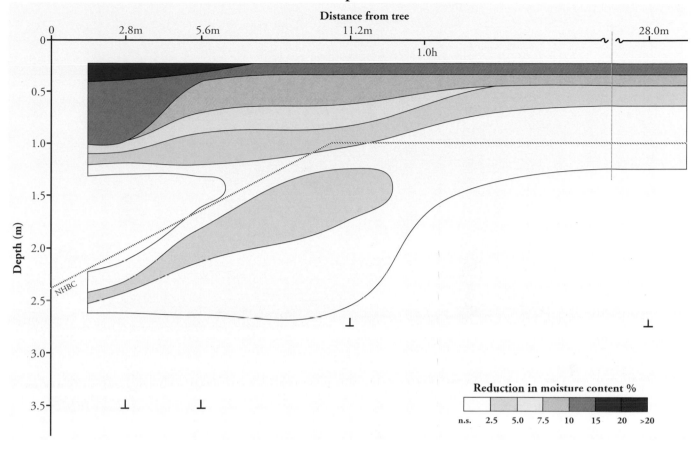

Soil moisture deficit on 18/9/84 compared with 21/4/82

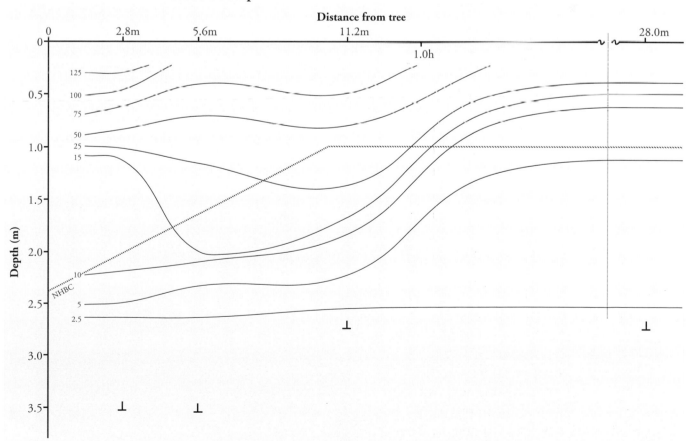

Reduction in soil moisture content on 29/10/91 compared with 21/4/82

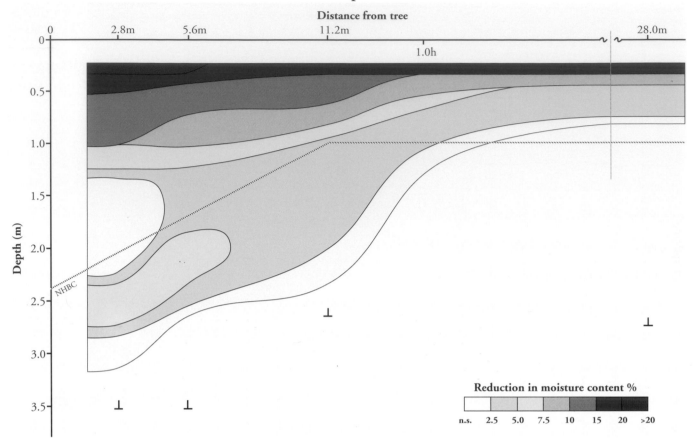

Soil moisture deficit on 29/10/91 compared with 21/4/82

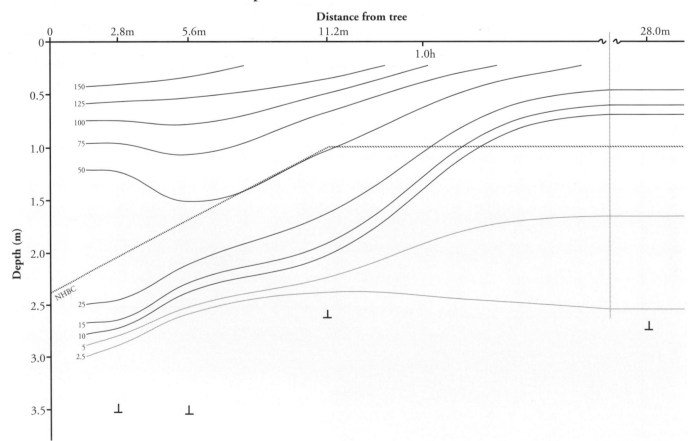

Development of persistent deficit between 21/4/82 and 19/4/94

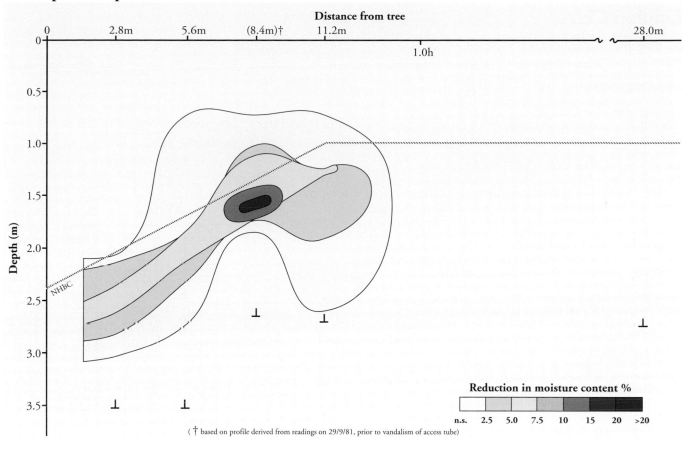

(† based on profile derived from readings on 29/9/81, prior to vandalism of access tube)

Persistent moisture deficit on 19/4/94 compared with 21/4/82

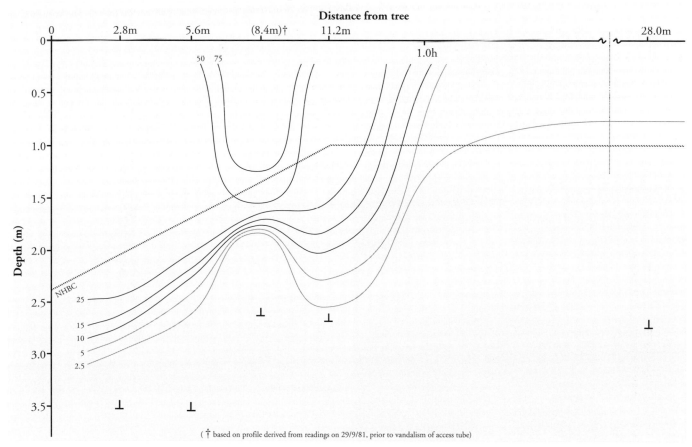

(† based on profile derived from readings on 29/9/81, prior to vandalism of access tube)

Horse chestnut
London Clay

Location: King Edward VII Park, Wembley.   Map ref: TQ 181 856   Tree height: 12m (1981); 14m (1991)   b.h.d.: 45cm (1992).

Current status: Site prone to flooding, and so routine readings have been suspended.

Site: At base of gentle slope. Tree is part of a row of mixed trees. The access tubes are in the mown grass of a playing field, in a line to the NE of the tree, at right angles to the slope. There is a tarmac car park 10m to the west.

Soil profile:	Distance from tree (m) x height (in 1981)	2.4 0.2	4.8 0.4	7.2 0.6	9.6 0.8	24.0 2.0

Soil classification tests:

Distance from tree (m)	2.4	4.8
Depth (m)	2.0	1.5
Plastic limit	26	31
Liquid limit	75	64
Plasticity index	49	33
% linear shrinkage	13.4	12.1

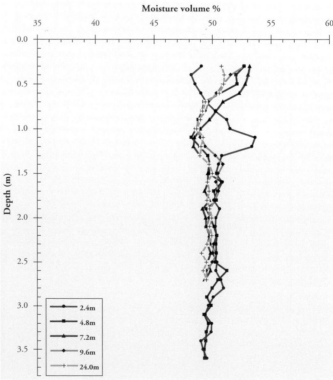

Spring soil moisture content profiles

Legend:
- 2.4m
- 4.8m
- 7.2m
- 9.6m
- 24.0m

Comments: Similar moisture profiles at all access tubes.

Seasonal fluctuations in soil moisture deficit at 1.0m depth.

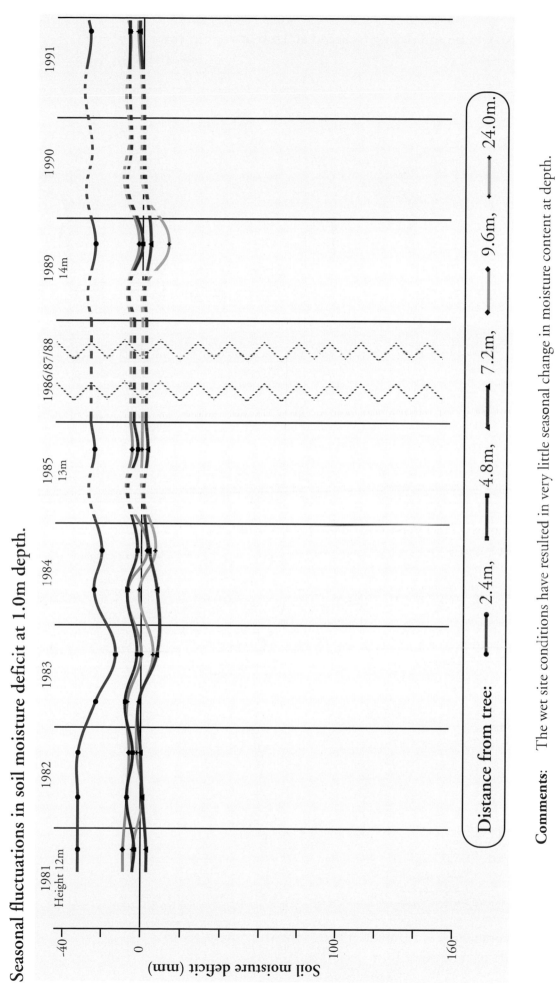

Distance from tree: 2.4m, 4.8m, 7.2m, 9.6m, 24.0m.

Comments: The wet site conditions have resulted in very little seasonal change in moisture content at depth.

23

Maximum soil drying recorded at 2.4m in various years

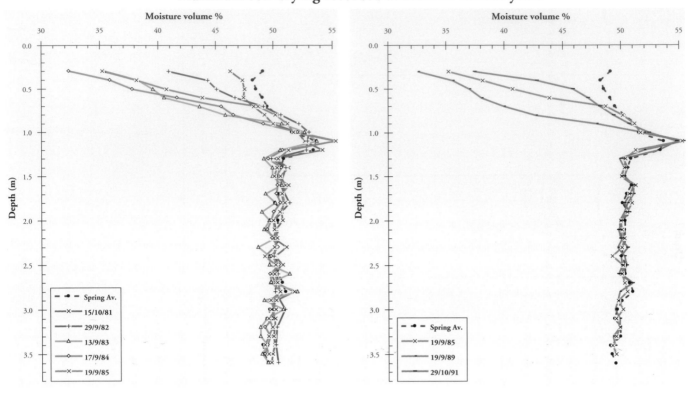

Comments: Driest conditions recorded in 1983, 1984 and 1989.

Seasonal (and persistent) deficit 2.4m from tree

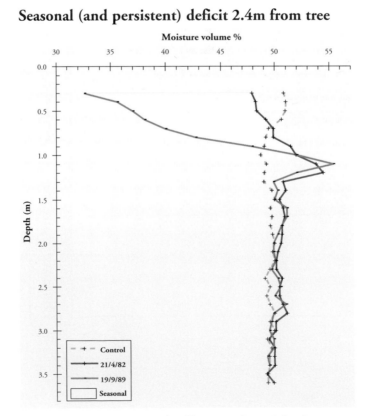

Comments: Seasonal effects only, with these restricted to surface 1.0m.

Reduction in soil moisture content on 19/9/89 compared with spring average

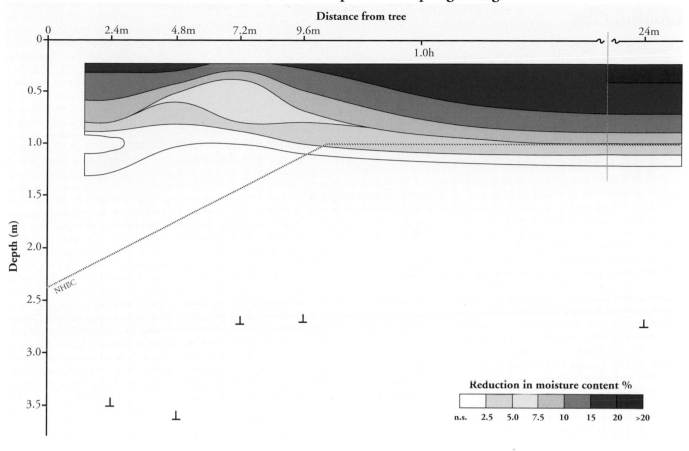

Soil moisture deficit on 19/9/89 compared with spring average

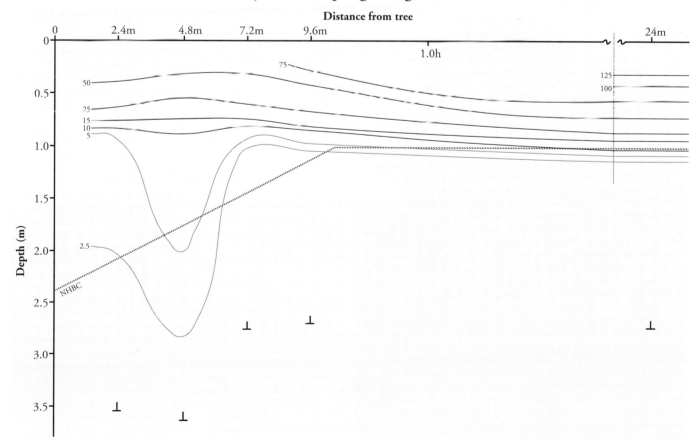

Horse chestnut
London Clay

Location: Barham Park,
Wembley   Map ref: TQ 174 851

Size: Height: 12m (1981); 14 m (1994)
b.h.d.: 71cm (1992).

Current status: Intermittent readings still in progress.

Site: Southernmost tree of group including another similar sized horse chestnut and several small hawthorns. The access tubes are situated in a line to the west in rough mown grass. The ground slopes up gradually to the west.

Soil profile:	Distance from tree (m)	2.4	4.8	7.2	9.6	24.0
	x height (in 1981)	0.2	0.4	0.6	0.8	2.0

Soil classification tests:

Distance from tree (m)	2.4	4.8
Depth (m)	2.0	1.5
Plastic limit	27	29
Liquid limit	84	67
Plasticity index	57	38
% linear shrinkage	12.4	12.1

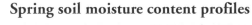

Spring soil moisture content profiles

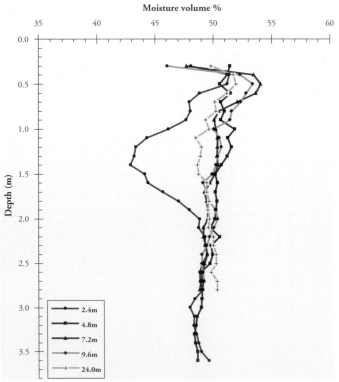

Comments: Profile 2.4m from tube is considerably drier than others down to 2.2m depth, implying presence of persistent deficit.

Seasonal fluctuations in soil moisture deficit at 1.0m depth

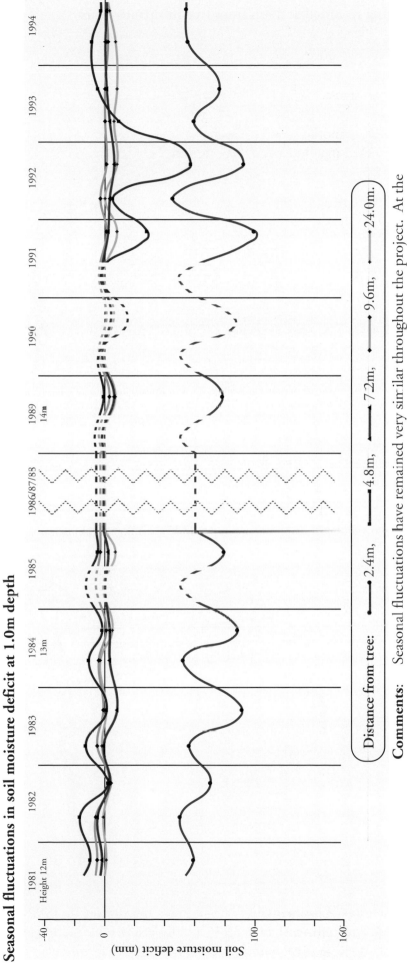

Distance from tree: ●— 2.4m, ●— 4.8m, ●— 7.2m, ●— 9.6m, ●— 24.0m.

Comments: Seasonal fluctuations have remained very similar throughout the project. At the access tube 4.8m from the tree there was an increase in drying in 1991 with a further increase in 1992, but this was not maintained in 1993 (see profiles overleaf).

27

Maximum soil drying recorded at 2.4m from tree in various years

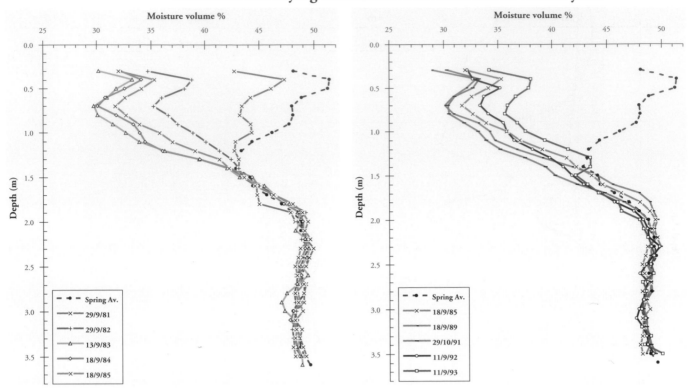

Comments: Near the surface the driest conditions were recorded in 1983, 1984 and 1991, but there was additional drying between 1.8 amd 2.5m depth in 1992 and 1993.

Seasonal and persistent deficits

2.4m from tree

4.8m from tree

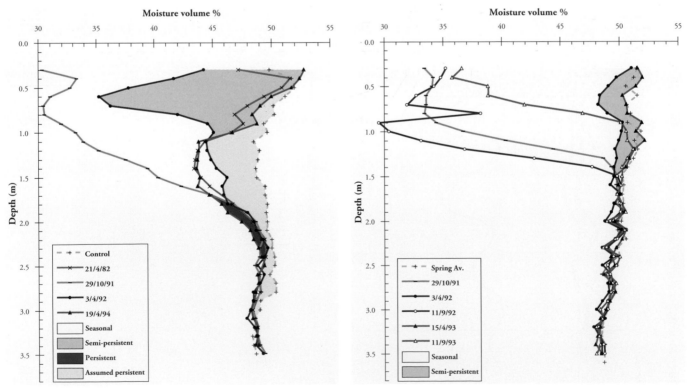

Comments: The slight persistent deficit which developed was associated with extra drying in 1992 and 1993, rather than the dry summer of 1991.

Comments: At this tube the drying in 1992 was greater than in 1991, but far less in 1993. Effects were seasonal with full recovery during each winter.

Reduction in soil moisture content on 29/10/91 compared with spring average

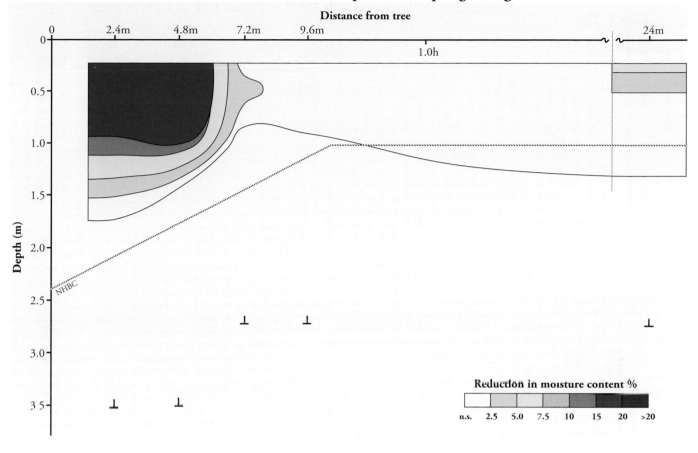

Soil moisture deficit on 29/10/91 compared with spring average

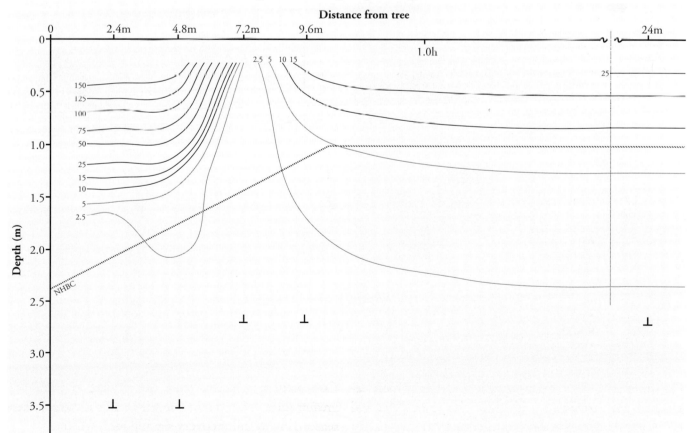

Horse chestnut
London Clay

Location: Woodside Park,   **Size:** Height: 12m (1979); 13 m (1984)
              Haringey   Map ref: TQ 309 913   b.h.d.: 54cm (1979).

Current status: Site destroyed in 1985 by engineering works.

Site: Part of a row of similar horse chestnuts adjacent to path. Access tubes to south of tree, running across slight slope. Mown grass over whole site.

Soil profile:	Distance from tree (m)		2.4	4.8	9.6	24.0
	x height (in 1979)		0.2	0.4	0.6	2.0

Soil classification tests:

Distance from tree (m)	2.4	2.4	2.4
Depth (m)	1.0	1.5	2.0
Plastic limit	31	30	31
Liquid limit	73	65	69
Plasticity index	42	35	38
% linear shrinkage	12.8	10.6	12.2

Spring soil moisture content profiles.

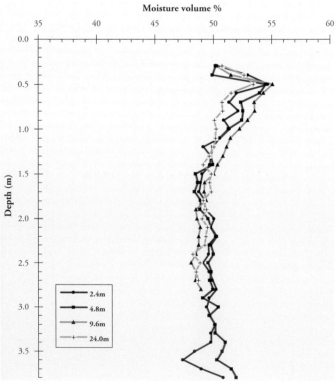

Comments: Similar soil conditions at all access tubes with no evidence of persistent deficit.

Seasonal fluctuations in soil moisture deficit at 1.0m depth

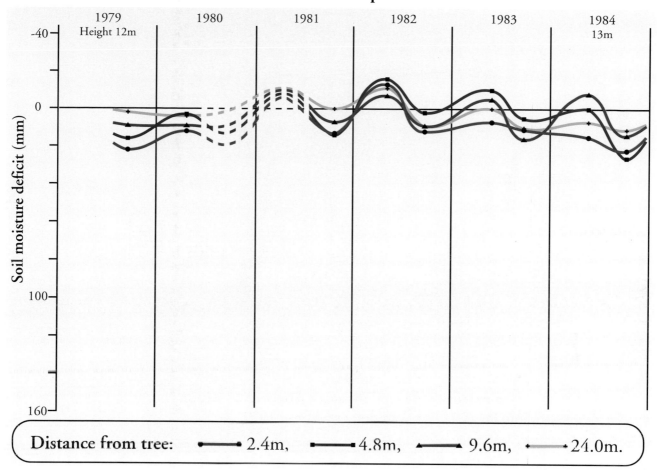

Comments: Similar seasonal changes at all access tubes, with no evidence of persistent deficit.

Maximum soil drying recorded at 2.4m from tree in various years

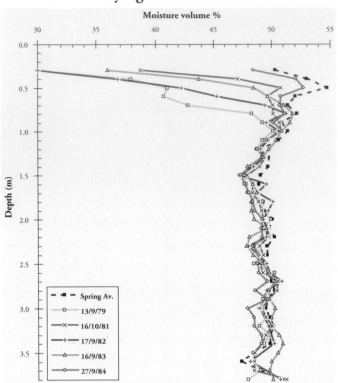

Comments: Seasonal changes restricted to within 0.8m of surface, with driest profiles in 1979.

Seasonal and persistent deficits 2.4m from tree

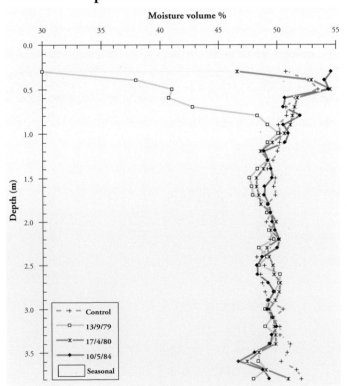

Comments: Seasonal deficit only.

Reduction in soil moisture content on 13/9/79 compared with spring average

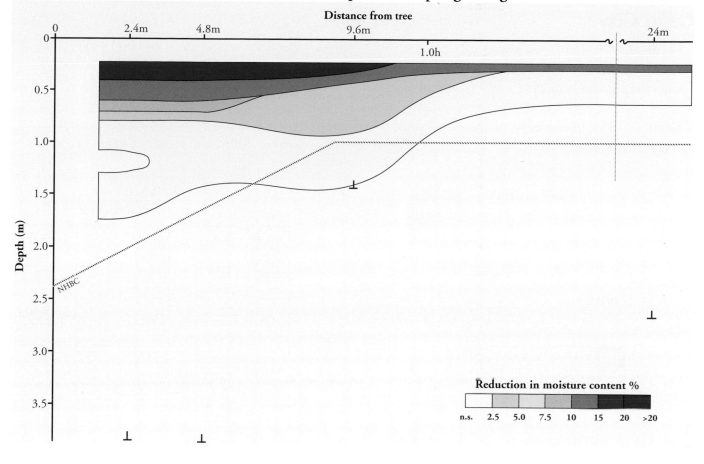

Soil moisture deficit on 13/9/79 compared with spring average

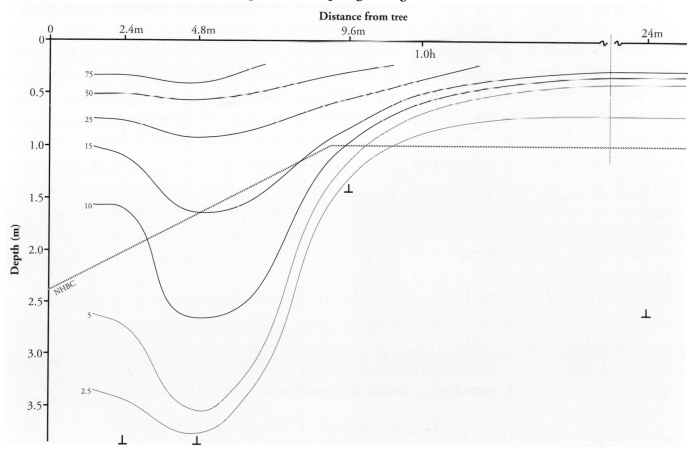

Horse chestnut
Gault Clay

Location: St. John's College,   **Size:** Height:12 m (1981); 14 m (1993)
Cambridge   Map ref: TL 440 587   b.h.d.: 76cm (1992).
Current status: Routine readings still in progress.

Site: Part of row of horse chestnuts along western boundary of playing fields. Access tubes sited in close mown grass of the playing field, aligned east from the tree. 200m to the east the Gault is covered by Alluvium and River Gravels.

Soil profile:	Distance from tree (m) x height (in 1981)	2.4 0.2	4.8 0.4	7.2 0.6	9.6 0.8	24.0 2.0

Soil classification tests:

Distance from tree (m)	4.8	7.2
Depth (m)	2.0	1.5
Plastic limit	31	34
Liquid limit	82	57
Plasticity index	51	23
% linear shrinkage	15.8	11.1

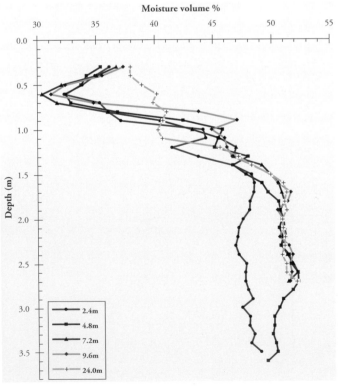

Spring soil moisture content profiles

Comments: Superficial deposits in surface 1.0m produce low values of moisture content. Significant assumed persistent deficit at access tube closest to tree.

Seasonal fluctuations in soil moisture deficit at 1.0m depth

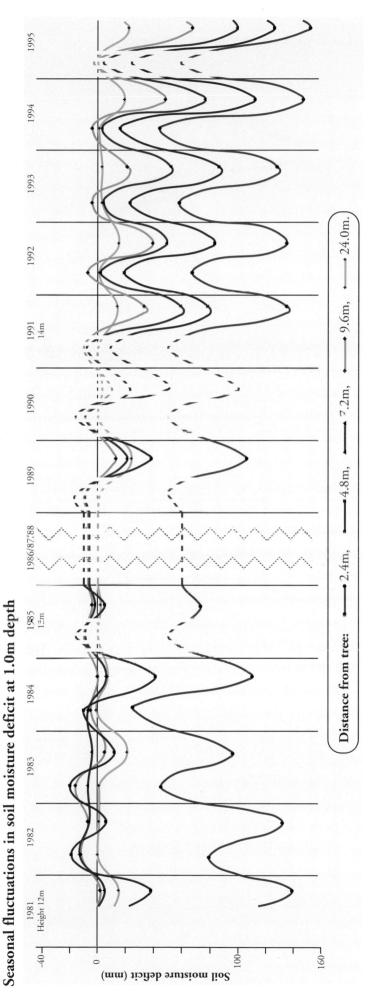

Distance from tree: ——— 2.4m, ——— 4.8m, ——— 7.2m, ——— 9.6m, ——— 24.0m.

Comments: At the access tube 2.4m from tree, there was a slight trend of the deficit reducing from 1981-1985, then increasing from 1989-1991, and then again reducing from 1991-1994. Seasonal deficits at all other access tubes close to tree were negligible prior to 1989, but increase considerably in 1991 and subsequent years, with development of slight persistent deficit 4.8m from tree.

35

Maximum soil drying recorded at 2.4m from tree in various years

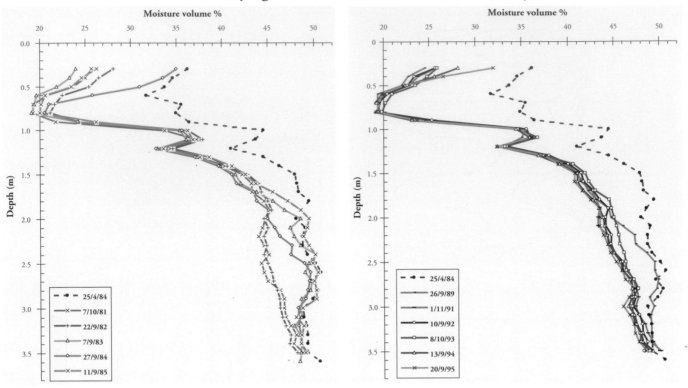

Comments: Significant increase in moisture content below 2.0m from 1981-1983, slightly drier in 1984, but then wetter again in 1985.

Comments: After 1989, all profiles remain very similar.

Seasonal development of soil drying at 2.4m from tree during 1983

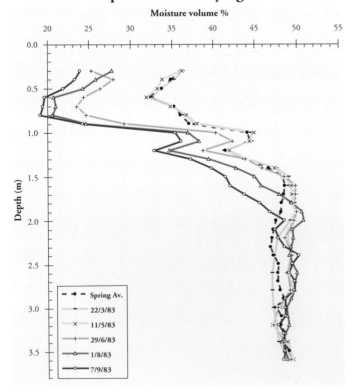

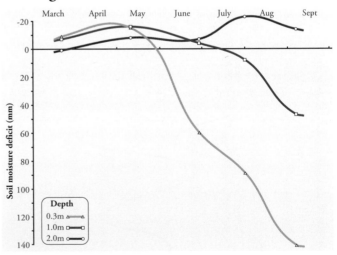

Comments: The soil was still recovering below 2.0m depth in March. Seasonal drying only extended to 2.2m depth by the end of the summer.

Seasonal development of soil drying at 2.4m from tree during 1984

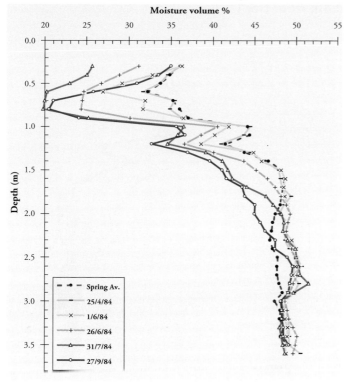

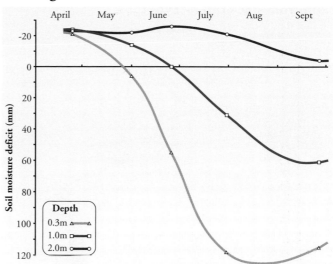

Comments: In 1984 slight seasonal drying extended to 2.6m depth at access tube 2.4m from tree.

Seasonal development of soil drying at 4.8m from tree during 1984

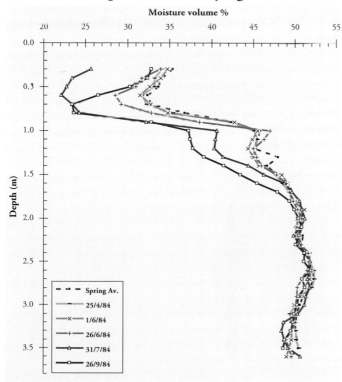

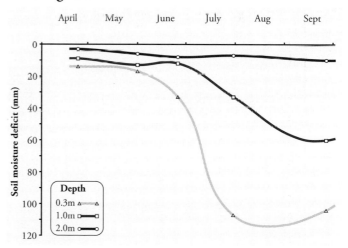

Comments: At 4.8m from tree, seasonal drying in 1984 extended to 1.8m depth.

Seasonal and Persistent deficits

2.4m from tree (1982 - 1984)

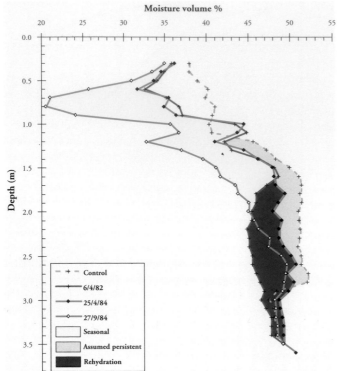

Comments: Considerable rehydration from 1982-1984.

2.4m from tree (1984 - 1994)

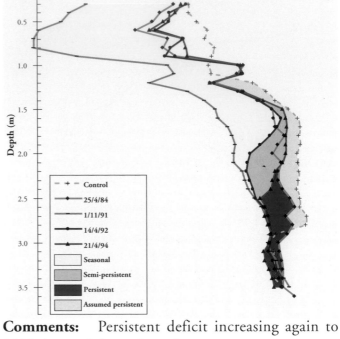

Comments: Persistent deficit increasing again to 1991, but mainly semi-persistent.

4.8m from tree

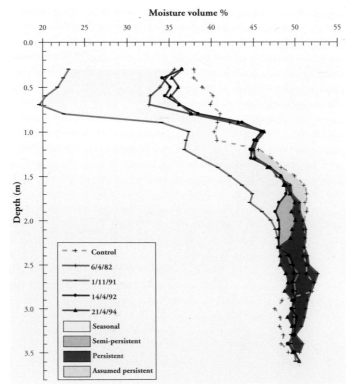

Comments: At 4.8m from tree, slight development of a persistent deficit.

Reduction in soil moisture content on 26/9/89 compared with 25/4/84

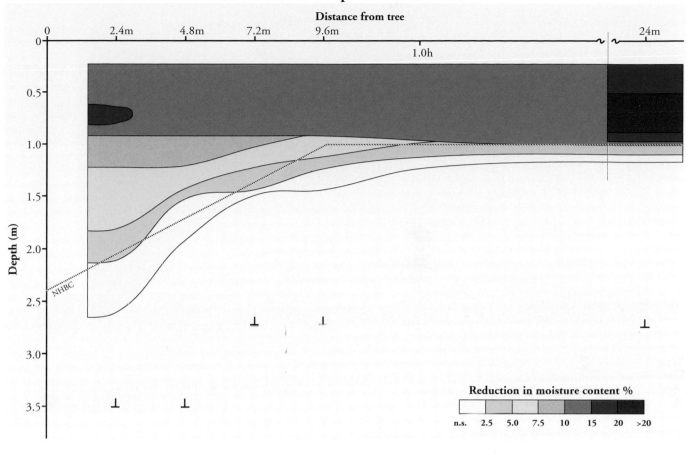

Soil moisture deficit on 26/9/89 compared with 25/4/84

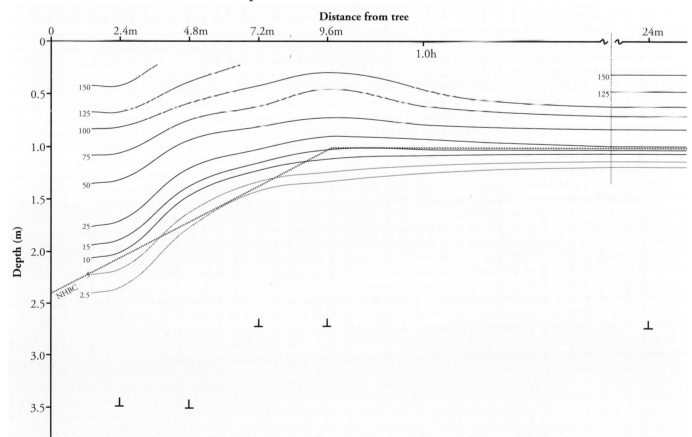

Reduction in soil moisture content on 1/11/91 compared with 25/4/84

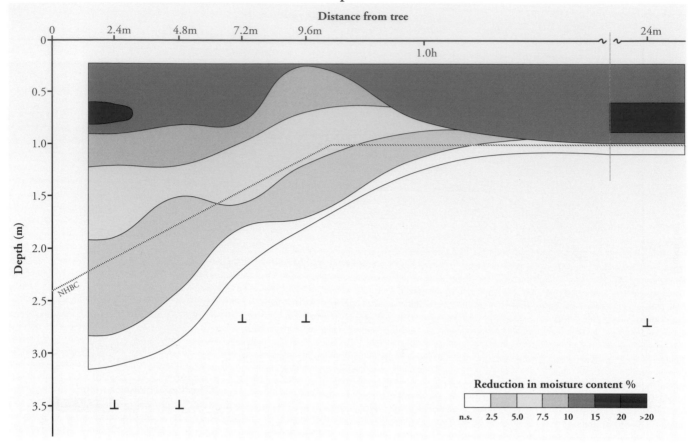

Soil moisture deficit on 1/11/91 compared with 24/4/84

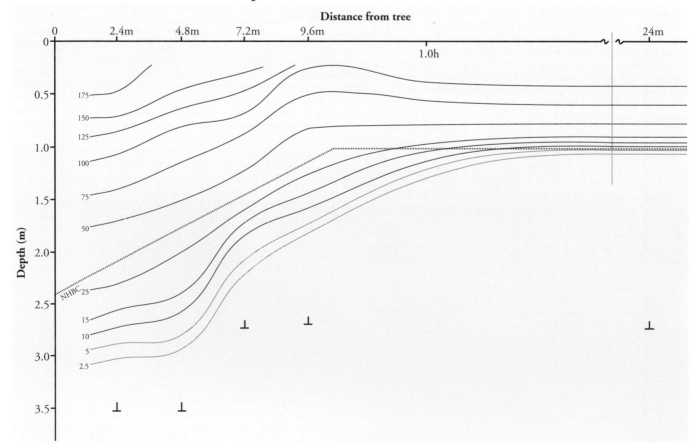

Development of persistent deficit between 25/4/84 and 21/4/94

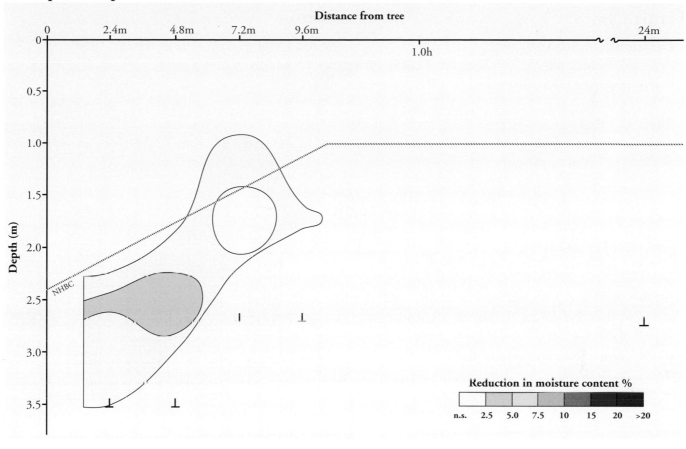

Persistent moisture deficit on 21/4/94 compared with 25/4/84

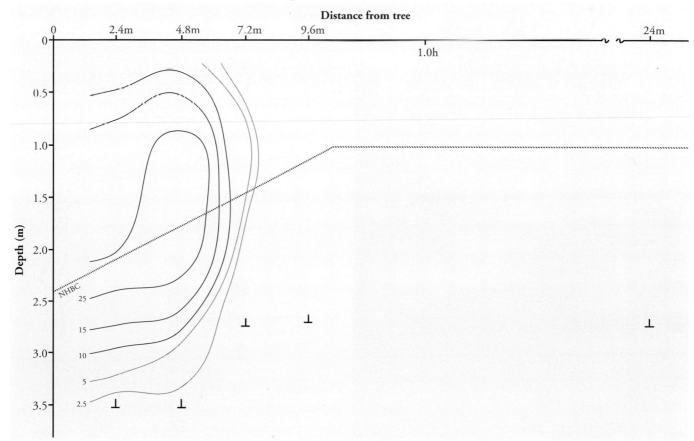

Horse chestnut
Gault Clay

Location: St. John's College, Cambridge   Map ref: TL 441 587

Size: Height:12 m (1981); 15 m (1993)
b.h.d.: 67cm (1992).

Current status: Routine readings still in progress.

Site: Part of a row of trees along south boundary of playing fields. Access tubes sited in the close mown grass of the playing field aligned to the north of the tree. Alluvium and River Gravels outcrop 150m to the east.

| **Soil profile:** | Distance from tree (m) | 2.4 | 4.8 | 7.2 | 9.6 | 24.0 |
| | x height (in 1981) | 0.2 | 0.4 | 0.6 | 0.8 | 2.0 |

Soil classification tests:

Distance from tree (m)	4.8
Depth (m)	2.0
Plastic limit	35
Liquid limit	81
Plasticity index	46
% linear shrinkage	15.4

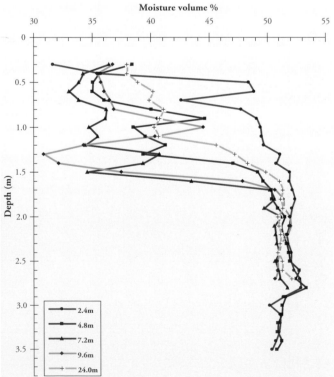

Spring soil moisture content profiles

Comments: Superficial sandy loam causes low values of moisture content to about 1.7m depth; all profiles very similar below 1.7m.

42

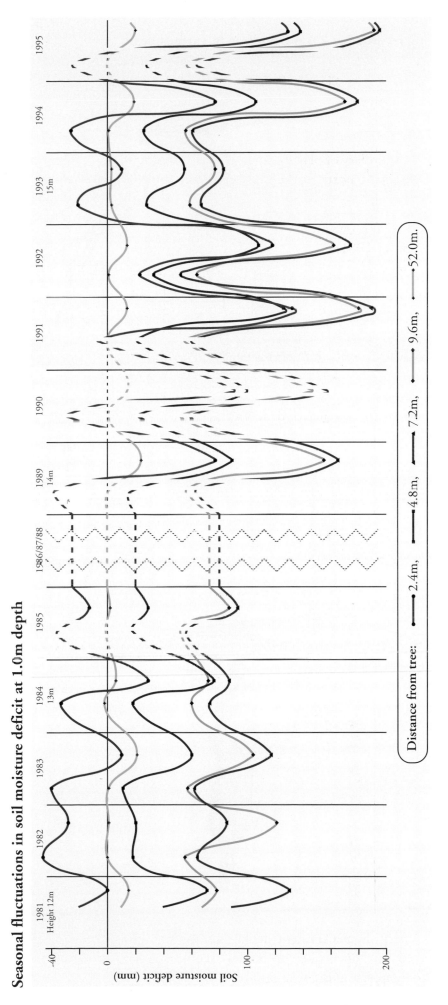

Seasonal fluctuations in soil moisture deficit at 1.0m depth

Tree 6. Horse chestnut, Gault Clay

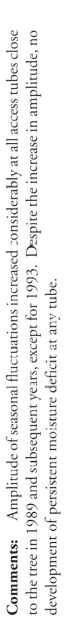

Distance from tree: —•— 2.4m, —•— 4.8m, —•— 7.2m, —•— 9.6m, —•— 52.0m.

Comments: Amplitude of seasonal fluctuations increased considerably at all access tubes close to the tree in 1989 and subsequent years, except for 1993. Despite the increase in amplitude, no development of persistent moisture deficit at any tube.

43

Maximum soil drying recorded at 2.4m from tree in various years

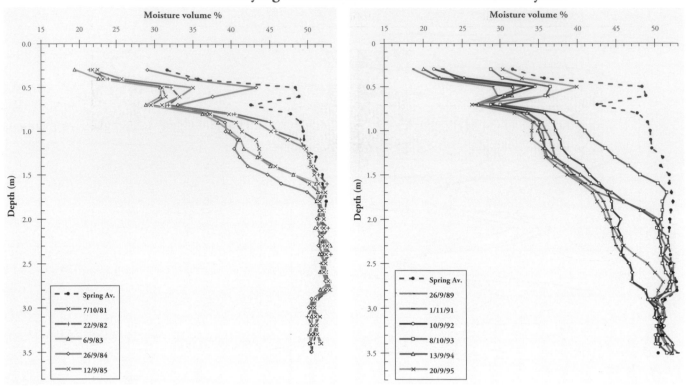

Comments: In 1984 the seasonal changes were restricted to a depth of 1.8m; the depth was similar in 1989, but had increased to 2.9m in 1991. Drying in 1992 was very similar to 1991, but by 1993 the depth reverted to only 1.7m. It increased again slightly in 1995.

Seasonal and persistent deficit 2.4m from tree

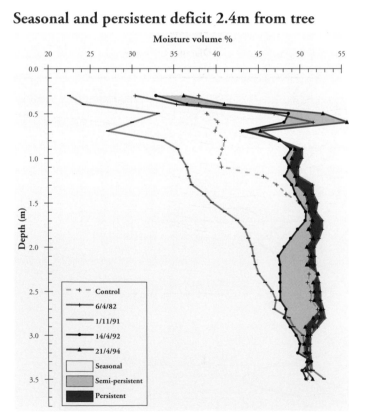

Comments: A very slight persistent deficit has apparently developed, but this is likely to be only semi-persistent and to disappear in the future.

Reduction in soil moisture content on 26/9/89 compared with spring average

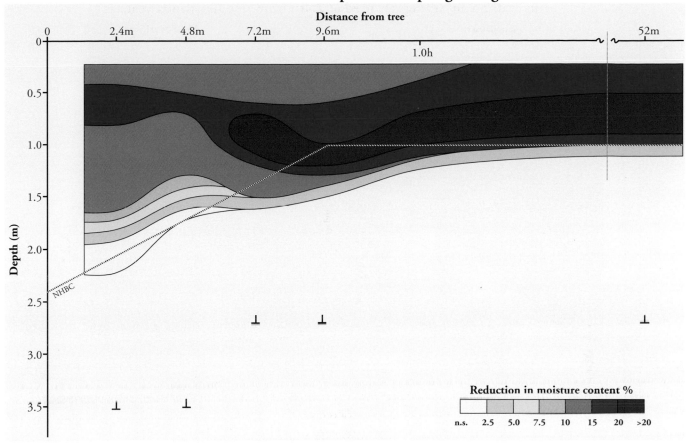

Soil moisture deficit on 26/9/89 compared with spring average

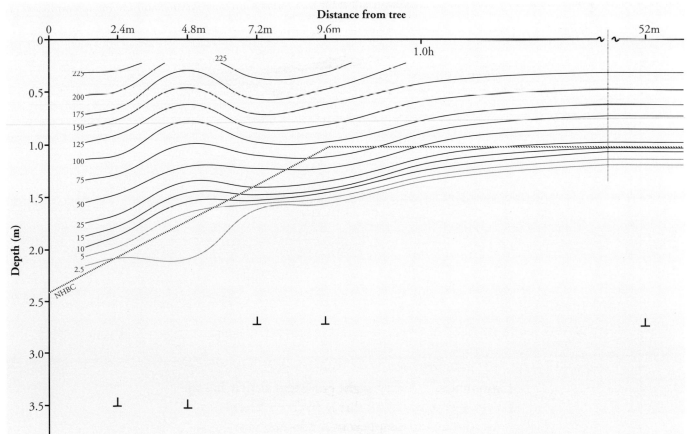

Reduction in soil moisture content on 1/11/91 compared with spring average

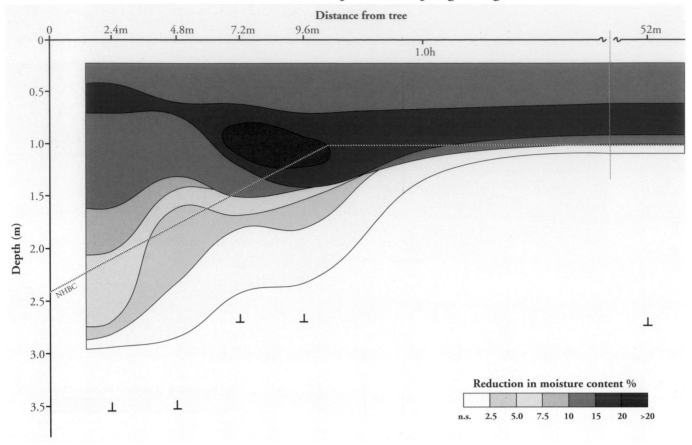

Soil moisture deficit on 1/11/91 compared with spring average

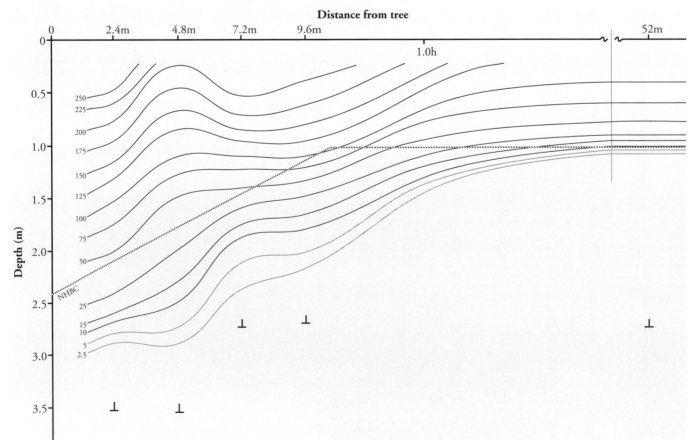

Reduction in soil moisture content on 8/10/93 compared with 7/4/93

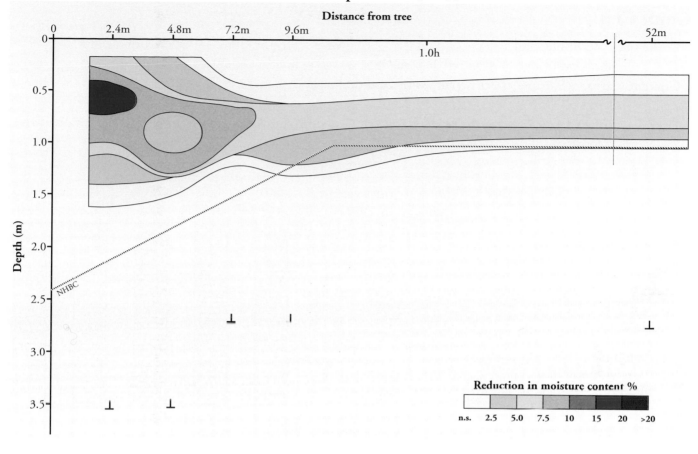

Soil moisture deficit on 8/10/93 compared with 7/4/93

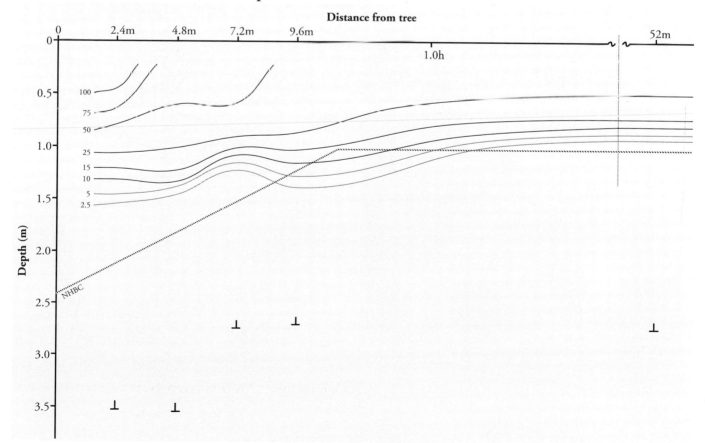

Horse chestnut
Gault Clay

Location: Wimpole Hall,
 Nr. Cambridge   Map ref: TL 332 505

Size: Height: 20m (1981); 20m (1985)
 b.h.d.: 85cm (1981).

Current status: Site and tubes destroyed by land drainage work in 1985.

Site: One of pair of trees in parkland, with access tubes in rough grazed grass aligned to east of tree. Metalled, single track road 7m to north of tree.

| **Soil profile:** | Distance from tree (m) | 4.0 | 8.0 | 12.0 | 16.0 | 40.0 |
| | x height (in 1981) | 0.2 | 0.4 | 0.6 | 0.8 | 2.0 |

Soil classification tests:

Distance from tree (m)	8.0	8.0
Depth (m)	1.0	2.0
Plastic limit	23	28
Liquid limit	44	81
Plasticity index	21	53
% linear shrinkage	10.9	-

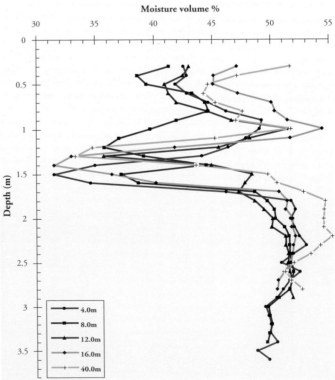

Spring soil moisture content profiles

Legend:
- 4.0m
- 8.0m
- 12.0m
- 16.0m
- 40.0m

Comments: Profiles strongly influenced by sandy loam to 1.7m.

Seasonal fluctuations in soil moisture deficit at 1.0m depth

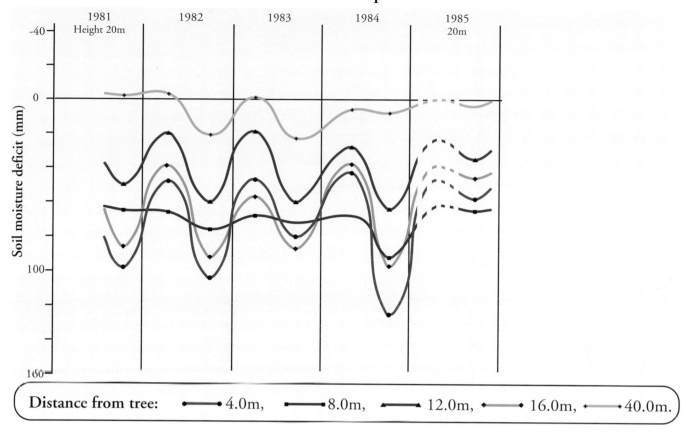

Comments: Amplitude of seasonal drying variable between the access tubes, with negligible drying at the tube 8.0m from the tree but greater effects at the more distant tubes.

Maximum soil drying recorded at 4.0m from tree in various years

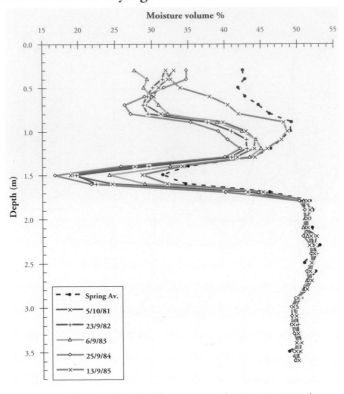

Comments: Marginally greater drying in 1984.

Seasonal (and persistent) deficits 4.0m from tree

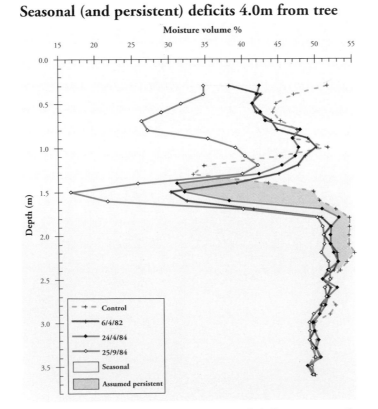

Comments: Considerable seasonal deficit, primarily within the sandy loam.

Reduction in soil moisture content on 25/9/84 compared with spring average

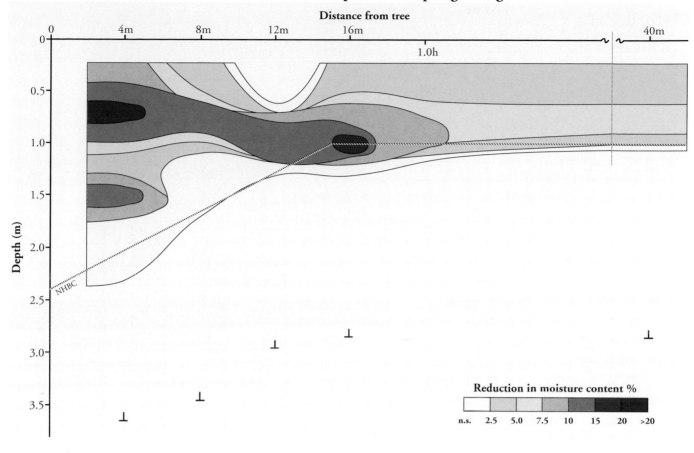

Soil moisture deficit on 25/9/84 compared with spring average

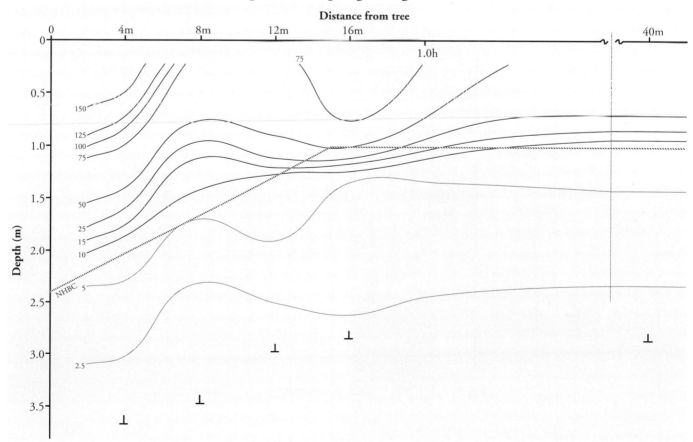

Horse chestnut
Oxford Clay

Location: College of Further Education,
Bletchley   Map ref: SP 886 335

Current status: Intermittent readings still in progress.

Size: Height:14m (1979); 15m (1993)
b.h.d.: 80cm (1992).

Site: Edge of playing field, with close mown grass over whole site. Holes aligned to east of tree.

Soil profile:				Distance from tree (m) x height (in 1979)	1.8 0.13	3.8 0.27	6.6 0.47	11.2 0.8	28.0 2.0
Soil classification tests:									
Distance from tree (m)	3.8	3.8	6.6	6.6					
Depth (m)	1.0	2.0	1.0	2.0					
Plastic limit	29	27	27	27					
Liquid limit	67	63	68	62					
Plasticity index	38	36	41	35					
% linear shrinkage	13.6	11.6	12.1	9.8					

Spring soil moisture content profiles

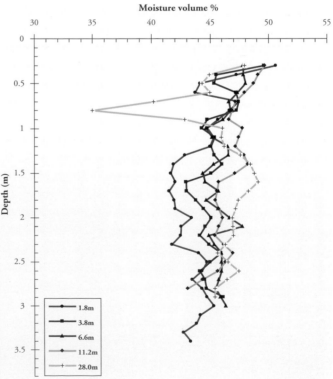

Legend:
- 1.8m
- 3.8m
- 6.6m
- 11.2m
- 28.0m

Comments: Profiles suggest slight persistent deficits at start.

Seasonal fluctuations in soil moisture deficit at 1.0m depth

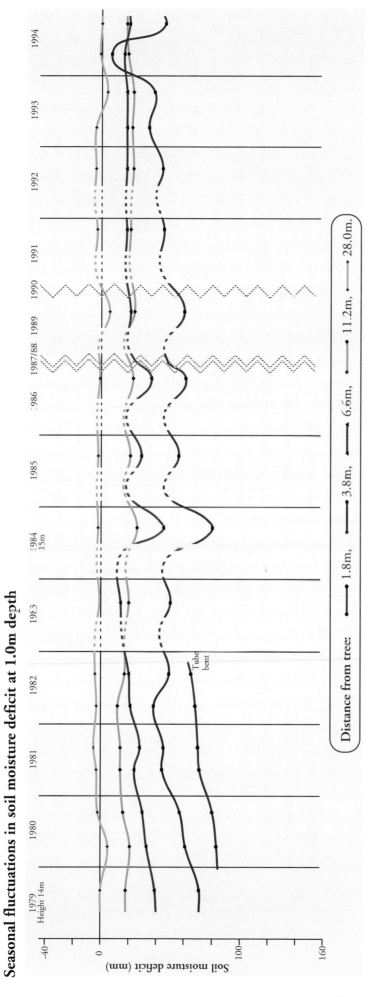

Distance from tree: 1.8m, 3.8m, 6.6m, 11.2m, 28.0m.

Comments: Persistent deficit at the three access tubes closest to the tree diminish progressively during the period 1979 - 1982. They remain fairly steady from 1982 - 1989, with further reduction in the persistent deficit since 1991. Dieback of twigs in the periphery of the crown has become apparent since 1990. The access tube closest to the tree was bent at a depth of 0.7m, presumably caused by lateral swelling of the clay.

Maximum soil drying recorded at 3.8m from tree in various years

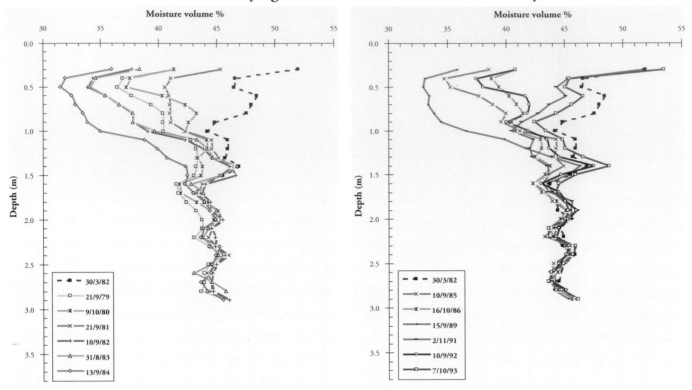

Comments: Below 1.6m the driest profile was in 1979, with subsequent rehydration below this depth. Near the surface the driest profile was in 1984, with a similar profile in 1989, but the drying in those years does not extend below 1.7m. The recordings in 1991 were too late to record drying in that year.

Seasonal development of soil drying at 3.8m from tree during 1984

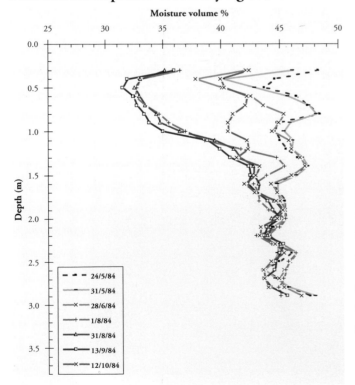

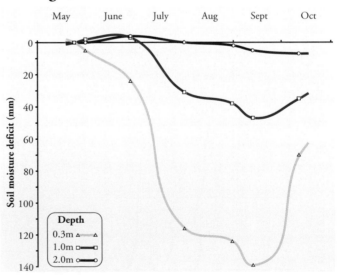

Comments: The onset of wet weather in early September of 1984 allowed rapid recovery by October both at 0.3m and 1.0m depth.

Seasonal and persistent deficits

1.8m from tree

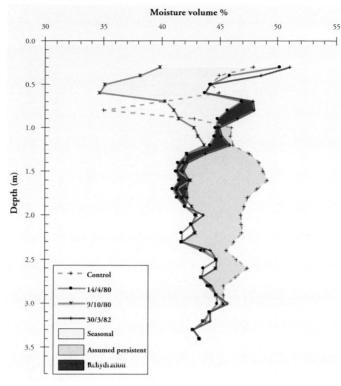

Comments: Recovery was occurring prior to the bending of the access tube. This damage to the tube prevented determination of any further recovery of the assumed persistent deficit.

3.8m from tree

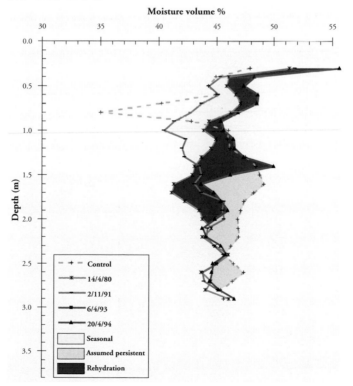

Comments: Extensive recovery has occurred from the persistent deficit, but further recovery of the assumed persistent deficit may continue.

Reduction in soil moisture content on 13/9/84 compared with 30/3/82

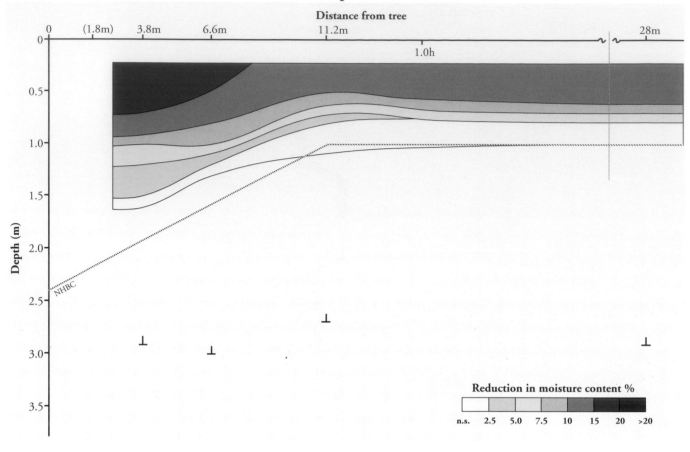

Soil moisture deficit on 13/9/84 compared with 30/3/82

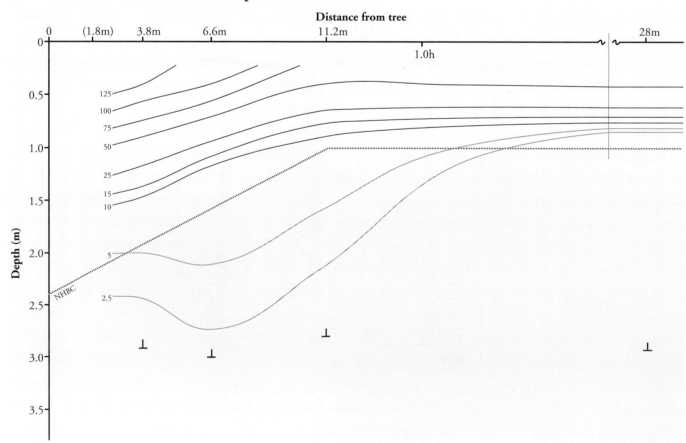

Increase in soil moisture content on 20/4/94 compared with 14/4/80

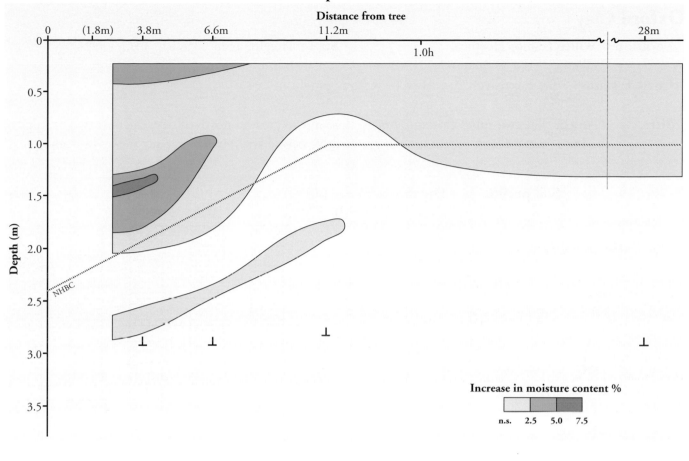

Rehydration on 20/4/94 compared with 14/4/80

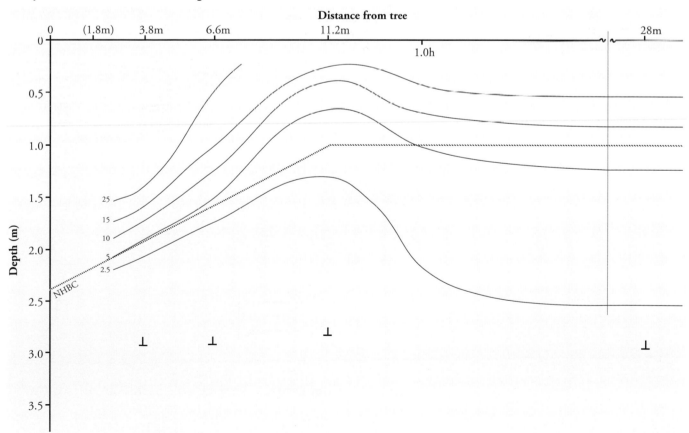

Horse chestnut
Oxford Clay

Location: Willen Manor Hospice,   **Size:** Height: 15m (1978); 15m (1984)
Willen   Map ref: SP 879 441   b.h.d.: 80cm (1978).

Current status: Site extensively disturbed by redevelopment in 1985.

Site: Garden. The two tubes closest to tree in close mown grass to north of tree; the next two on edge of herbaceous border. Control tube in gravel drive beside lawn, with large ivy stem 3m from hole.

Soil profile:			Distance from tree (m)	1.5	3.0	6.0	11.0	28.0
			x height (in 1978)	0.1	0.2	0.4	0.7	1.9
Soil classification tests:								
Distance from tree (m)	1.5	1.5	1.5					
Depth (m)	1.0	1.5	2.0					
Plastic limit	35	37	37					
Liquid limit	78	66	70					
Plasticity index	43	29	33					
% linear shrinkage	13.6	14.3	-					

Spring soil moisture content profiles

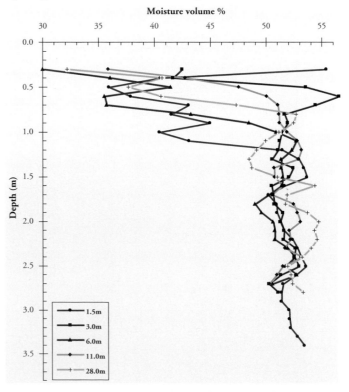

Comments: Very variable profiles in surface 1m.

Seasonal fluctuations in soil moisture deficit at 1.0m depth

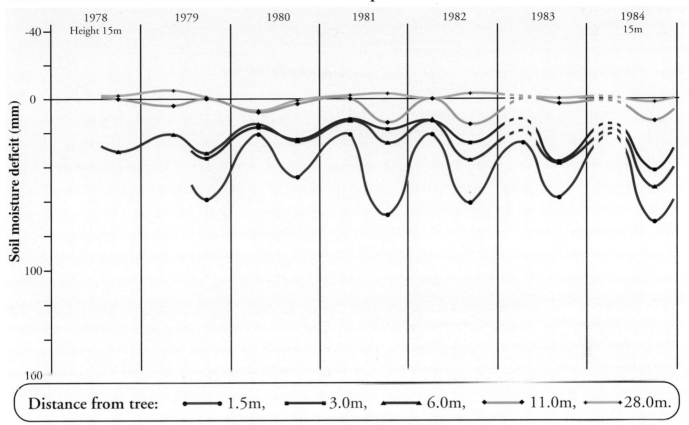

Comments: Seasonal deficits remain similar throughout period, with slight increase in amplitude in 1984.

Maximum soil drying recorded at 1.5m from tree in various years

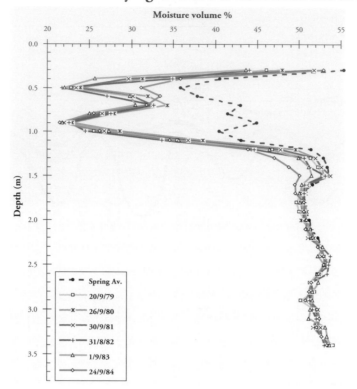

Comments: Very similar profiles every year, except for slight extra drying in 1984 between 1.2 to 1.6m depth.

Seasonal (and persistent) deficits 1.5m from tree

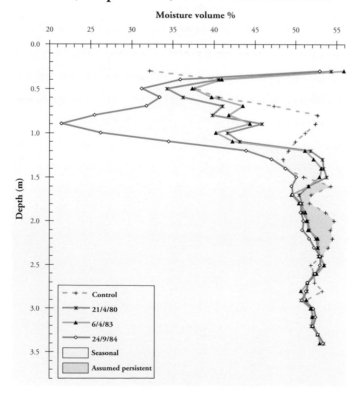

Comments: Considerable seasonal change, with slight assumed persistent deficit.

Reduction in soil moisture content on 24/9/84 compared with spring average

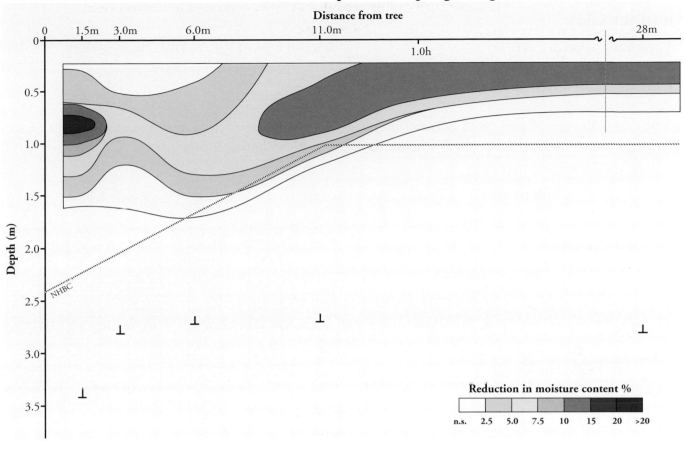

Soil moisture deficit on 24/9/84 compared with spring average

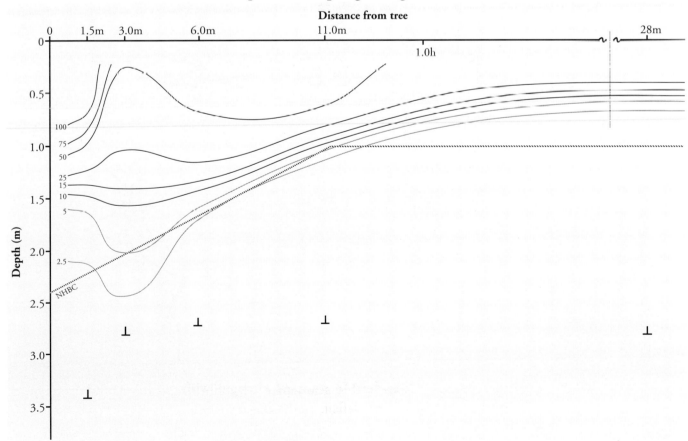

Horse chestnut
Boulder Clay

Tree 10

Location: Church Green,
Bletchley   Map ref: SP 863 336

Size: Height:15 m (1978); 16m (1989)
b.h.d.: 78cm (1989).

Current status: No readings since 1989.

Site: On edge of park, with adjacent building and rear garden. Close mown grass over most of site, except tube at 3.3m which is in centre of small path with loose gravel surface. Holes aligned to NE of tree.

| **Soil profile:** | Distance from tree (m) | 1.6 | 3.3 | 6.4 | 12.1 | 43.4 |
| | x height (in 1978) | 0.1 | 0.2 | 0.4 | 0.8 | 2.9 |

Soil classification tests:

Distance from tree (m)	1.6
Depth (m)	1.5
Plastic limit	23
Liquid limit	46
Plasticity index	23
% linear shrinkage	10.6

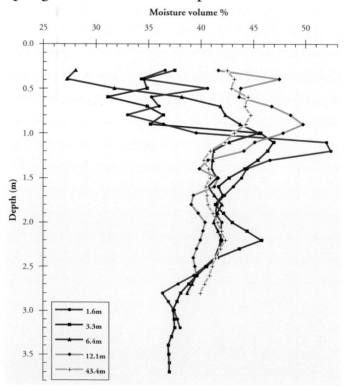

Spring soil moisture content profiles

Comments: Rubble fill and gravel produce very variable profiles near surface.

Seasonal fluctuations in soil moisture deficit at 1.0m depth

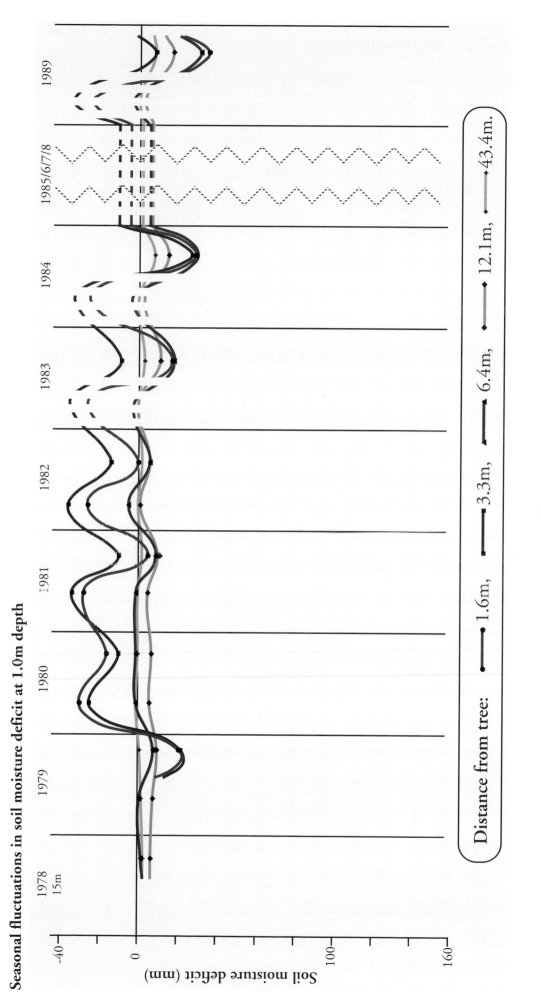

Distance from tree:

1.6m, 3.3m, 6.4m, 12.1m, 43.4m.

Comments: Seasonal deficits remain similar, with slight increase in amplitude in 1984 and 1989.

Maximum soil drying recorded at 1.6m from tree in various years

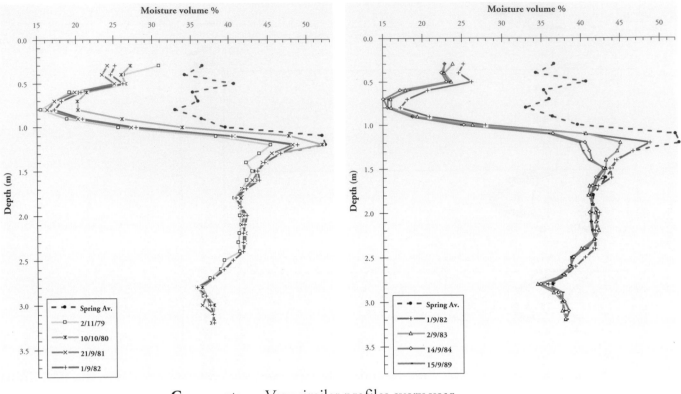

Comments: Very similar profiles every year.

Seasonal (and persistent) deficit 1.6m from tree

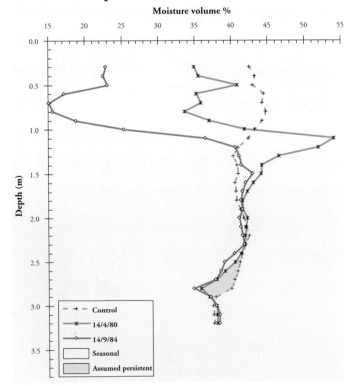

Comments: Considerable seasonal drying near surface associated with rubble fill.

Reduction in soil moisture content on 15/9/89 compared with spring average

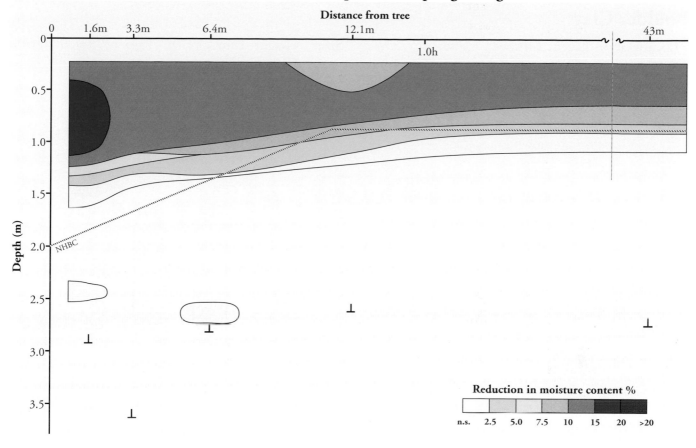

Soil moisture deficit on 15/9/89 compared with spring average

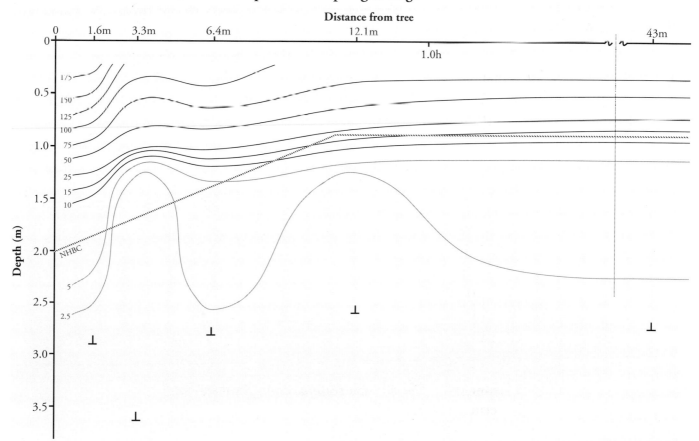

Horse chestnut
Boulder Clay

Location: Adjacent Turnberry Close, Bletchley   Map ref: SP 845 331

Size: Height: 15m (1979); 15m (1984)
b.h.d.: 82cm (1980).

Current status: Site destroyed by engineering works.

Site: On edge of dry ditch beside main road. Access tubes aligned to NE of tree in 16m wide grass verge of rough mown grass.

Soil profile:		Distance from tree (m) x height (in 1979)	1.5 0.1	3.0 0.2	5.8 0.4	12.0 0.8	30.0 2.0
Soil classification tests:							
Distance from tree (m)	3.0	3.0					
Depth (m)	1.5	2.0					
Plastic limit	18	21					
Liquid limit	39	39					
Plasticity index	21	18					
% linear shrinkage	9.9	-					

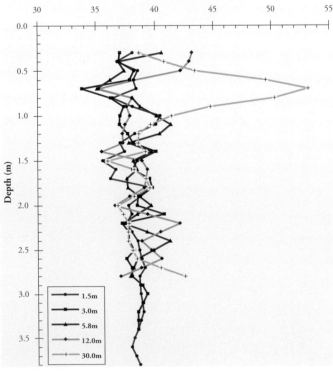

Spring soil moisture content profiles

Comments: Variable profiles.

66

Seasonal fluctuations in soil moisture deficit at 1.0m depth

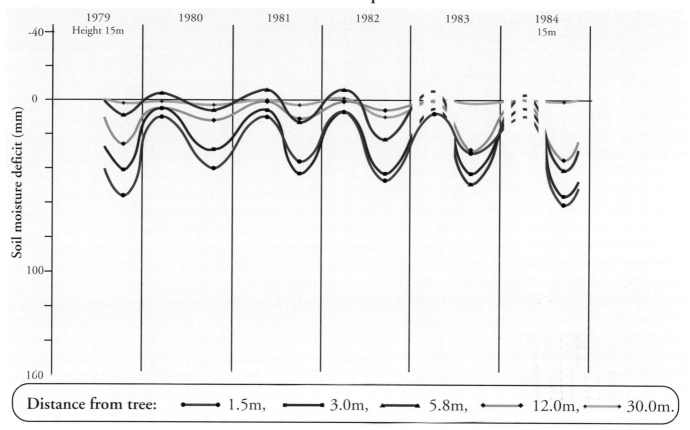

Comments: Seasonal fluctuations similar throughout, with slight increase in amplitude in dry years of 1979 and 1984.

Maximum soil drying recorded at 1.5m from tree in various years

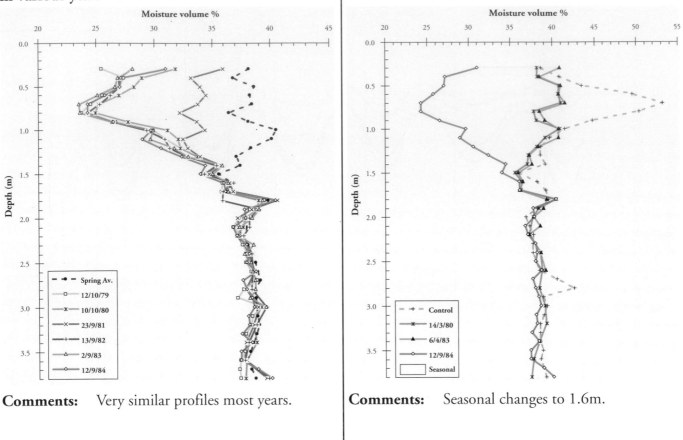

Comments: Very similar profiles most years.

Seasonal deficit 1.5m from tree

Comments: Seasonal changes to 1.6m.

Seasonal development of soil drying at 3.0m from tree during 1984

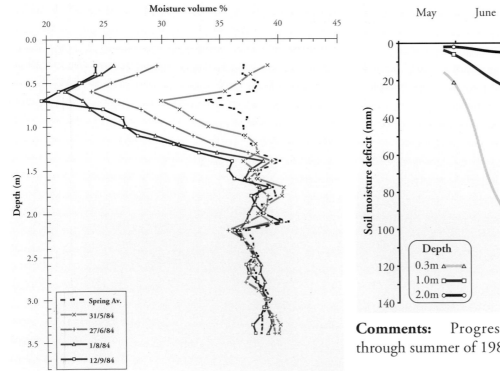

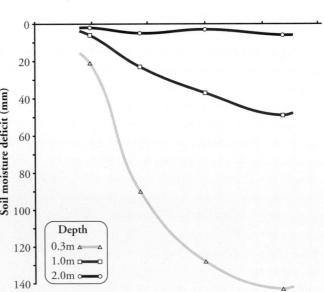

Comments: Progressive development of deficit through summer of 1984.

Reduction in soil moisture content on 12/9/84 compared with spring average

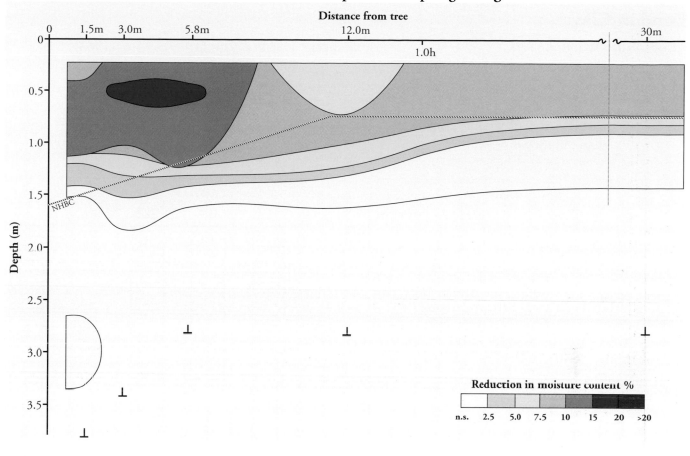

Soil moisture deficit on 12/9/84 compared with spring average

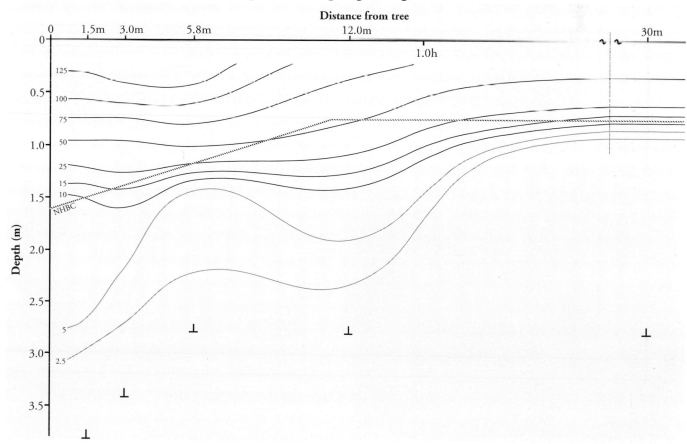

Lime
London Clay

Location: Woodside Park,   **Size:** Height: 17m (1979); 17m (1984)
         Haringey   Map ref: TQ 309 912   b.h.d.: 68cm (1979).

Current status: Site destroyed in 1985 by engineering works.

Site: Part of a row of similar limes along edge of park. Access tubes aligned to east, on slight upward slope, in mown grass.

Soil profile:	Distance from tree (m) x height (in 1979)			
	3.4 / 0.2	6.8 / 0.4	13.6 / 0.8	34.0 / 2.0

Soil classification tests:

Distance from tree (m)	3.4	3.4	6.8	6.8
Depth (m)	1.0	2.0	1.0	2.0
Plastic limit	33	29	30	28
Liquid limit	82	66	89	76
Plasticity index	49	37	59	48
% linear shrinkage	14.4	10.8	-	-

Spring soil moisture content profiles

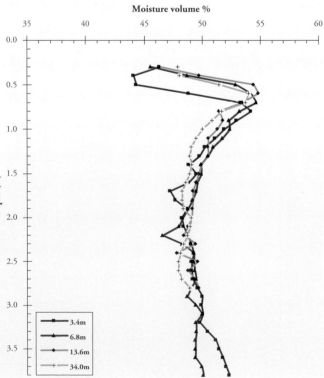

Comments: Similar profiles at all positions.

Seasonal fluctuations in soil moisture deficit at 1.0m depth

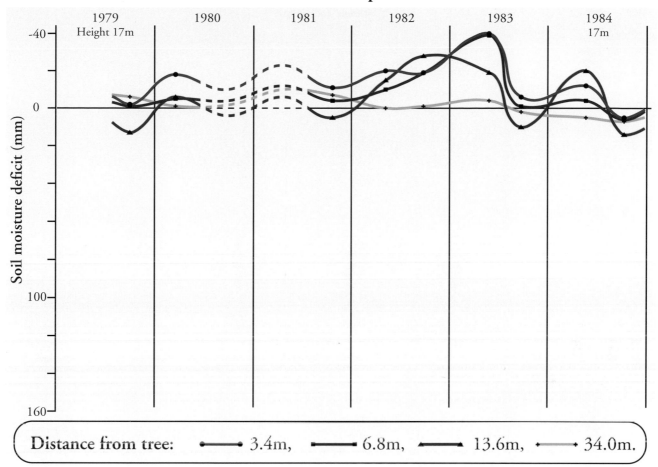

Comments: Slight rehydration prior to 1983.

Maximum soil drying recorded at 3.4m from tree in various years

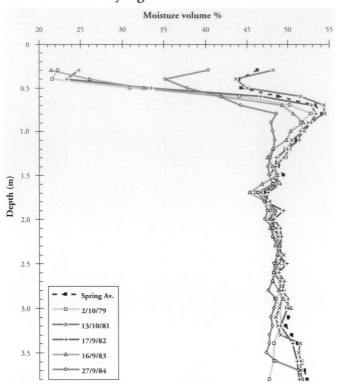

Comments: Additional drying extending to near base of access tube in dry years such as 1979 and 1984.

Seasonal deficits 3.4m from tree

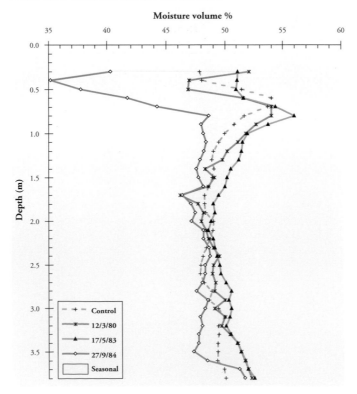

Comments: Seasonal drying extending to base of access tube in 1984.

Reduction in soil moisture content on 27/9/84 compared with spring average

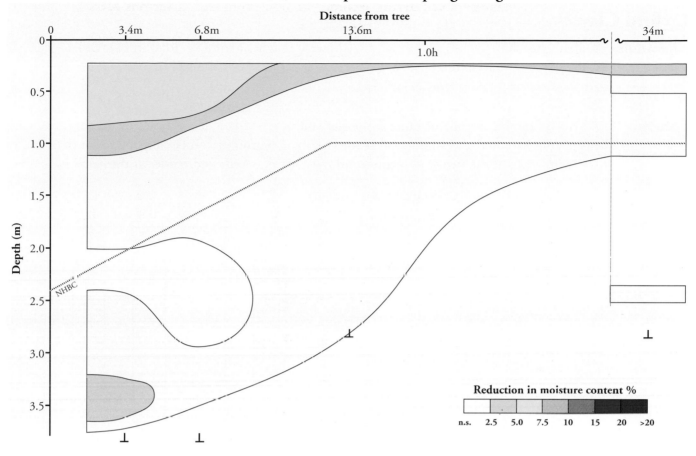

Soil moisture deficit on 27/9/84 compared with spring average

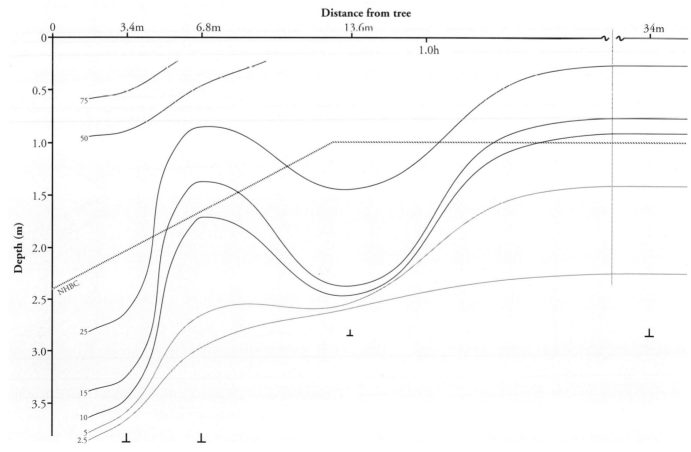

Lime
Oxford Clay

Tree 13

Location: Willen Church,
Willen   Map ref: SP 878 412

Size: Height: 15m (1979); 15m (1984)
b.h.d.: 65cm (1979).

Current status: Site disturbed by redevelopment.

Site: End tree of double avenue of limes (opposite end to tree 14). Access holes in rough gravel path between old barn and a retaining wall at edge of Church grounds. Tubes aligned to south of tree in short worn grass at the two closest tubes and the control; weeds and nettles at the other two tubes.

Soil profile:	Distance from tree (m)	1.5	3.0	6.0	12.0	30.0
	x height (in 1979)	0.1	0.2	0.4	0.8	2.0

Soil classification tests: None

Spring soil moisture content profiles

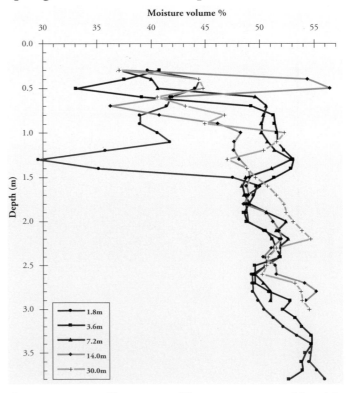

Comments: Closest profile suggests considerable persistent deficit extending only to 1.5m.

Seasonal fluctuations in soil moisture deficit at 1.0m depth

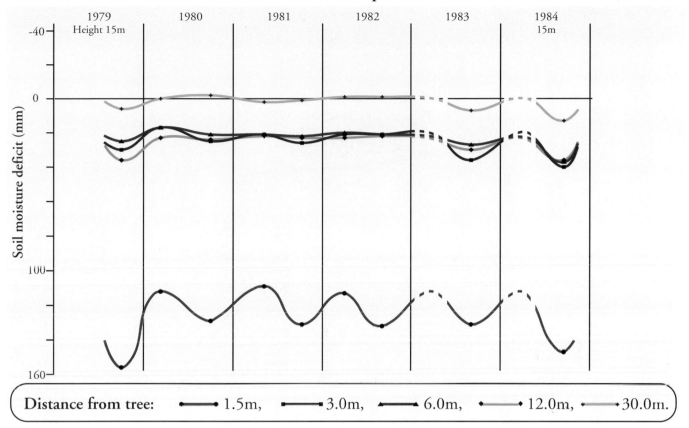

Comments: Seasonal fluctuations restricted to the closest access tube, with slight increase in amplitude in dry summers of 1979 and 1984.

Maximum soil drying recorded at 1.5m from tree in various years

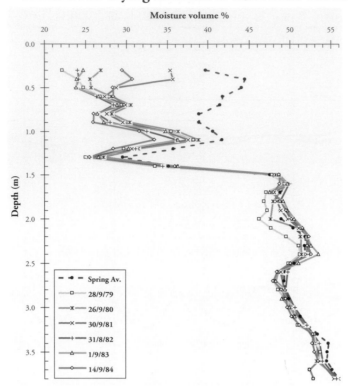

Comments: Very similar profiles most years, but some additional drying between 1.7 and 2.3m depth in 1979.

Seasonal (and persistent) deficits 1.5m from tree

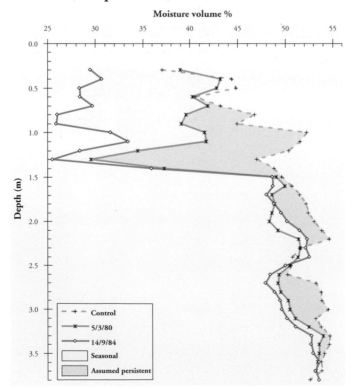

Comments: The slight seasonal changes which occur to the full depth of the access tube, together with the similarity in profiles each year, suggests that the assumed persistent deficit is not genuine.

Reduction in soil moisture content on 28/9/79 compared with spring average

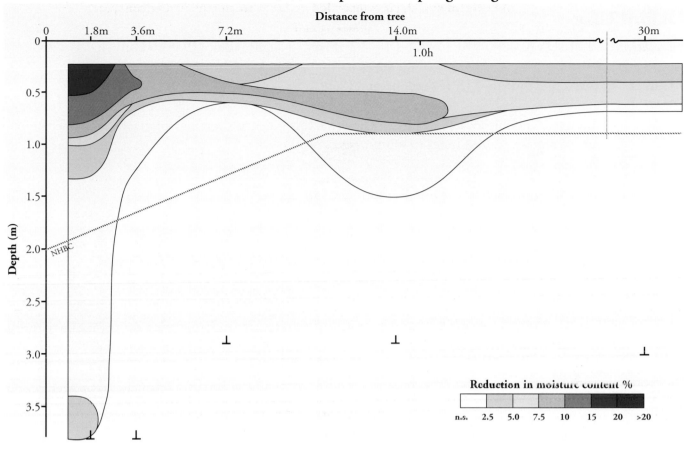

Soil moisture deficit on 28/9/79 compared with spring average

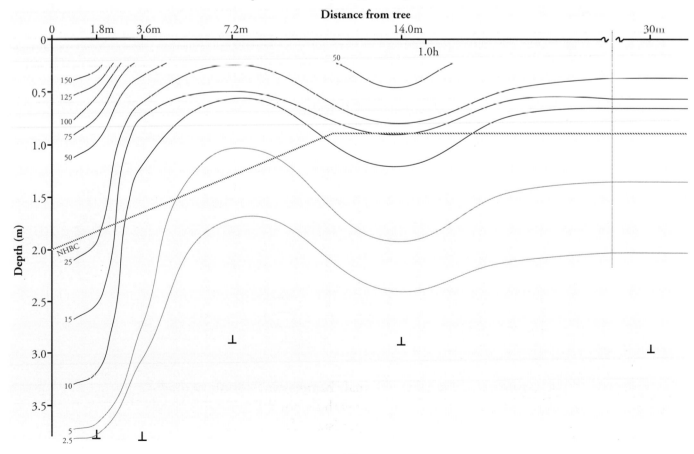

Lime
Oxford Clay

Tree 14

Location: Willen Priory,
Willen   Map ref: SP 878 412

Current status: Site disturbed by redevelopment.

Size: Height: 12m (1978); 16 m (1984)
b.h.d.: 47cm (1978).

Site: End tree of double avenue of limes. Closest access tubes in short mown grass, remainder in long unmown grass. Access tubes to south of tree.

Soil profile:	Distance from tree (m)		1.2	2.4	4.8	9.6	26.0
	x height (in 1978)		0.1	0.2	0.4	0.8	2.0

Soil classification tests:

Distance from tree (m)	2.4	2.4	2.4
Depth (m)	1.0	1.5	2.0
Plastic limit	29	21	34
Liquid limit	63	47	66
Plasticity index	34	26	32
% linear shrinkage	11.3	10.8	13.8

Spring soil moisture content profiles

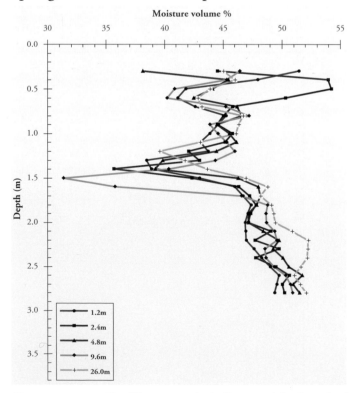

Comments: Profiles strongly influenced by band of sand around 1.5m.

Seasonal fluctuations in soil moisture deficit at 1.0m depth

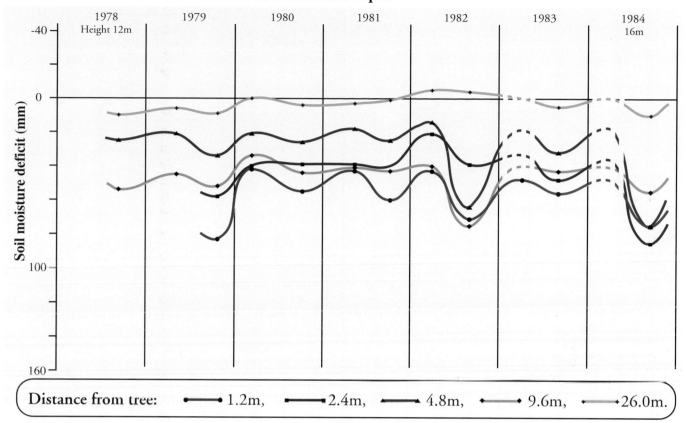

Comments: Different access tubes show very different amplitude of movement in different years. For instance, the tube 9.6m from the tree has an increased deficit in 1982 but very little in 1984; the tube 2.4m from the tree shows the opposite pattern.

Maximum soil drying recorded at 1.2m from tree in various years

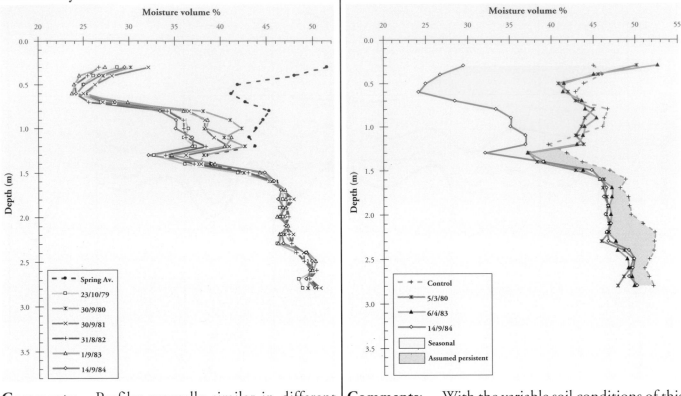

Comments: Profiles generally similar in different years.

Seasonal (and persistent) deficits 1.2m from tree

Comments: With the variable soil conditions of this site, it is unlikely that the assumed persistent deficit is genuine.

Seasonal development of soil drying at 2.4m from tree during 1984

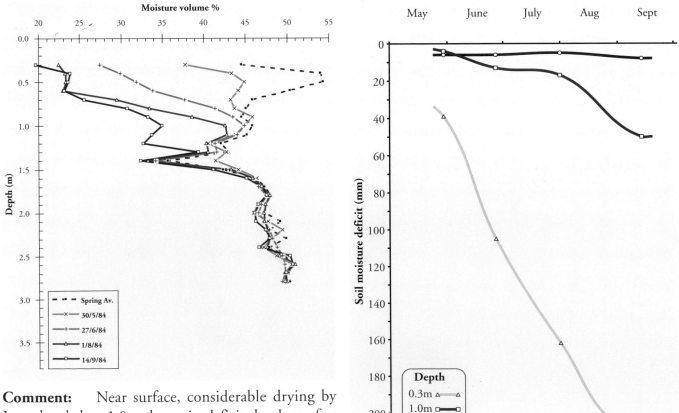

Comment: Near surface, considerable drying by June, but below 1.0m the main deficit develops after July.

Reduction in soil moisture content on 14/9/84 compared with spring average

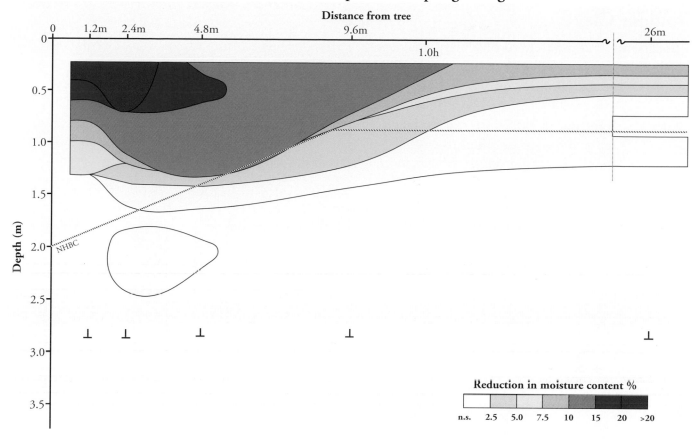

Soil moisture deficit on 14/9/84 compared with spring average

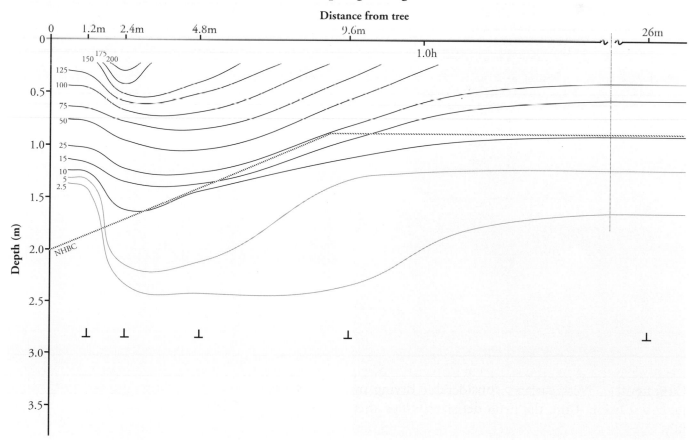

Lime
Boulder Clay

Location: Park adjacent to Bletchley Church of
England School.   Map ref: SP 860 334

Size: Height: 14m (1979); 16 m (1993)
b.h.d.:   57cm (1992).

Current status: Routine readings still in progress.

Site: On edge of park, with rear gardens of properties immediately adjacent to south. Access tubes in close mown grass, oriented NW of tree. The surface of the park has been drained in the past by producing slight ridges; the tubes were placed in the top of these.

Soil profile:	Distance from tree (m) x height (in 1979)	1.4 0.1	2.8 0.2	5.6 0.4	11.2 0.8	28.0 2.0

Soil classification tests:

Distance from tree (m)	2.8	2.8	2.8
Depth (m)	1.0	1.5	2.0
Plastic limit	-	20	20
Liquid limit	42	43	40
Plasticity index	-	23	20
% linear shrinkage	10.8	9.9	9.1

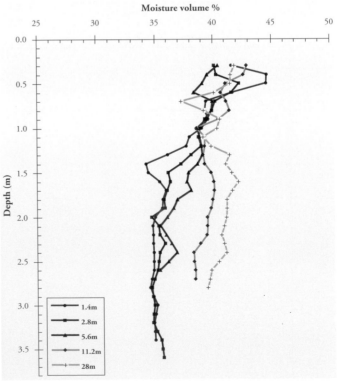

Spring soil moisture content profiles

Comments: Significantly drier profiles for the three access tubes closest to the tree.

Seasonal fluctuations in soil moisture deficit at 1.0m depth

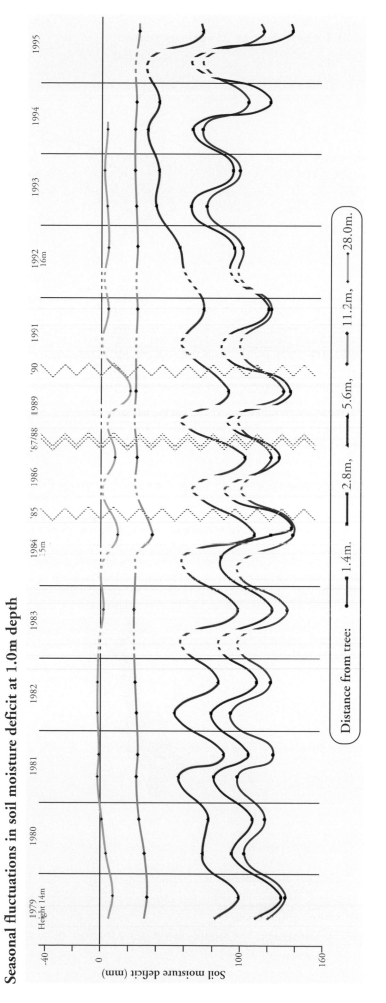

Distance from tree: ⟶ 1.4m. ⟶ 2.8m, ⟶ 5.6m, ⟶ 11.2m, ⟶ 28.0m.

Comments: The two access tubes furthest from the tree show negligible fluctuation throughout. The three closest access tubes show very similar fluctuations, all apparently with a superimposed persistent deficit (see page 84). At the tube 5.6m from the tree gradual rehydration of this persistent deficit started in 1984 and has continued progressively since then apart from 1995; at the two closest tubes there has been similar rehydration since 1989, again reversing in 1995 (page 87).

Maximum soil drying recorded at 1.4m from tree in various years

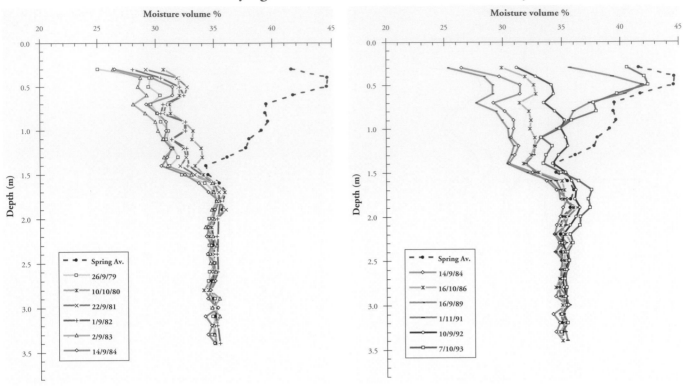

Comments: During this period the driest profile was in 1983.

Comments: Driest profile in 1989, with markedly wetter profile in 1993.

Seasonal (and persistent) deficits 1.4m from tree

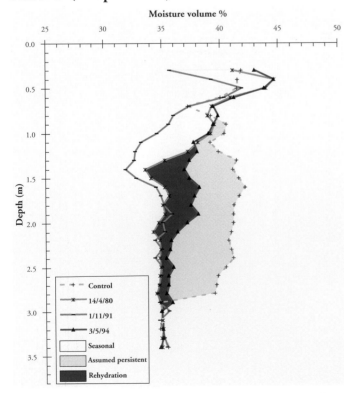

Comments: Considerable assumed persistent deficit, but with partial rehydration by 1994.

Seasonal (and persistent) deficits 5.6m from tree

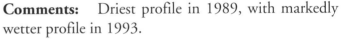
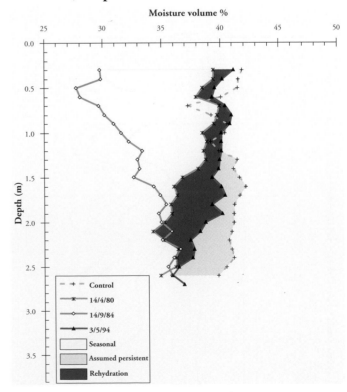

Comments: Considerable rehydration occurring between 1980 and 1994.

Seasonal development of soil drying during summer 1984, and subsequent rehydration, 2.8m from tree

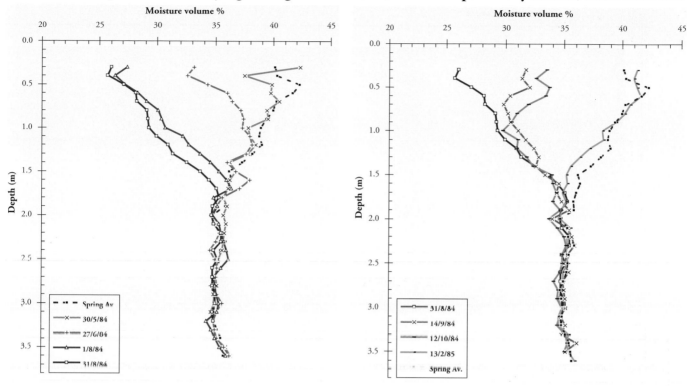

Seasonal changes in soil moisture deficit at 2.8m from tree during 1984/5

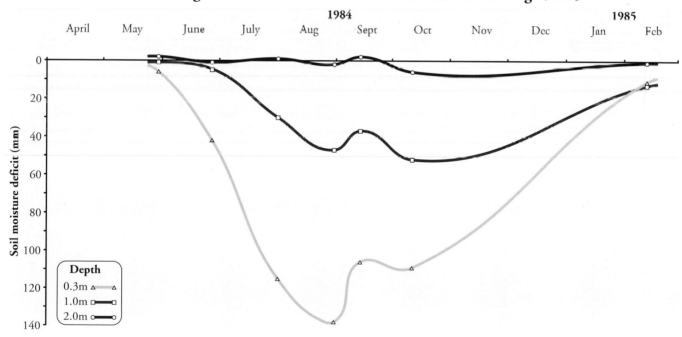

Comments: Considerable drying occurred through to the end of August, with significant recovery as a result of heavy rain in early September. There was then a slight increase in the deficit again in early October. Seasonal recovery was almost complete by mid-February 1985.

Reduction in soil moisture content on 16/9/89 compared with spring average

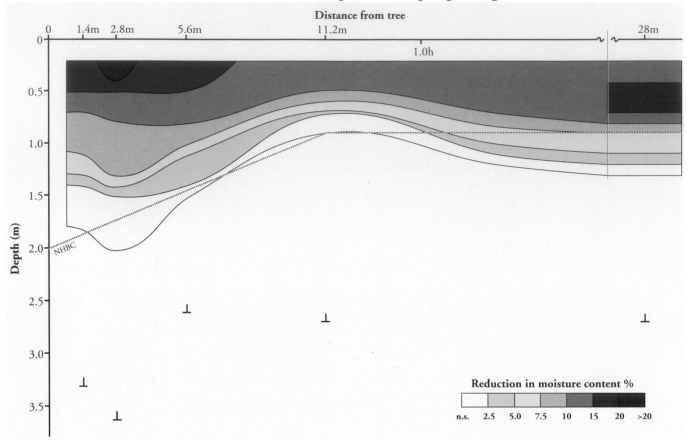

Soil moisture deficit on 16/9/89 compared with spring average

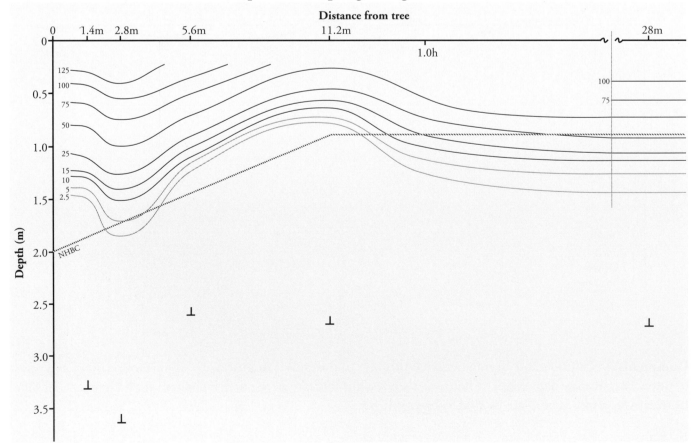

Increase in soil moisture content on 3/5/94 compared with 14/4/80

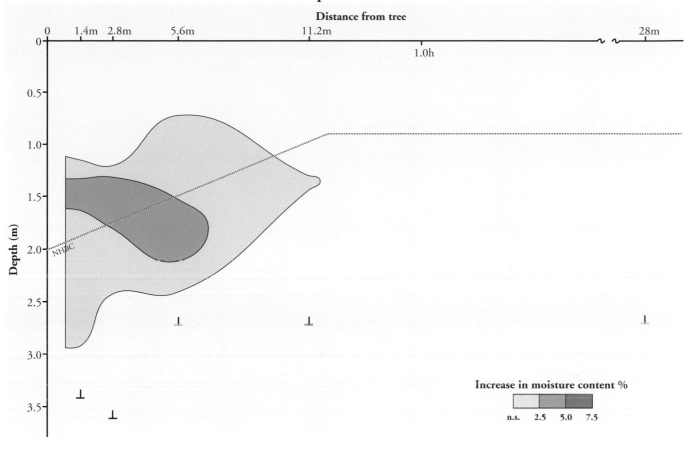

Rehydration on 3/5/94 compared with 14/4/80

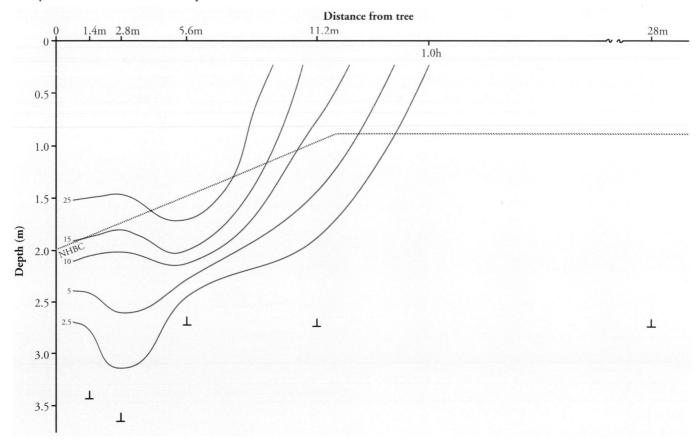

Lime
Boulder Clay

Location: Stacey Hall,
Wolverton   Map ref: SP 821 404

Size: Height: 15m (1978); 16m (1984)
b.h.d.: 68cm (1978).

Current status: Site destroyed by new development.

Site: Isolated tree close to edge of field grazed by horses. Access tubes aligned to SW of tree, with slight slope down to SW.

Soil profile:				Distance from tree (m) x height (in 1978)	1.4 0.09	3.0 0.2	4.9 0.33	10.0 0.66	30.0 2.0
Soil classification tests:									
Distance from tree (m)	1.4	3.0	3.0	3.0					
Depth (m)	2.0	1.0	1.5	2.0					
Plastic limit	29	18	17	17					
Liquid limit	45	36	36	34					
Plasticity index	16	18	19	17					
% linear shrinkage	-	-	-	8.9					

Spring soil moisture content profiles

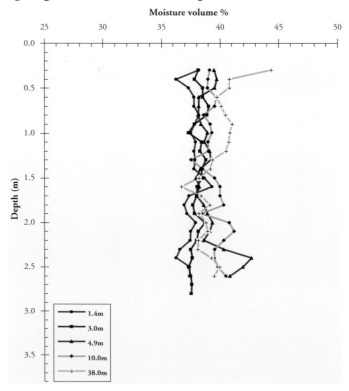

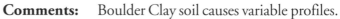

Comments: Boulder Clay soil causes variable profiles.

Seasonal fluctuations in soil moisture deficit at 1.0m depth

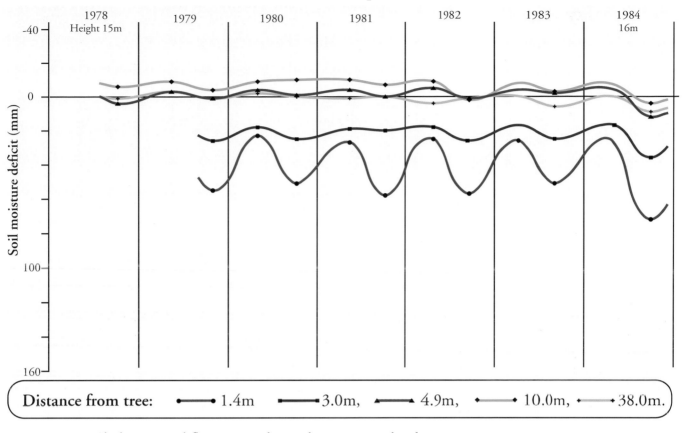

Comments: Slight seasonal fluctuation, but only at access tube closest to tree.

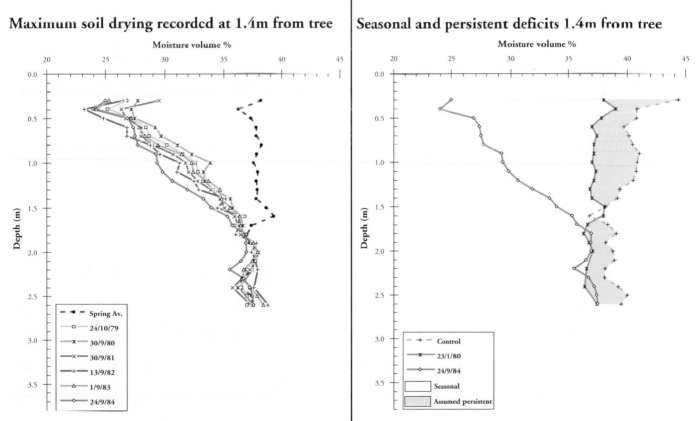

Maximum soil drying recorded at 1.4m from tree

Seasonal and persistent deficits 1.4m from tree

Comments: Very similar profiles, with maximum drying in 1984.

Comments: Assumed persistent deficit is unlikely to be genuine, except possibly below 1.5m.

Seasonal development of soil drying during summer 1979, and subsequent rehydration, 1.4m from tree

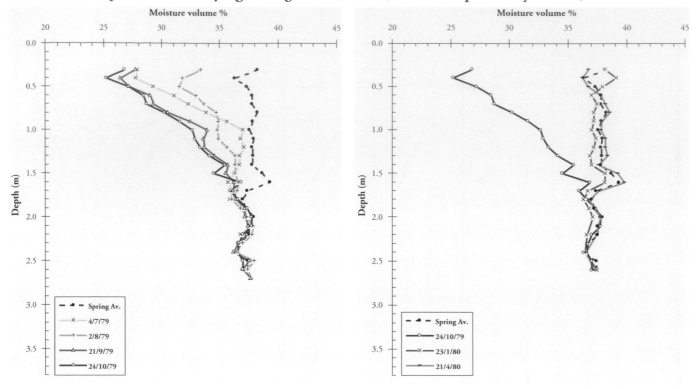

Seasonal changes in soil moisture deficit at 1.4m from tree during 1979/80

Comments: Readings did not start until mid-summer, by which time the seasonal deficit was already partially established, particularly at 0.3m depth.

Seasonal development of soil drying during summer 1979, and subsequent rehydration, 4.9m from tree

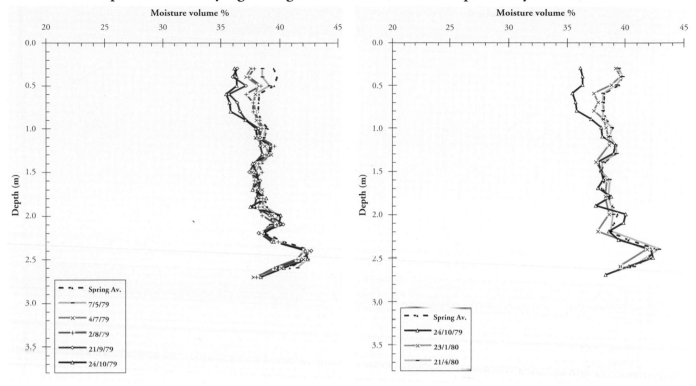

Seasonal changes in soil moisture deficit at 4.9m from tree during 1979/80

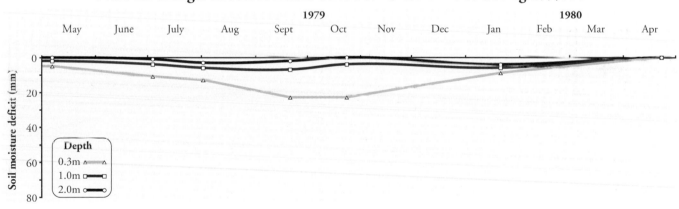

Comments: At this distance the tree was having negligible influence, even close to the surface.

Seasonal development of soil drying at 1.4m from tree during 1983

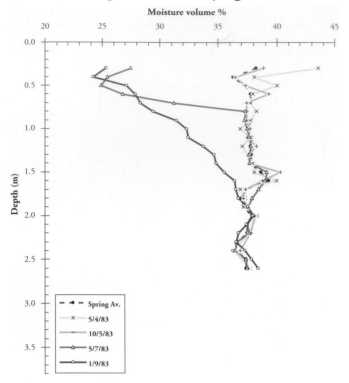

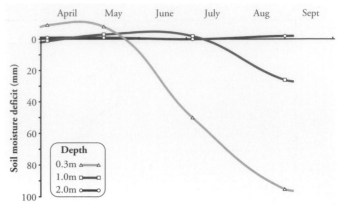

Comments: Seasonal drying extends to 1.8m depth.

Seasonal development of soil drying at 3.0m from tree during 1984

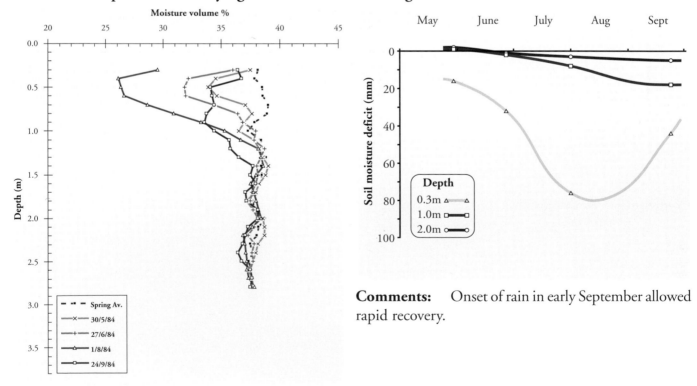

Comments: Onset of rain in early September allowed rapid recovery.

Reduction in soil moisture content on 24/9/84 compared with spring average

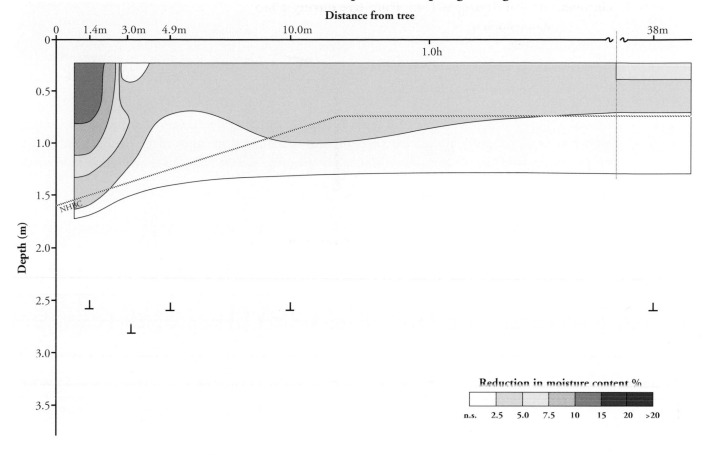

Soil moisture deficit on 24/9/84 compared with spring average

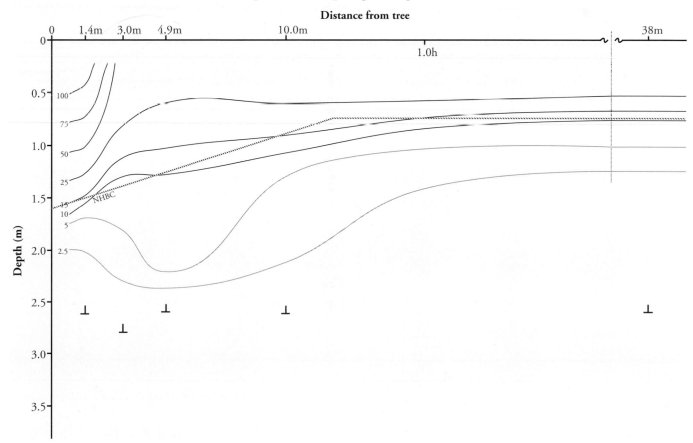

Norway maple
London Clay

Tree 17

Location: Centenary Park,   **Size:** Height: 11m (1983); 12m (1991)
Stanmore   Map ref: TQ 176 904   b.h.d.: 42cm (1991).

Current status: Routine readings ceased because of negligible effects even in 1991.

Site: One of a pair of Norway maple (the other is tree 18) situated near eastern boundary of the park adjacent to a school playground. Trees are growing on a slight slope upwards to the boundary fence, with some surface run-off from the adjacent playground. Access tubes in mown grass to the west.

Soil profile:	Distance from tree (m)	2.2	4.4	7.2	9.4	22.6
	x height (in 1983)	0.2	0.4	0.7	0.9	2.1

Soil classification tests: None

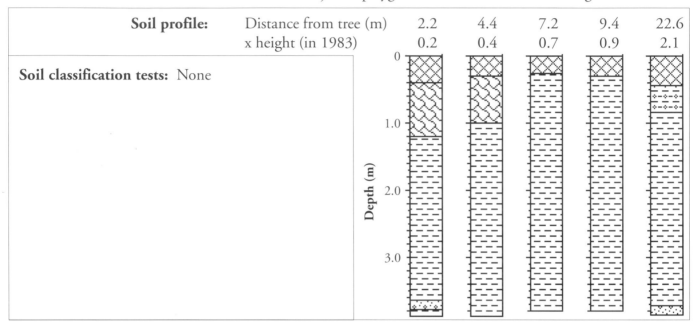

Spring soil moisture content profiles

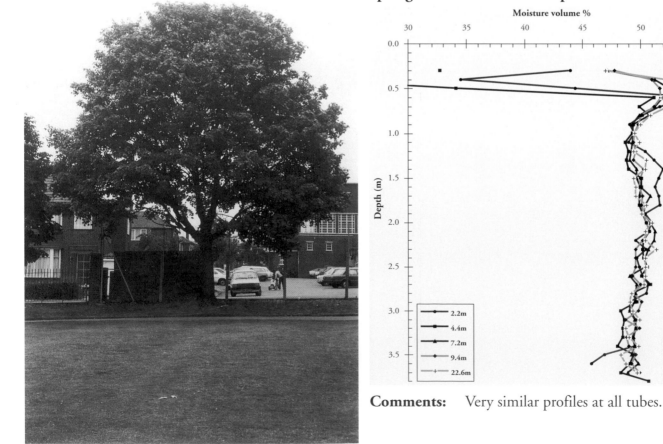

Comments: Very similar profiles at all tubes.

Seasonal fluctuations in soil moisture deficit at 1.0m depth

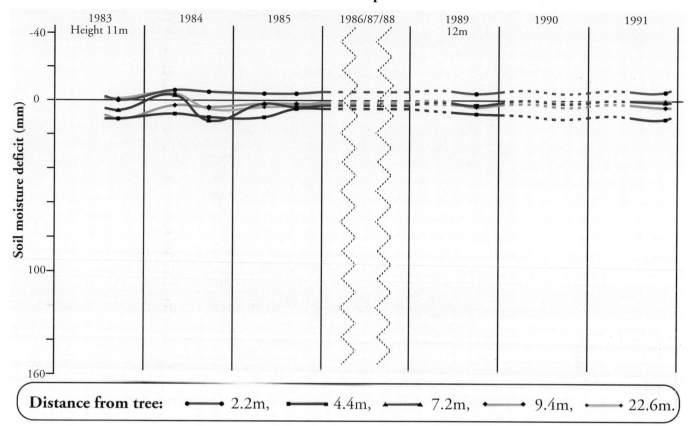

Comments: Negligible fluctuation at any of the access tubes, even in dry years.

Maximum soil drying recorded at 2.2m from tree in various years

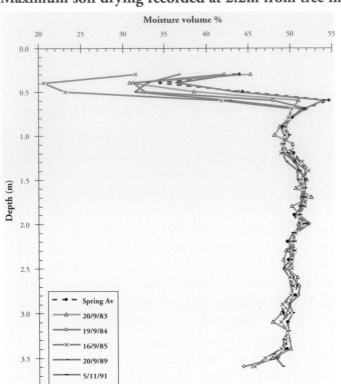

Comments: The driest profile was in 1985, probably because partial recovery had occurred in other years.

Seasonal deficit 2.2m from tree

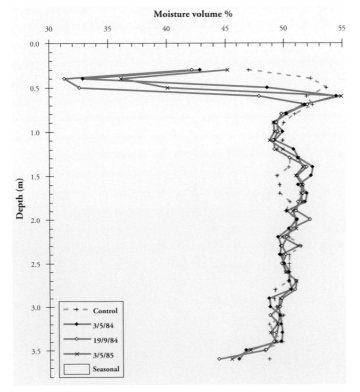

Comments: Seasonal effects only extend to 0.7m.

Reduction in soil moisture content on 20/9/89 compared with spring average

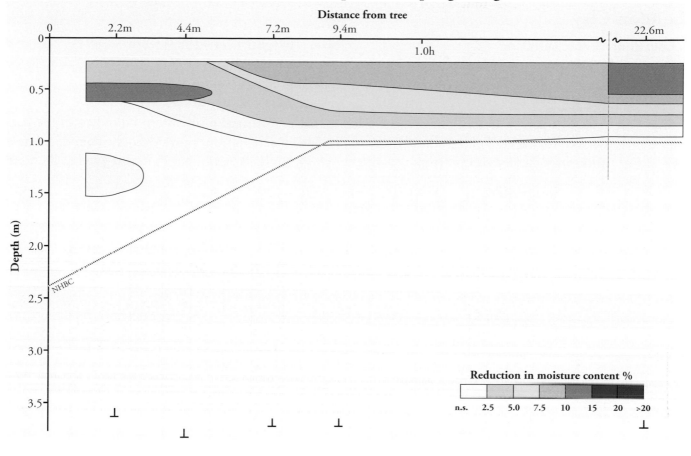

Soil moisture deficit on 20/9/89 compared with spring average

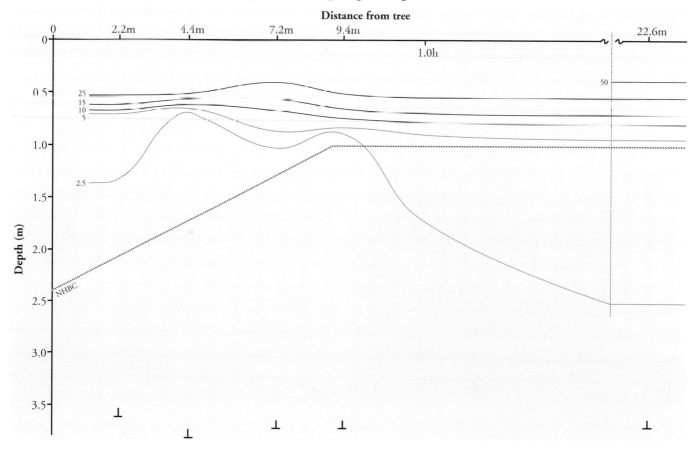

Norway maple
London Clay

Location: Centenary Park,   **Size:** Height: 11m (1983); 12m (1991)
Stanmore   Map ref: TQ 176 904   b.h.d.: 38cm (1991).

Current status: Routine readings ceased because of negligible effects even in 1991.

Site: One of a pair of Norway maple (the other is tree 17) situated near eastern boundary of the park adjacent to a school playground. Trees are growing on a slight slope upwards to the boundary fence, with some surface run-off from the adjacent playground. Access tubes in mown grass to the west.

Soil profile:	Distance from tree (m)	2.2	4.4	6.8	8.8	23.0
	x height (in 1983)	0.2	0.4	0.6	0.8	2.1

Soil classification tests: None

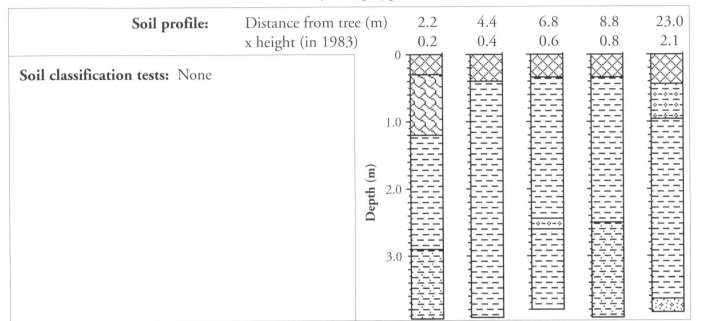

Spring soil moisture content profiles

Comments: Similar profiles at all tubes.

Seasonal fluctuations in soil moisture deficit at 1.0m depth

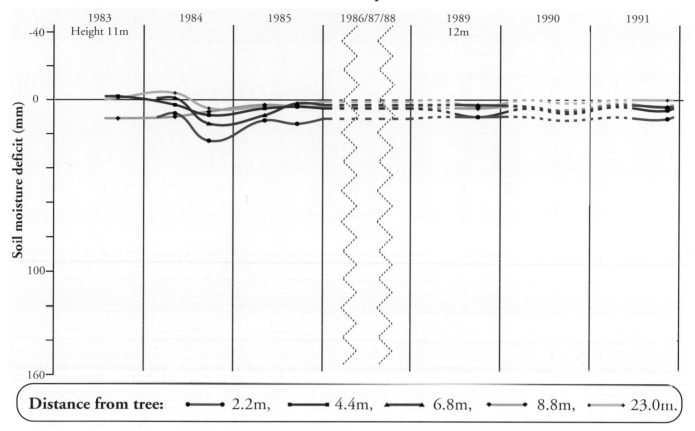

Comments: Negligible fluctuation at any of the access tubes, even in dry years.

Maximum soil drying recorded at 2.2m from tree in various years

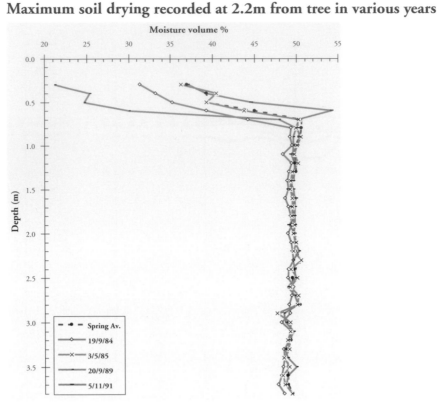

Comments: Driest profile in 1989; delayed readings
in 1991 allowed full recovery.

Seasonal deficit 2.2m from tree

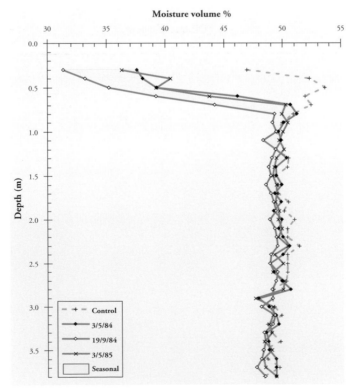

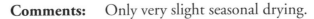

Comments: Only very slight seasonal drying.

Reduction in soil moisture content on 20/9/89 compared with spring average

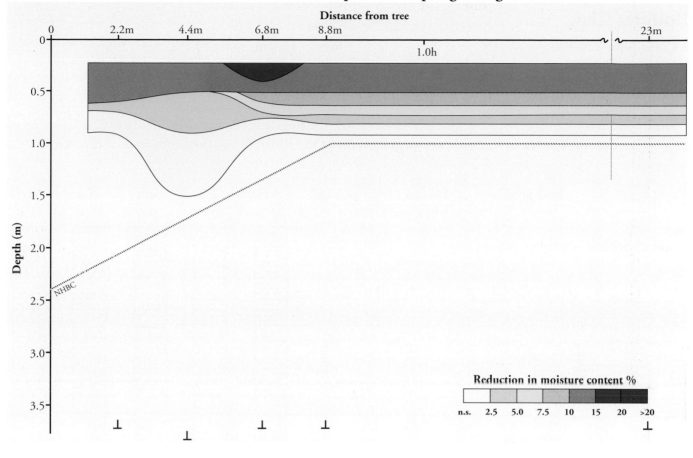

Soil moisture deficit on 20/9/89 compared with spring average

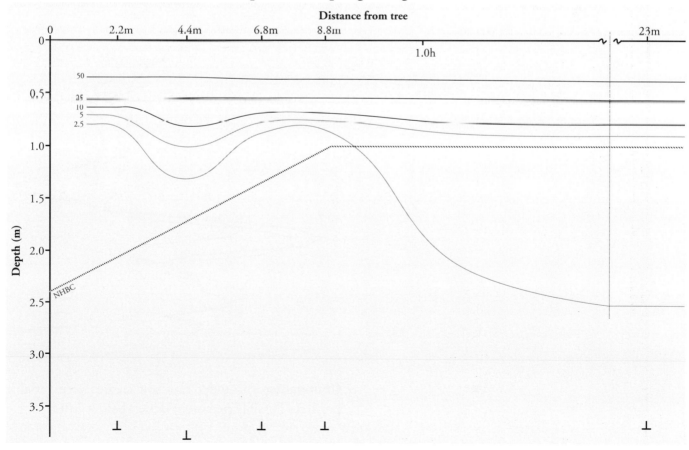

Norway maple
Boulder Clay

Location: The Ridgeway,
                Welwyn   Map ref: TL 255 127

Size: Height: 8m (1983); 8m (1985)
            b.h.d.: 40cm (1985).

Current status: Growth of other trees in locality now likely to interfer with results.

Site: Part of a widely-spaced group of ornamental plantings adjacent to an old hedge. The access tubes are positioned in the wide mown grass verge of the Ridgeway to the south west of the tree.

Soil profile:	Distance from tree (m)	1.6	3.2	4.8	6.4	16.0
	x height (in 1983)	0.2	0.4	0.6	0.8	2.0

Soil classification tests: None

Spring soil moisture content profiles

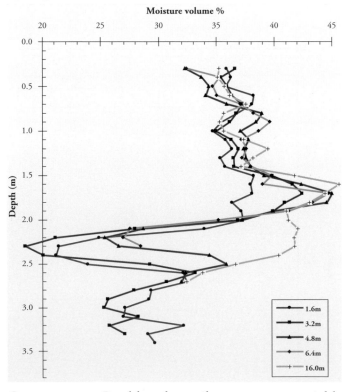

Comments: Boulder clay soil creates very variable profiles. Possible persistent deficit below 2.0m.

Seasonal fluctuations in soil moisture deficit at 1.0m depth

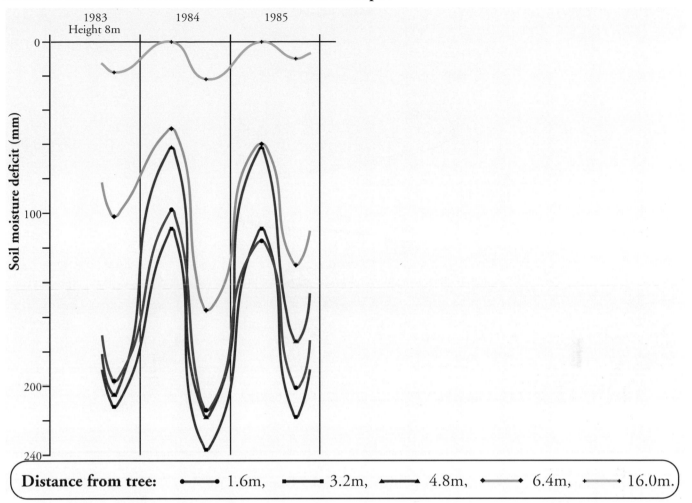

Comments: Considerable seasonal fluctuation on the sandy boulder clay soil.

Maximum soil drying recorded at 1.6m from tree in various years

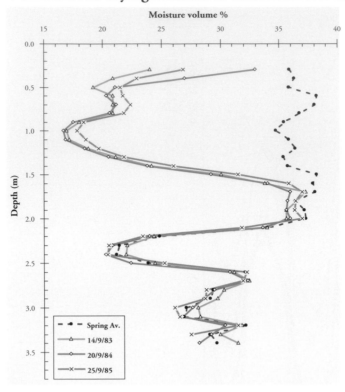

Comments: Very similar profiles developing each year.

Seasonal (and persistent) deficits 1.6m from tree

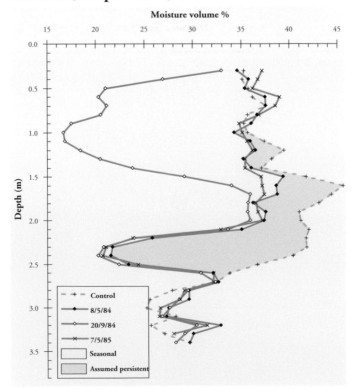

Comments: Seasonal drying extending to 2.0m. The very variable soil conditions make assumptions about a persistent deficit unreliable.

Reduction in soil moisture content on 14/9/83 compared with spring average

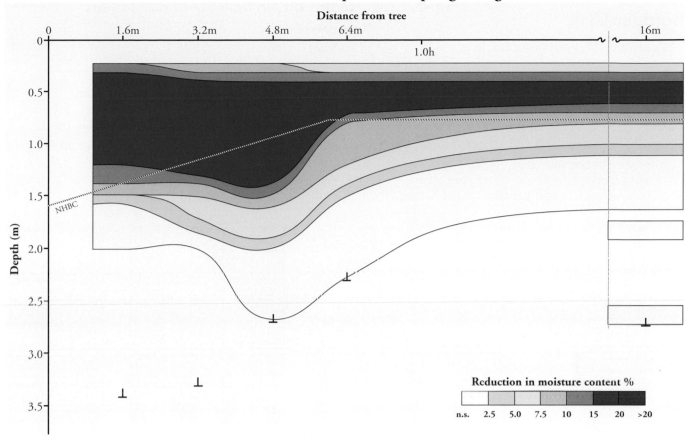

Soil moisture deficit on 14/9/83 compared with spring average

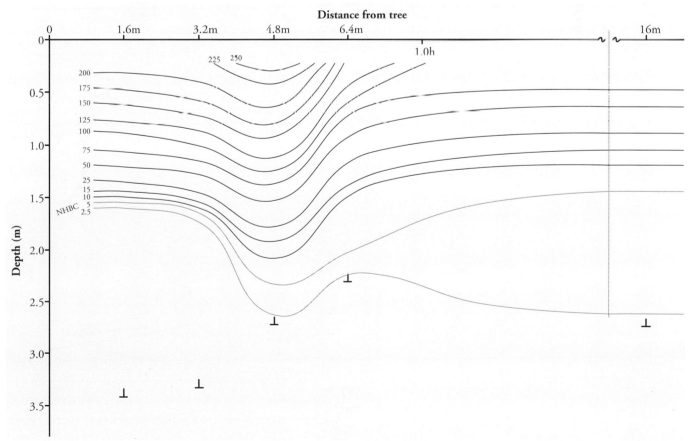

Norway maple
Boulder Clay

Location: Parkway Junior School,   **Size:**   Height: 14m (1983); 14m (1985)
Welwyn   Map ref: TL 235 124   b.h.d.: 37cm (1985).

Current status: Variable soil conditions make site of dubious value.

Site: One of a row of trees, mainly Norway maples, which form the boundary between the tarmac playground and a grassed area. The access holes are to the south of the tree in the close mown grass of the play area.

Soil profile:	Distance from tree (m)	2.8	5.6	8.4	11.2	27.0
	x height (in 1983)	0.2	0.4	0.6	0.8	2.0

Soil classification tests: None

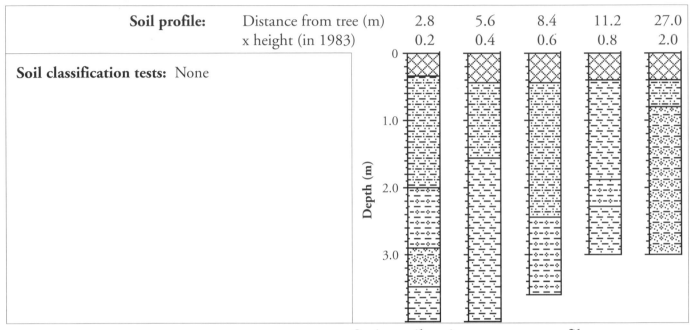

Spring soil moisture content profiles

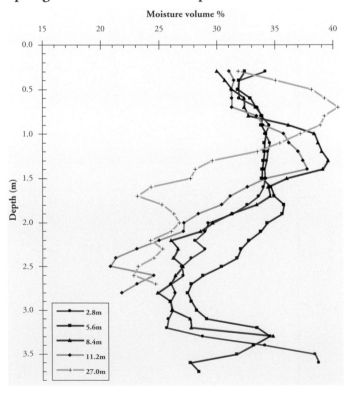

Comments: Boulder clay creates variable profiles, with the control generally drier than other access tubes.

Seasonal fluctuations in soil moisture deficit at 1.0m depth

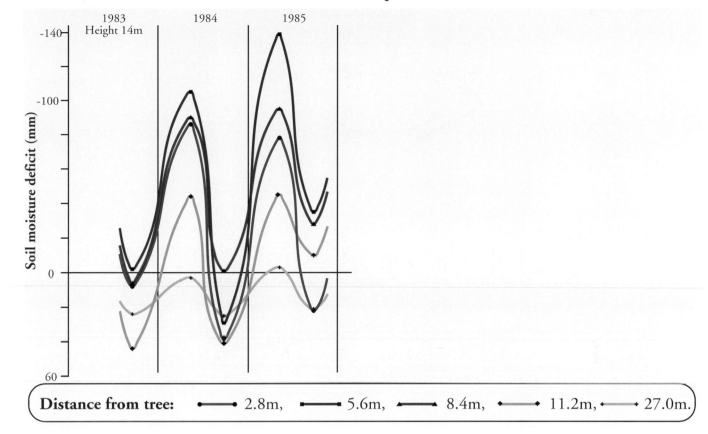

Distance from tree: 2.8m, 5.6m, 8.4m, 11.2m, 27.0m.

Comments: Considerable seasonal fluctuation at all access tubes, particularly those closest to the tree.

Maximum soil drying recorded at 2.8m from tree in various years

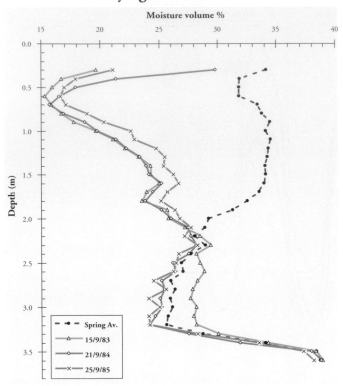

Comments: Variable profiles, with additional drying in 1984 and 1985.

Seasonal and persistent deficits 2.8m from tree

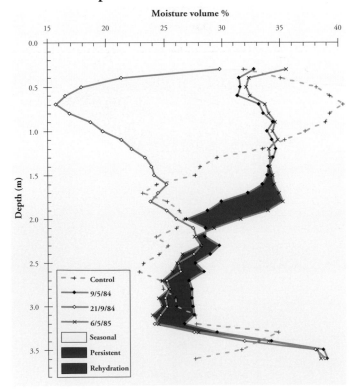

Comments: An unusual pattern of drying, with a persistent deficit developing below 2.2m but the soil rehydrating at shallower depths.

Reduction in soil moisture content on 14/9/83 compared with spring average

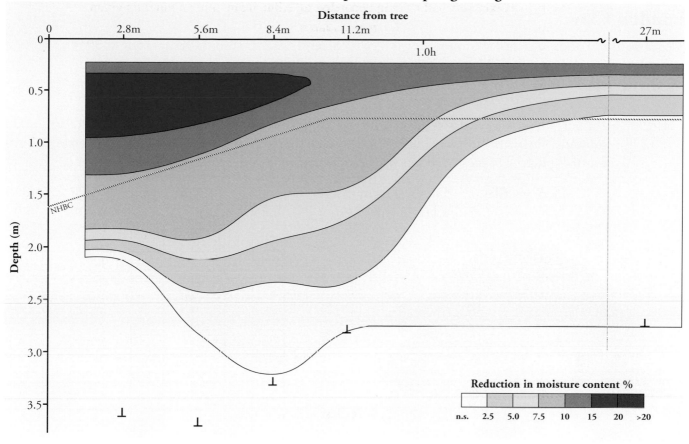

Soil moisture deficit on 14/9/83 compared with spring average

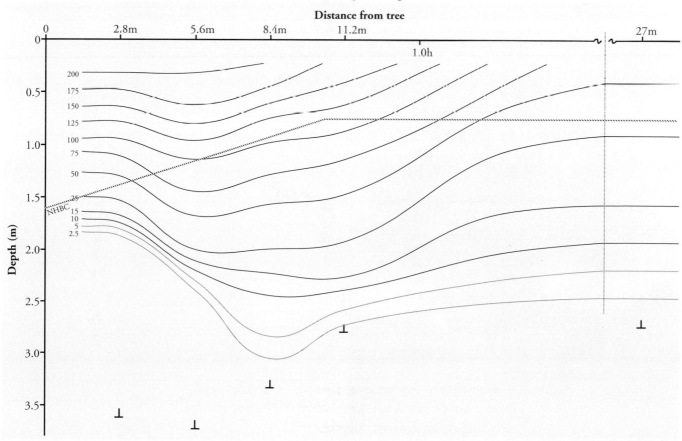

Oak
London Clay

Location: Roxeth Recreation Ground,
South Harrow   Map ref: TQ144 860

Size: Height: 16m (1983); 16m (1994)
b.h.d.: 89cm (1992).

Current status: Intermittent readings still in progress.

Site: Part of a widely spaced row of mature oak trees beside a footpath which bisects the recreation ground. The access tubes are in a line south east of the tree, sited in the mown grass of an occasional football pitch. Dieback of shoots has become apparent in the crown during the project.

Soil profile:	Distance from tree (m)	4.0	8.0	12.0	16.0	48.0
	x height (in 1983)	0.25	0.5	0.75	1.0	3.0

1983

1993

Spring soil moisture content profiles

Legend:
4.0m
8.0m
12.0m
12.0m
48.0m

Comments: Very similar profiles at all access tubes.

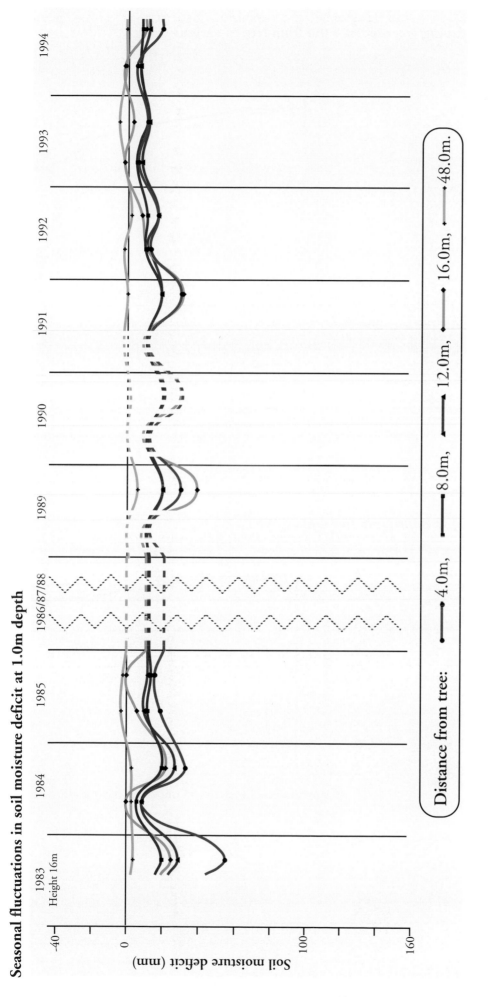

Seasonal fluctuations in soil moisture deficit at 1.0m depth

Distance from tree: 4.0m, 8.0m, 12.0m, 16.0m, 48.0m.

Comments: Trend towards reducing amplitude of fluctuation and increase in moisture content throughout project.

Maximum soil drying recorded at 4.0m from tree in various years

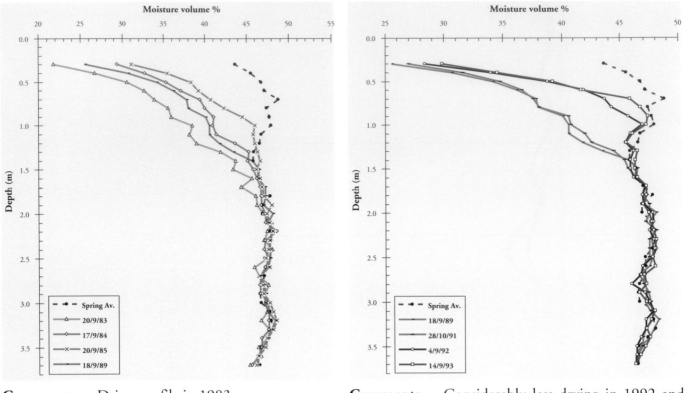

Comments: Driest profile in 1983.

Comments: Considerably less drying in 1992 and 1993.

Seasonal development of soil drying at 8.0m from tree during 1984

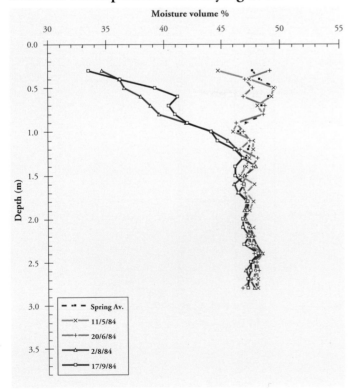

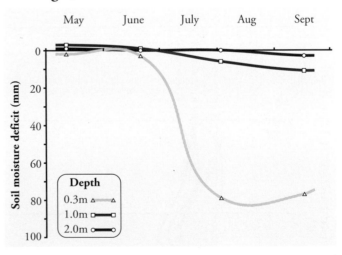

Comments: Restricted depth of drying allows rapid recovery.

Seasonal and persistent deficits

4.0m from tree

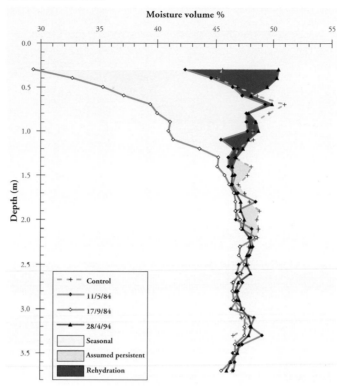

Comments: Increase in moisture content apparently only occurring at shallow depths.

8.0m from tree

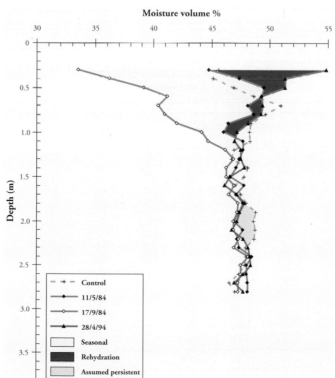

Comments: At this distance there is less seasonal deficit and rehydration.

Reduction in soil moisture content on 17/9/84 compared with spring average

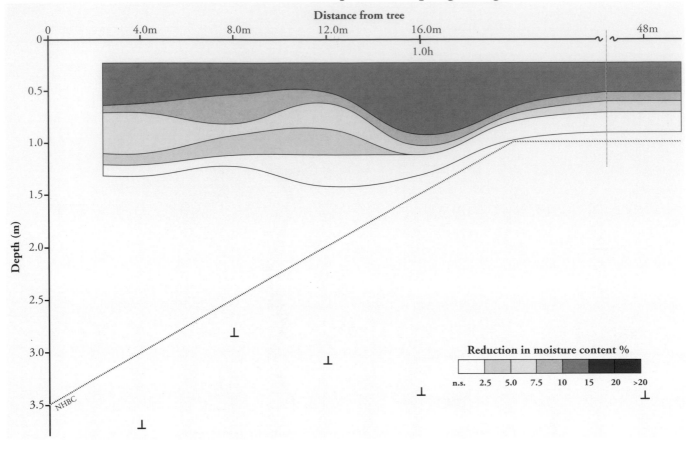

Soil moisture deficit on 17/9/84 compared with spring average

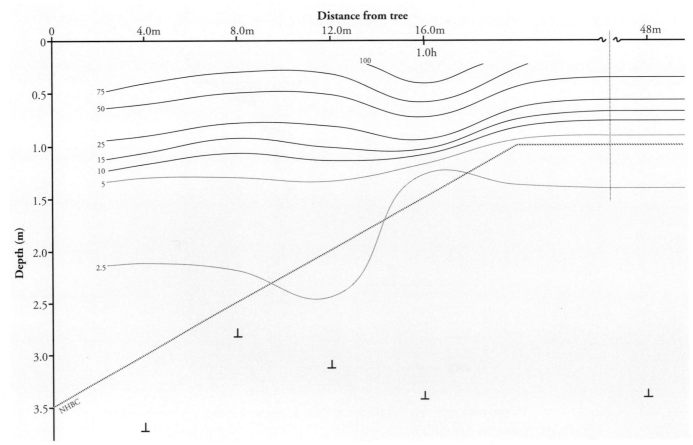

Reduction in soil moisture content on 20/9/94 compared with spring average

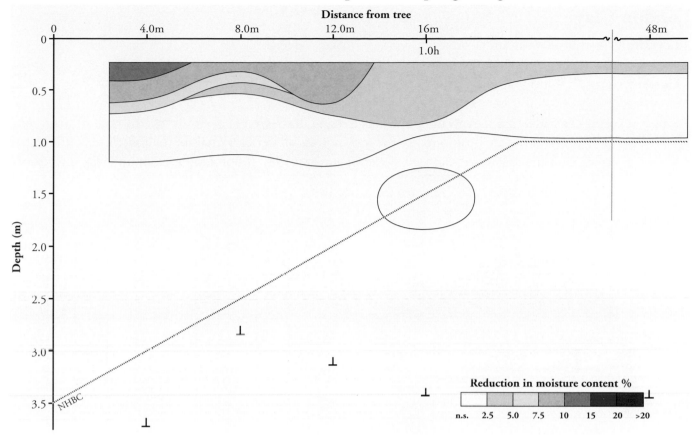

Soil moisture deficit on 20/9/94 compared with spring average

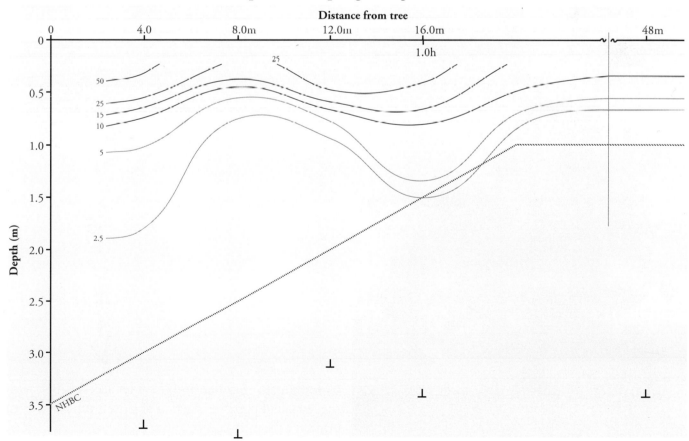

Oak
London Clay

Tree 22

Location: Roxeth Recreation Ground,
South Harrow   Map ref: TQ 144 860

Size: Height: 19m (1983); 15m (1994)
b.h.d.: 105cm (1992).

Current status: Routine readings still in progress.

Site: Part of a widely spaced row of mature oak trees, to north west of a path across the recreation ground. The access tubes are positioned in the mown grass of an occasional football pitch to south east of tree. Considerable storm damage to tree in autumn 1987 (photographs from opposite directions).

Soil profile:

| Distance from tree (m) | 4.8 | 9.5 | 14.2 | 19.0 | 43.0 |
| x height (in 1983) | 0.25 | 0.5 | 0.75 | 1.0 | 2.3 |

1983

1993

Spring soil moisture content profiles

Comments: Similar profiles at all access tubes, with suggestion of persistent deficit at closest tube at start of project.

116

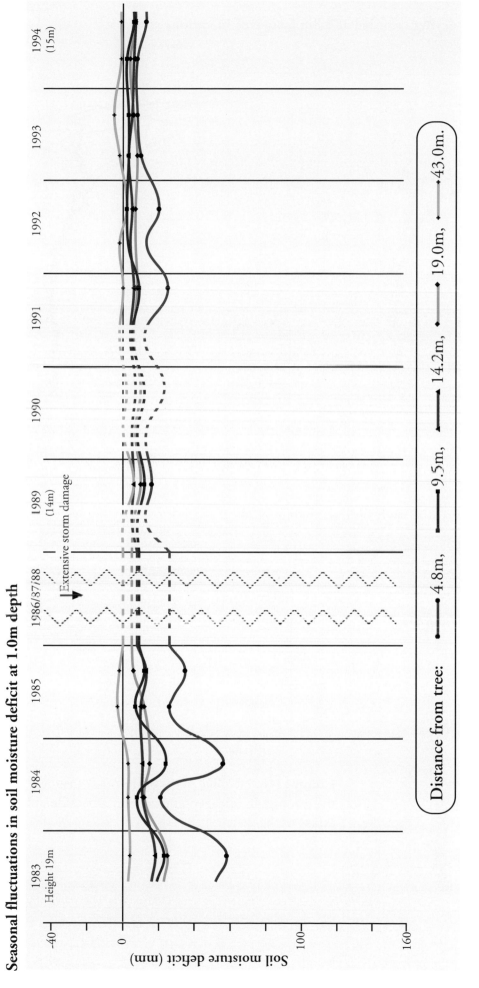

Seasonal fluctuations in soil moisture deficit at 1.0m depth

Comments: Trend of reducing amplitude of seasonal deficit and overall reduction in deficit at access tube closest to tree, particularly after the extensive storm damage which removed much of the top of this tree in 1987.

Maximum soil drying recorded at 4.8m from tree in various years

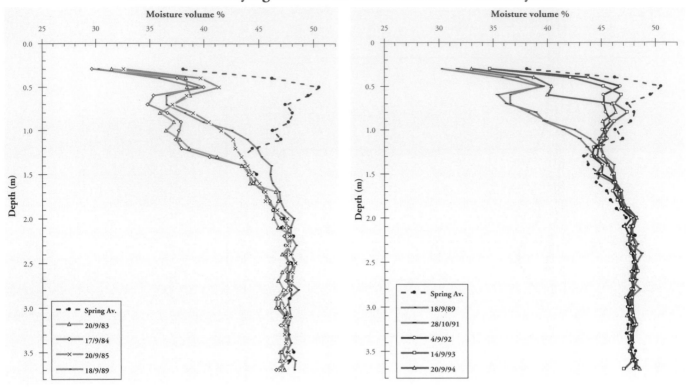

Comments: Profiles in 1983 and 1984 very similar, but considerably less drying in 1989 after the storm damage.

Comments: 1989 and 1991 very similar, but effects diminish further in subsequent years.

Seasonal development of soil drying at 9.5m from tree during 1984

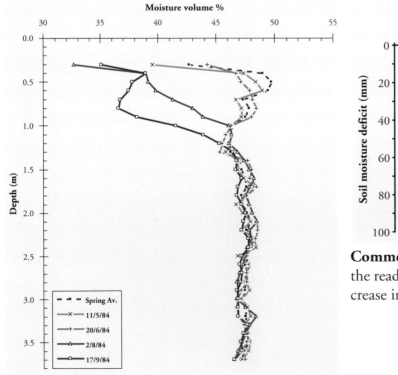

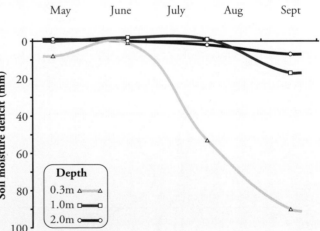

Comments: Unlike many of the other trees in 1984, the readings in mid-September show a considerable increase in the deficit.

Seasonal and persistent deficits

4.8m from tree

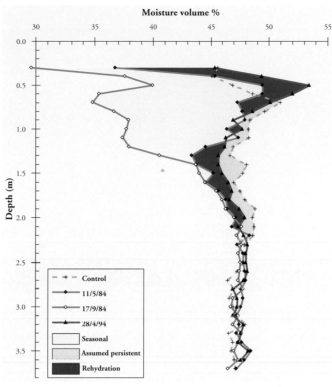

Comments: Significant rehydration extending to 2.1m

9.5m from tree

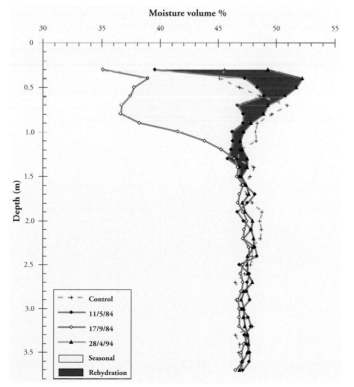

Comments: At this distance from the tree the rehydration is only a superficial effect caused by variation in readings near the surface.

Reduction in soil moisture content on 17/9/84 compared with spring average

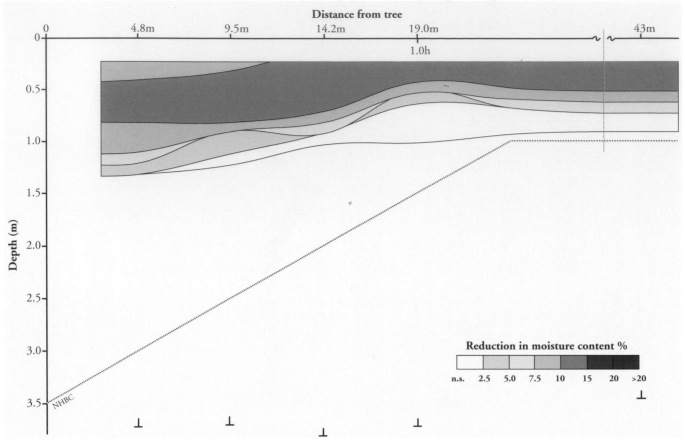

Soil moisture deficit on 17/9/84 compared with spring average

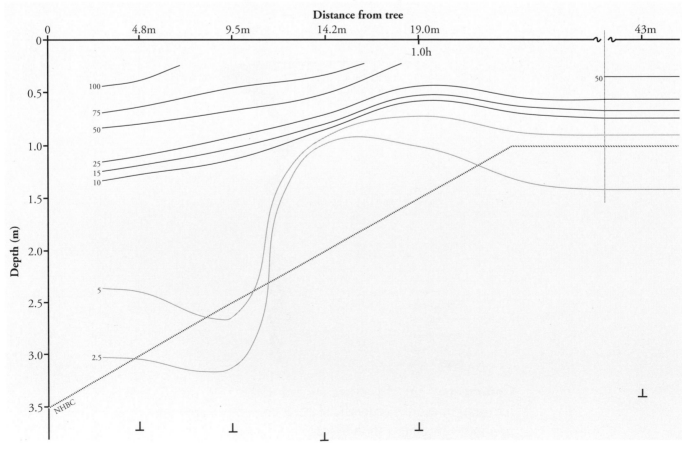

Increase in soil moisture content on 28/4/94 compared with 11/5/84

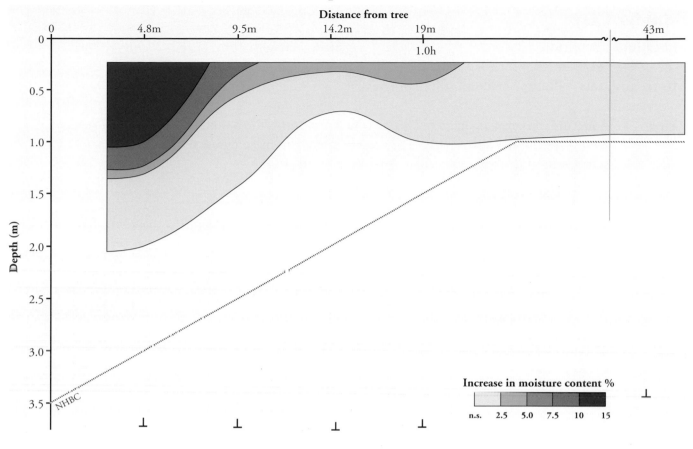

Rehydration on 28/4/94 compared with 11/5/84

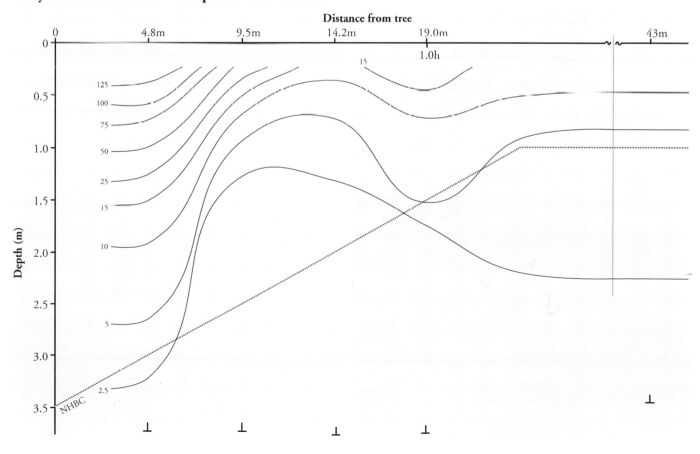

Oak
Boulder Clay

Location: Boxfield,
Welwyn   Map ref: TL 257 115

Current status: Routine readings still in progress.

Size: Height: 15m (1983); 15m (1993)
b.h.d.: 85cm (1992).

Site: A mature tree growing in an old hedge which now forms the boundary between rear gardens and an area of communal open space. The access tubes are in mown grass of the area of open space to the south west of the tree, on a slight slope up from the tree.

Soil profile:	Distance from tree (m)	3.8	7.5	11.2	15.0	44.0
	x height (in 1983)	0.25	0.5	0.75	1.0	3.0

Soil classification tests: None

Spring soil moisture content profiles

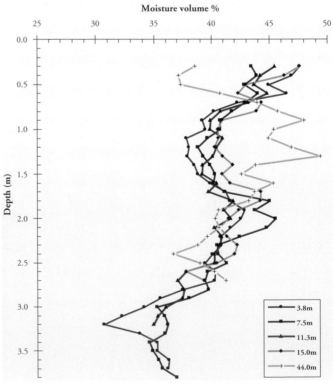

Comments: Variable profiles caused by sandy boulder clay soil.

Seasonal fluctuations in soil moisture deficit at 1.0m depth

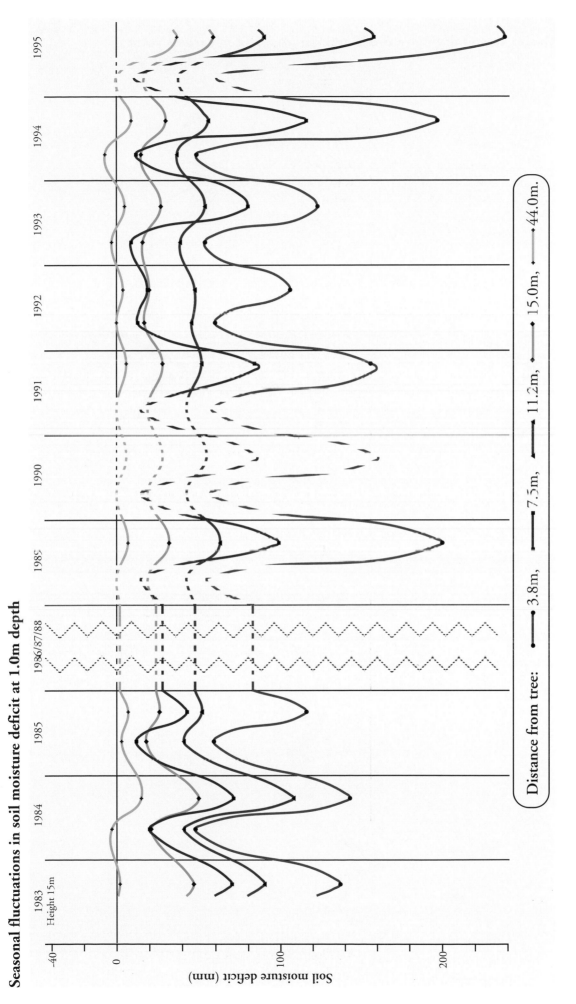

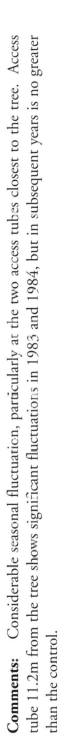

Distance from tree: — 3.8m, — 7.5m, — 11.2m, ◆ 15.0m, — 44.0m.

Comments: Considerable seasonal fluctuation, particularly at the two access tubes closest to the tree. Access tube 11.2m from the tree shows significant fluctuations in 1983 and 1984, but in subsequent years is no greater than the control.

Maximum soil drying recorded at 3.8m from tree in various years

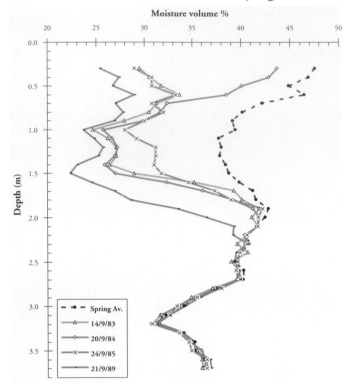

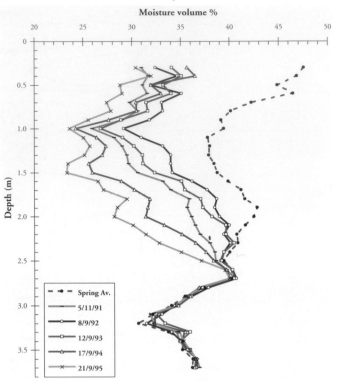

Comments: Soil drying in 1989 extends considerably deeper (to 2.3m) than in 1984 (1.9m).

Comments: Considerable additional drying in 1994 and 1995.

Seasonal and persistent deficits 3.8m from tree

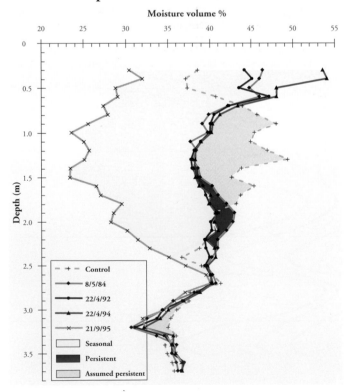

Comments: A slight persistent deficit developed, but the seasonal effects extend to below the depth of this persistent deficit.

Reduction in soil moisture content on 21/9/95 compared with spring average

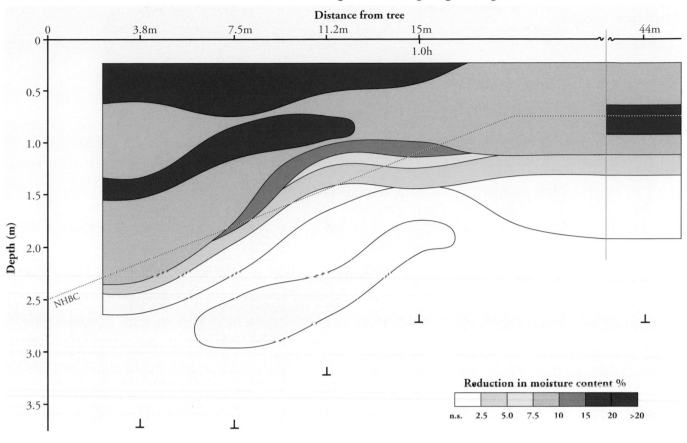

Soil moisture deficit on 21/9/95 compared with spring average

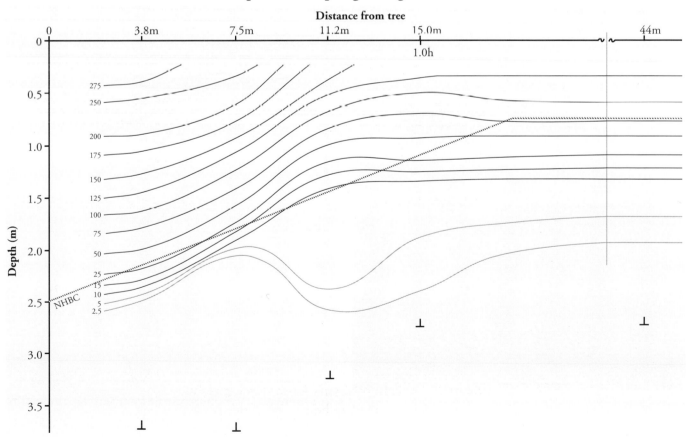

Oak
Boulder Clay

Tree 24

Location: Boxfield,
Welwyn   Map ref: TL 258 114

Size: Height: 15m (1983); 15m (1985)
b.h.d.: 100cm (1985).

Current status: Site destroyed by extensive engineering works in 1985.

Site: A mature tree growing in an old hedge which now forms the boundary between rear gardens and an area of communal open space to the rear of Boxfield. The access tubes are in mown grass to the west of the tree, with a slope up of 1:10 for a distance of 10m from the tree with level ground beyond.

Soil profile:	Distance from tree (m)	3.6	7.4	11.2	15.0	45.0
	x height (in 1983)	0.25	0.5	0.75	1.0	3.0

Soil classification tests: None

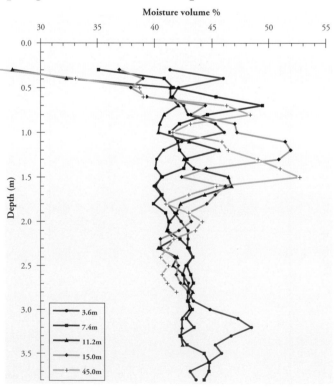

Spring soil moisture content profiles

Comments: Variable profiles caused by the sandy boulder clay.

126

Seasonal fluctuations in soil moisture deficit at 1.0m depth

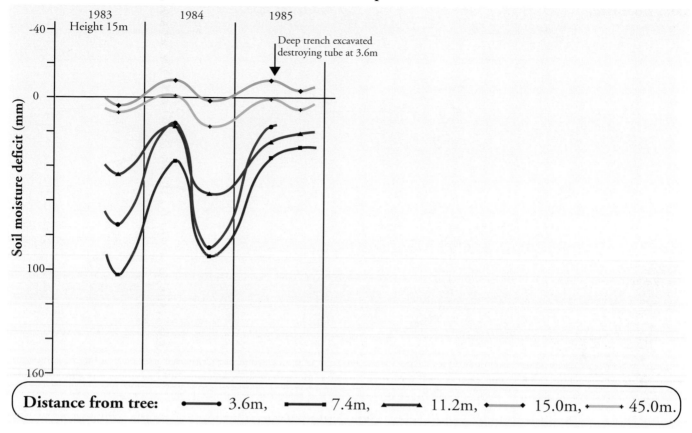

Distance from tree: 3.6m, 7.4m, 11.2m, 15.0m, 45.0m.

Comments: Considerable seasonal fluctuation in 1983 and 1984, but the excavation of a deep trench for engineering works in 1985 at the position of the closest access tube not only destroyed this tube but also stopped all further seasonal fluctuations in deficit at the more distant tubes.

Maximum soil drying recorded in various years

3.6m from tree.

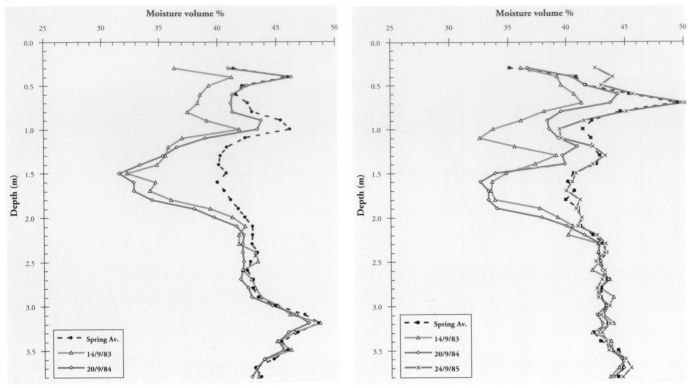

Comments: Very similar profiles in 1983 and 1984.

7.4m from tree.

Comments: Similar profiles in 1983 and 1984, but profile in September 1985 after excavation of trench is virtually identical to the spring readings.

Seasonal (and persistent) deficits 3.6m from tree

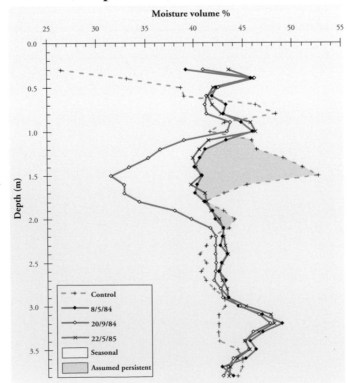

Comments: Seasonal deficit extending to 2.9m.

Reduction in soil moisture content on 20/9/84 compared with spring average

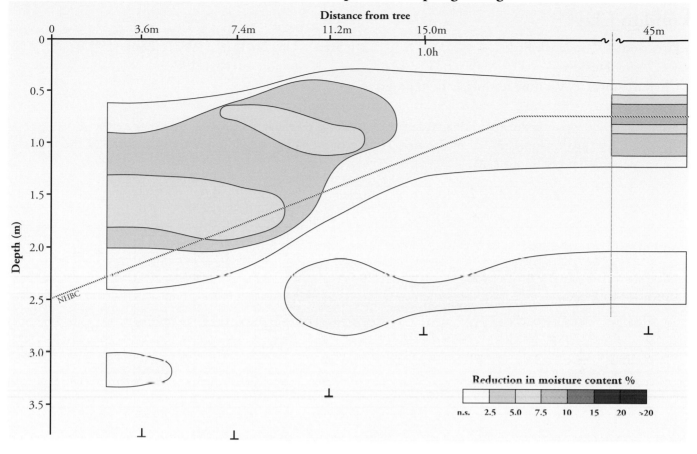

Soil moisture deficit on 20/9/84 compared with spring average

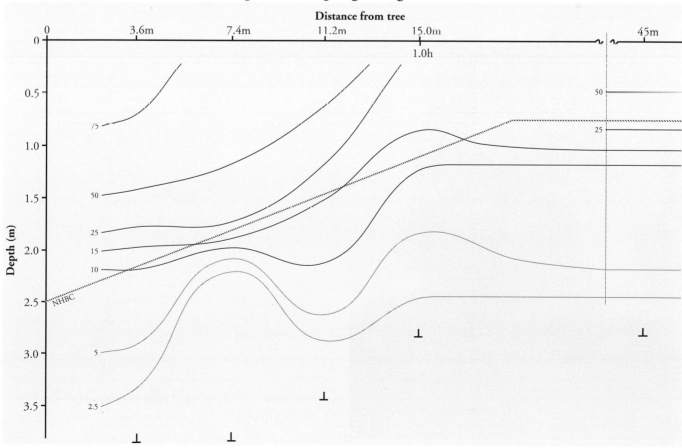

Poplar
London Clay

Location: Woodcock Park,
Harrow Map ref: TQ 177 885

Current status: Routine readings still in progress.

Size: Height: 18m (1981); 24m (1993)
b.h.d.: 61cm (1992).

Site: The western-most tree of a widespread group of poplars. The access tubes are in the short grass of the park aligned NNE of the tree. The ground slopes steadily downwards north of the tree at a gradient of about 1:25.

Soil profile:	Distance from tree (m)	4.5	9.0	18.0	27.0	54.0
	x height (in 1981)	0.25	0.5	1.0	1.5	3.0

Soil classification tests:

Distance from tree (m)	9.0	9.0
Depth (m)	1.0	2.0
Plastic limit	28	29
Liquid limit	64	61
Plasticity index	36	32
% linear shrinkage	11.9	13.2

Spring soil moisture content profiles

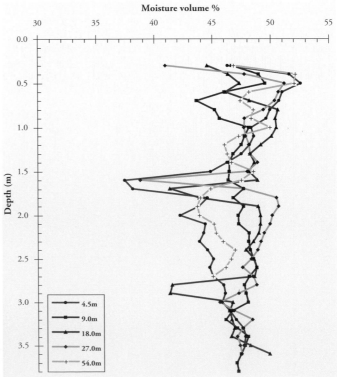

Comments: Variable profiles as a result of the layers of silt and gravel within this London Clay.

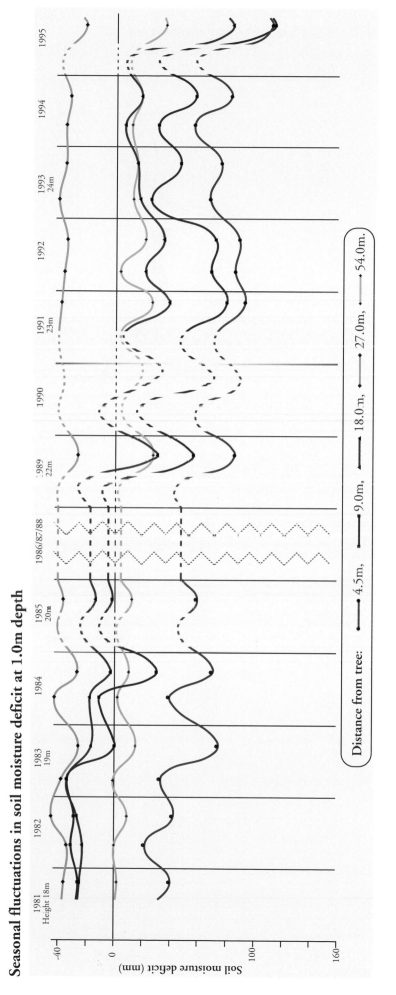

Seasonal fluctuations in soil moisture deficit at 1.0m depth

Soil moisture deficit (mm)

Distance from tree: 4.5m, 9.0m, 18.0m, 27.0m, 54.0m.

Tree 25. Poplar, London Clay

Comments: Progressive increase in deficit associated with the establishment of a persistent deficit, particularly at the access tube 9.0m from the tree. Access tube 18.0m from tree shows negligible fluctuation prior to 1991, but development of slight persistent deficit by 1991. All of these deficits reach a maximum in autumn 1991, with gradual reduction since then.

Maximum soil drying recorded at 4.5m from tree in various years

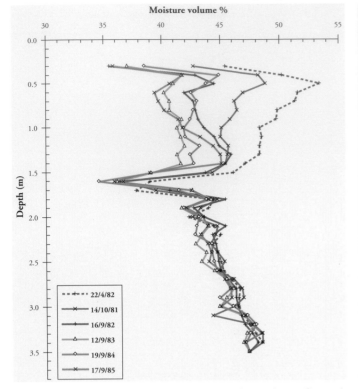

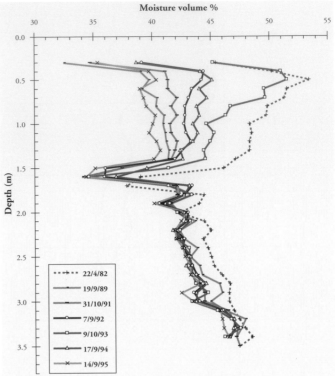

Comments: Profile in 1983 drier than that of 1984. Negligible change below 1.6m.

Comments: Driest profiles in 1995 and 1991, and significant increase in drying below 2.0m associated with development of persistent deficit.

Seasonal development of soil drying at 4.5m from tree during 1983

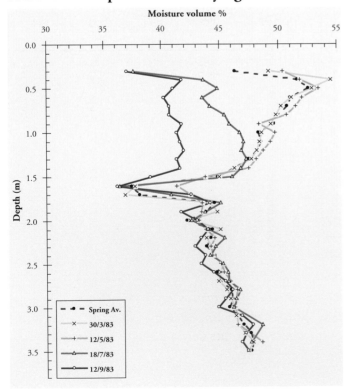

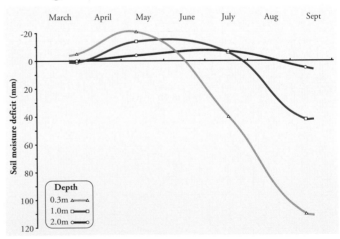

Comments: Soil drying does not start until after leaves have expanded in May (no readings taken in June; compare with diagrams opposite).

Seasonal development of soil drying at 4.5m from tree during 1984

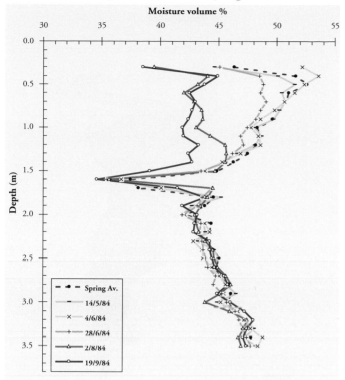

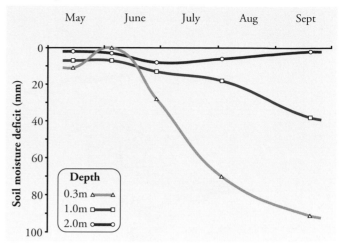

Comments: The readings taken at this tube in June show that the soil recovery was continuing until then.

Seasonal development of soil drying at 9.0m from tree during 1984

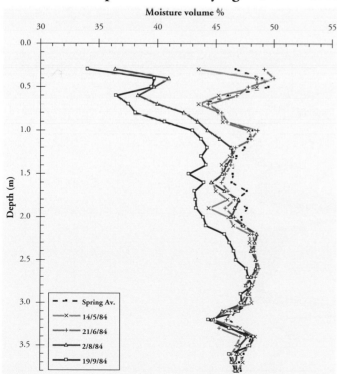

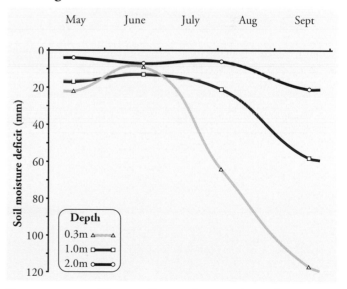

Comments: The readings taken at this tube in June also show that the soil recovery was continuing until then. Greater deficits develop at this distance from the tree than at 4.5m.

4.5m from tree

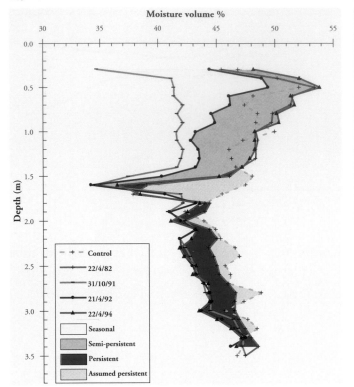

Comments: Persistent deficit established between 2.0m and base of access tube at 3.5m, and probably deeper. Assumed persistent deficit had probably established before start of project.

9.0m from tree

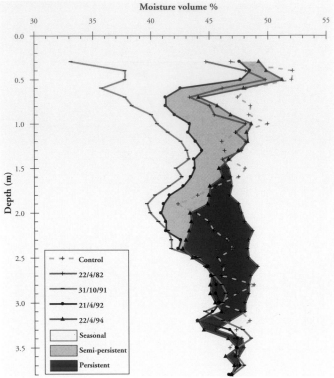

Comments: Considerable development of persistent deficit between 1.5 and 3.2m. Overlap of persistent and semi-persistent deficits between 1.5 and 2.5m suggests further recovery may occur.

18.0m from tree

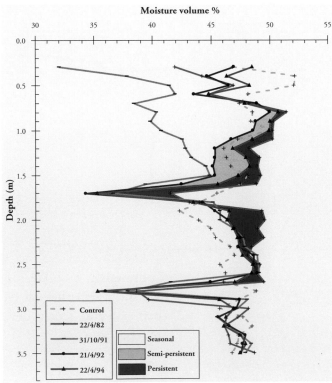

Comments: Slight persistent deficit establishing to 2.3m depth.

Seasonal reduction in soil moisture content on 14/9/95 compared with 22/4/94

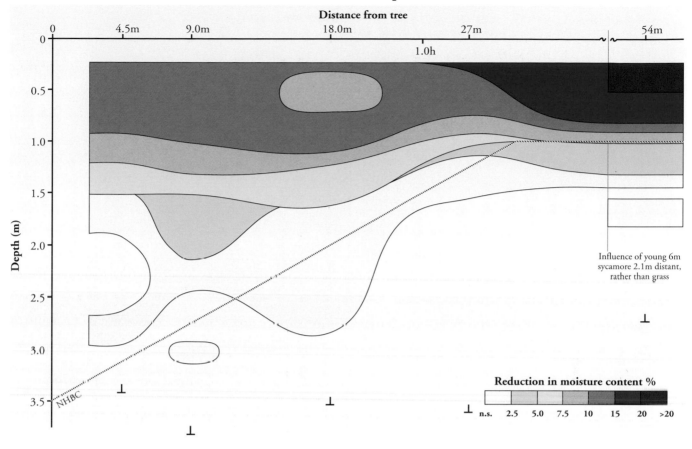

Seasonal soil moisture deficit on 14/9/95 compared with 22/4/94

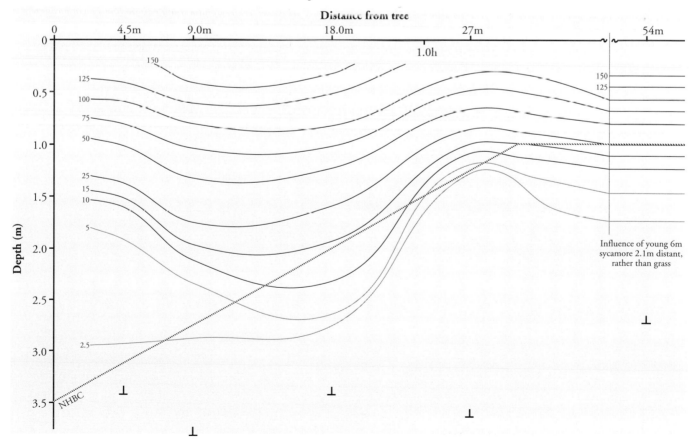

Development of persistent deficit between 22/4/82 and 22/4/94

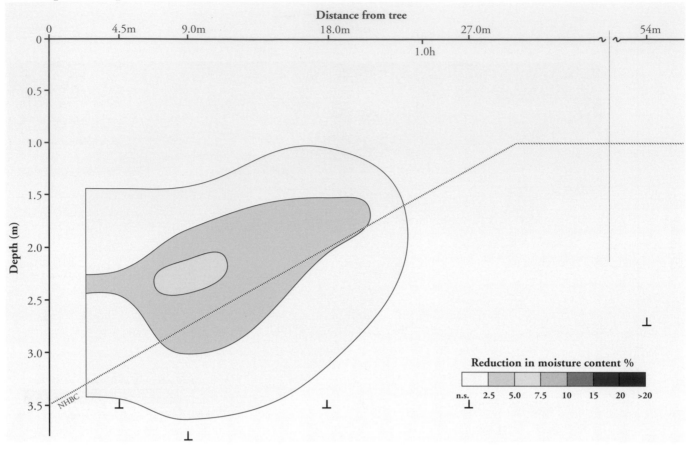

Persistent soil moisture deficit on 22/4/94 compared with 22/4/82

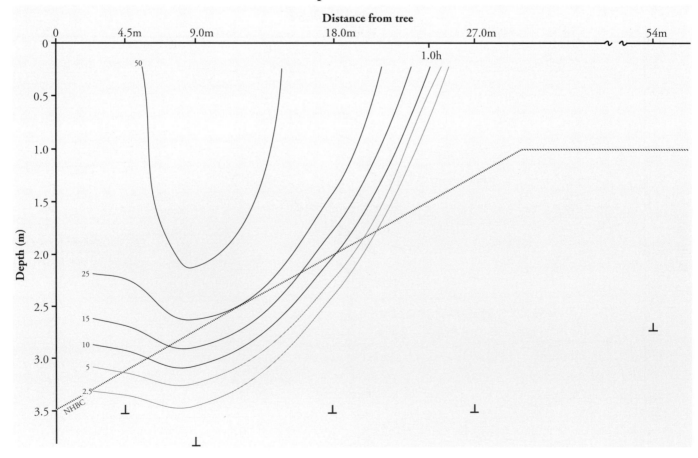

Total reduction in soil moisture content (seasonal + persistent) on 14/9/95 compared with spring 1982

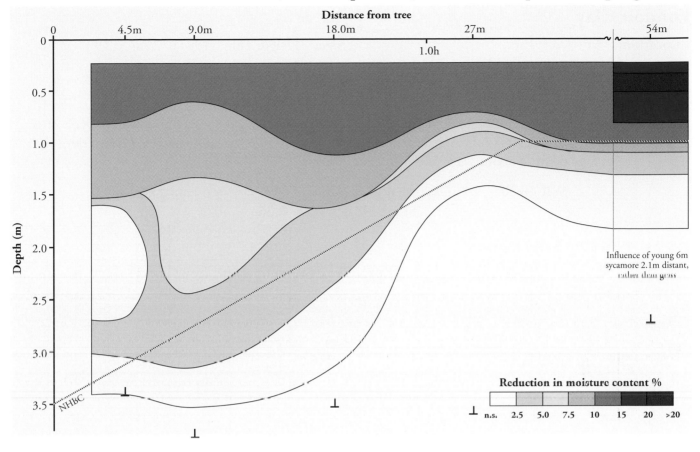

Total soil moisture deficit (seasonal + persistent) on 14/9/95 compared with spring 1982

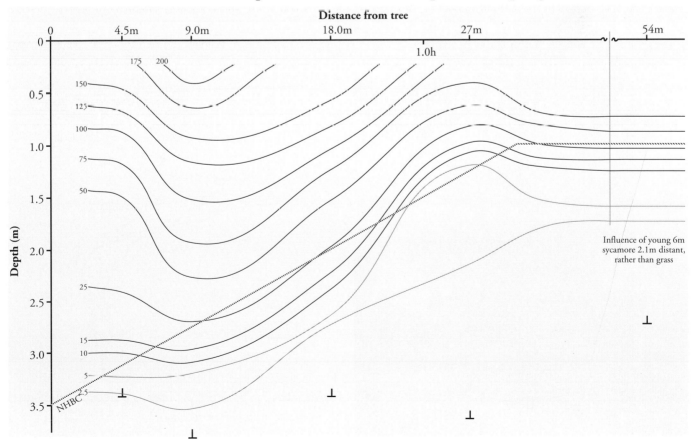

Poplar
London Clay

Tree 26

Location: Woodcock Park,
Harrow   Map ref: TQ 177 885

Size: Height:18m (1981); 24m (1993)
b.h.d.: 63cm (1992).

Current status: Routine readings still in progress.

Site: Part of the same group of poplars of which tree 25 is the westernmost. The access tubes are situated in the mown grass to the north of the tree. The ground slopes steadily downwards north of the tree at a gradient of about 1:25.

Soil profile:	Distance from tree (m) x height (in 1981)	4.5 0.25	9.0 0.5	18.0 1.0	27.0 1.5	54.0 3.0

Soil classification tests:

Distance from tree (m)	9.0
Depth (m)	2.0
Plastic limit	28
Liquid limit	81
Plasticity index	53
% linear shrinkage	14.5

Spring soil moisture content profiles

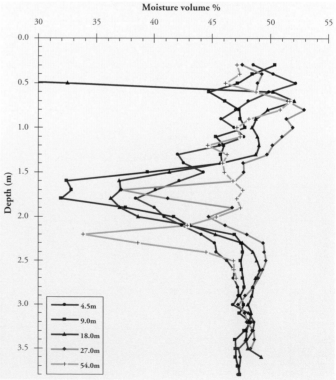

Comments: Variable profiles as a result of the layers of sand and gravel in the clay.

138

Seasonal fluctuations in soil moisture deficit at 1.0m depth

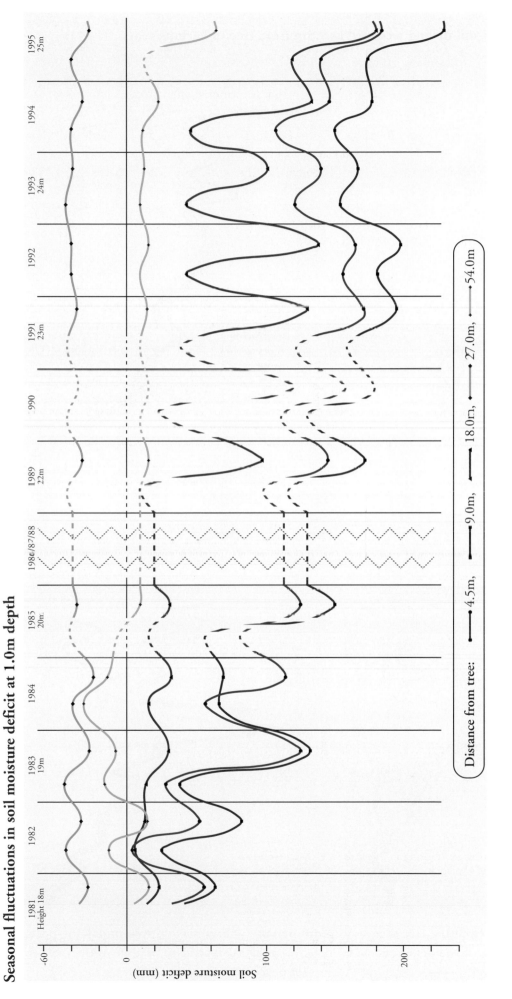

Distance from tree: 4.5m, 9.0m, 18.0m, 27.0m, 54.0m

Comments: At the two access tubes closest to the tree there is a progressive development of a persistent deficit through to 1991. At the tube 18.0m from the tree there are no significant seasonal effects up to and including 1985, but by 1989 it appears that root activity from the tree has developed at this position, producing considerable seasonal fluctuation and slight development of a persistent deficit. At all three of these tubes the seasonal drying was maintained, or even greater, in 1992 despite the wet conditions of that year. The deficits diminish in 1993, but again increase, particularly in 1995 to exceed the values of 1992. The access tube 27.0m from the tree shows no significant fluctuations throughout. The most distant tube shows an unexplained drift in 1983/1984, possibly associated with watering of other tree planting in the locality at that time. By 1995 the nearest of these trees (a lime, 8.3m from the tube) had reached a height of 9m; it probably accounts for the obvious deficit which suddenly occurred at this tube in that year.

Maximum soil drying recorded at 4.5m from tree in various years

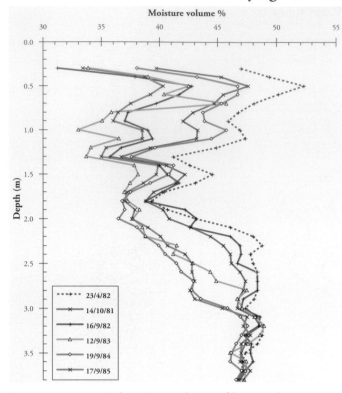

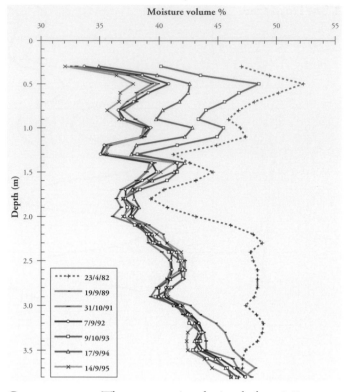

Comments: Below 1.5m the profiles are drying progressively each year with the establishment of a persistent deficit.

Comments: The progressive drying below 1.5m continues through to 1991, with slight further drying by 1995, particularly below 3.1m. Above 1.5m the profiles are very variable.

Maximum soil drying recorded at 9.0m from tree in various years

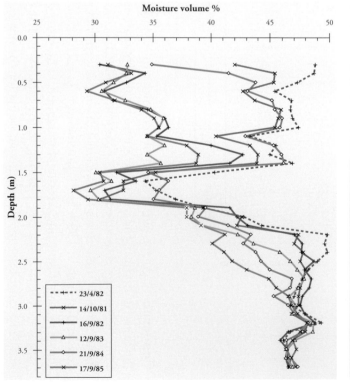

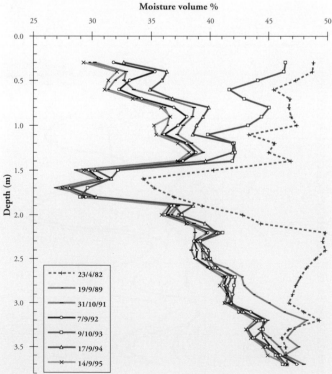

Comments: At this distance from the tree there is a similar progressive development of the persistent deficit (compare with diagram above).

Comments: Progressive development of persistent deficit similar to that at 4.5m (see above), except no further development since 1992.

Seasonal and Persistent deficits

4.5m from tree

9.0m from tree

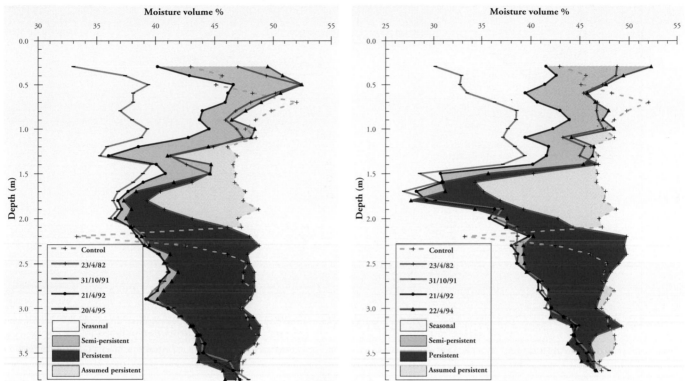

Comments: Extensive development of persistent deficit down to base of access tube, but deficit to 2.9m is partially semi-persistent.

Comments: Extensive development of persistent deficit extending to base of access tube.

18.0m from tree

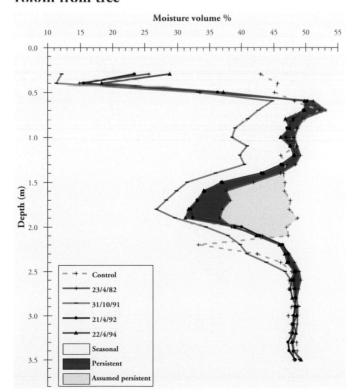

Comments: The slight persistent deficit which has developed is at comparatively shallow depth (down to 2.0m). However, seasonal deficits and recovery extend to 2.6m. Although water is clearly able to penetrate through the soil, there has been no recovery of the persistent deficit since 1992.

Seasonal reduction in soil moisture content on 21/9/84 compared with 14/5/84

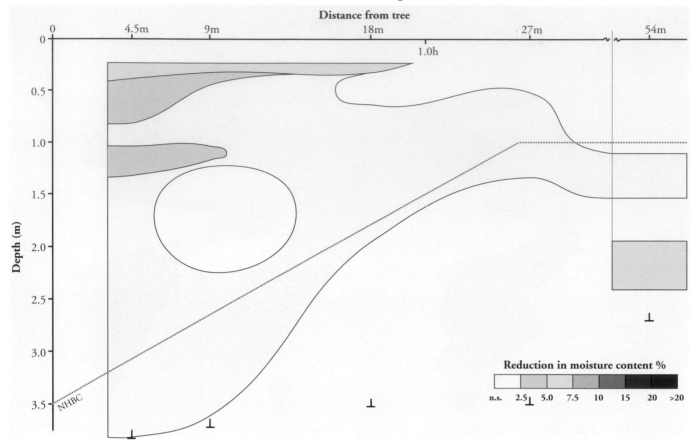

Seasonal soil moisture deficit on 21/9/84 compared with 14/5/84

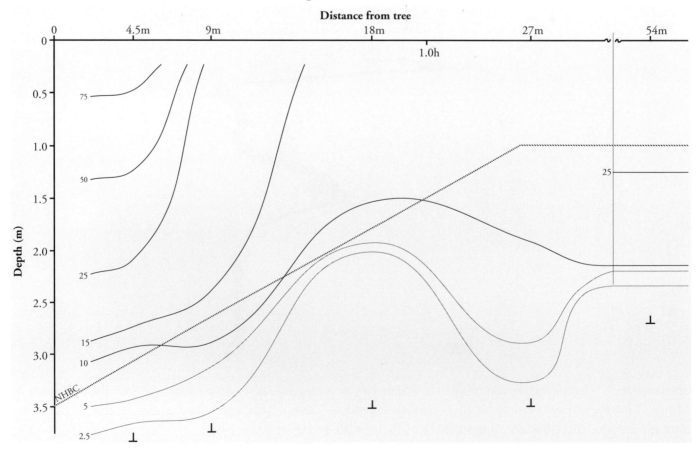

Seasonal reduction in soil moisture content on 14/9/95 compared with 20/4/95

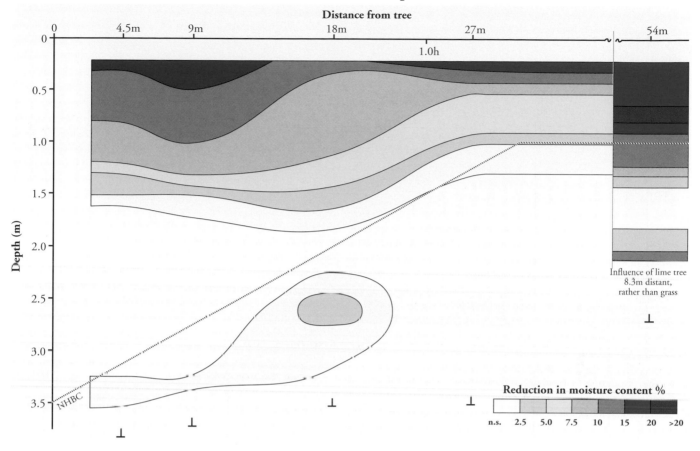

Seasonal soil moisture deficit on 14/9/95 compared with 20/4/95

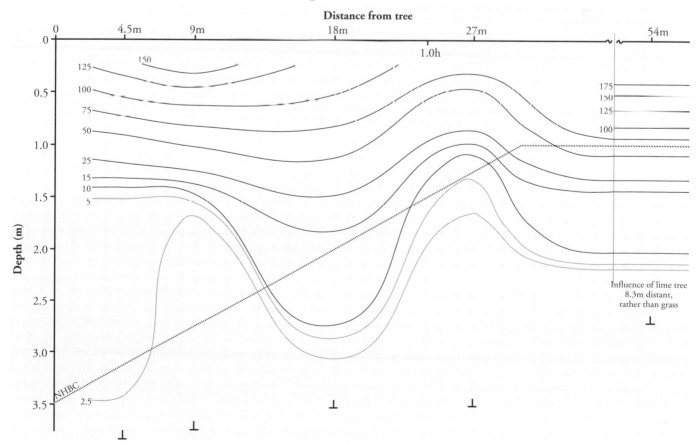

Development of persistent deficit between 20/4/95 and 22/4/94

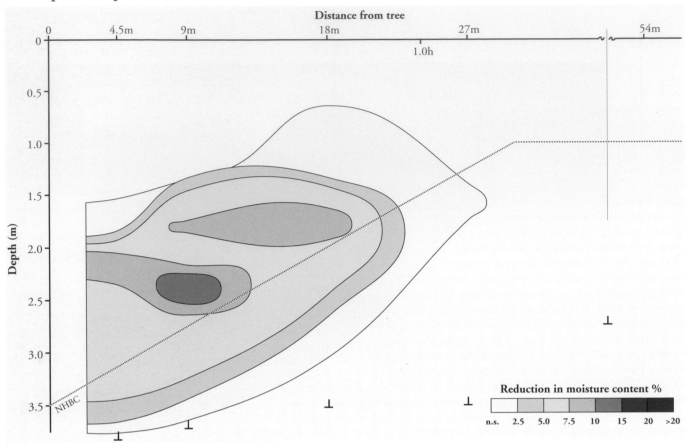

Persistent soil moisture deficit on 20/4/95 compared with 22/4/82

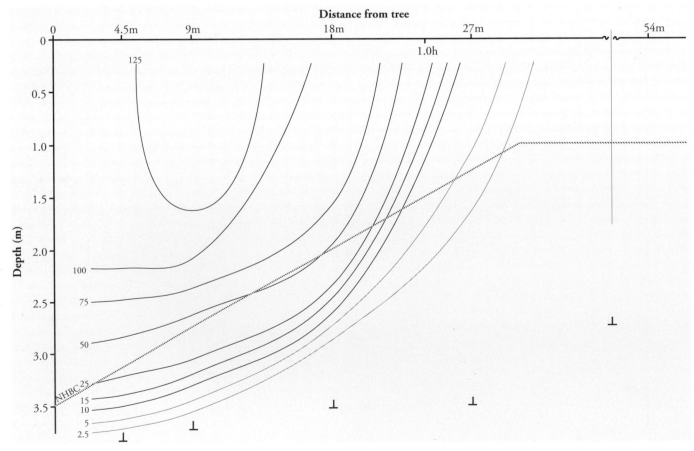

Total reduction in soil moisture content (seasonal + persistent) on 14/9/95 compared with spring 1982

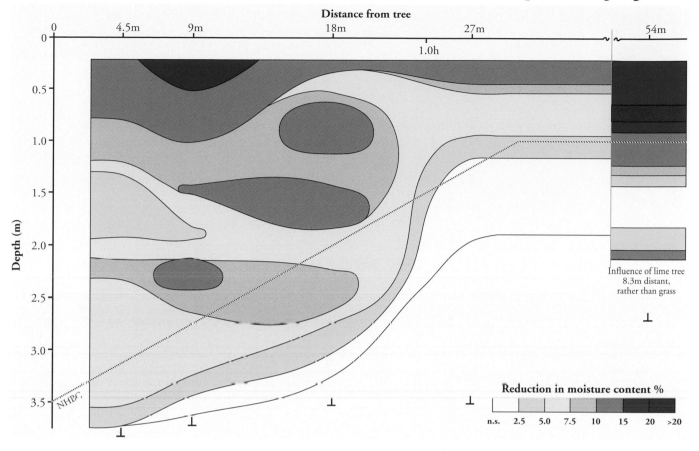

Influence of lime tree
8.3m distant,
rather than grass

Reduction in moisture content %

n.s. 2.5 5.0 7.5 10 15 20 >20

Total soil moisture deficit (seasonal + persistent) on 14/9/95 compared with spring 1982

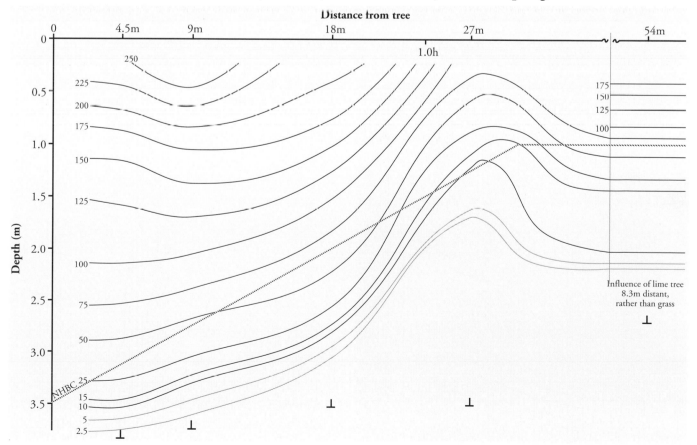

Influence of lime tree
8.3m distant,
rather than grass

Poplar
London Clay

Location: Downhills Park,   **Size:** Height: 20m (1981); 21m (1985)
     Wembley   Map ref: TQ 325 894   b.h.d.: 83cm (1985).

Current status: Readings discontinued since 1985.

Site: Part of row of poplars across centre of park. Tarmac path on either side of row, and flower beds to the east. Access holes in level rough-mown grass of a playing field, to west of tree.

Soil profile:	Distance from tree (m)	4.4	8.0	16.0	36.0
	x height (in 1981)	0.22	0.4	0.8	1.8

Soil classification tests: None

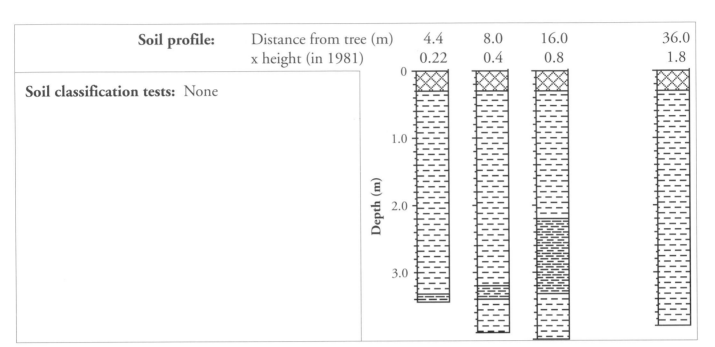

Spring soil moisture content profiles

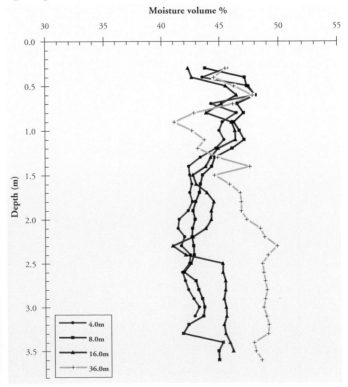

Comments: A considerable persistent deficit appears to have been present at the start of the project.

Seasonal fluctuations in soil moisture deficit at 1.0m depth

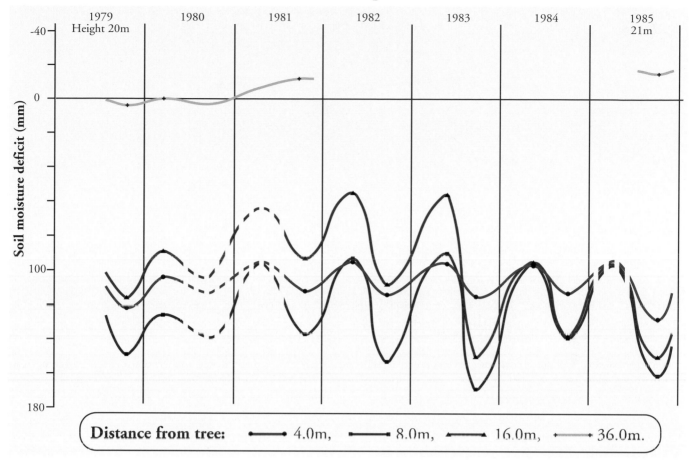

Comments: Similar seasonal fluctuations at all three access tubes close to the tree, with no significant change in the assumed persistent deficit.

Maximum soil drying recorded at 8.0m from tree in various year

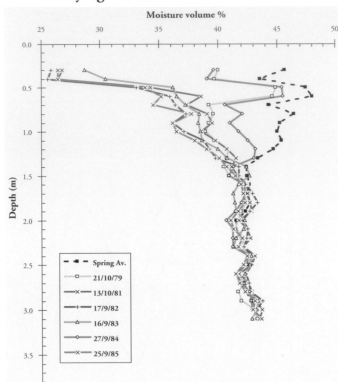

Comments: The seasonal deficits each year (above the assumed persistent deficit) only extend to about 1.5m. Early onset of rain in 1984 allowed extensive recovery prior to the readings being taken.

Seasonal and persistent deficits 8.0m from tree

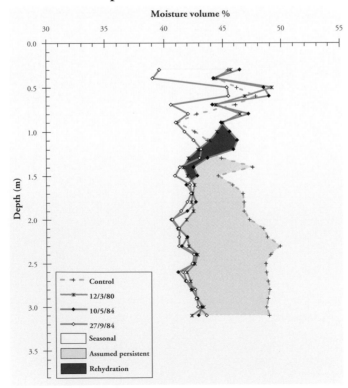

Comments: Massive assumed persistent deficit extending to below base of access tubes. Prior to 1984 there was some slight rehydration.

Reduction in soil moisture content on 25/9/85 compared with spring average

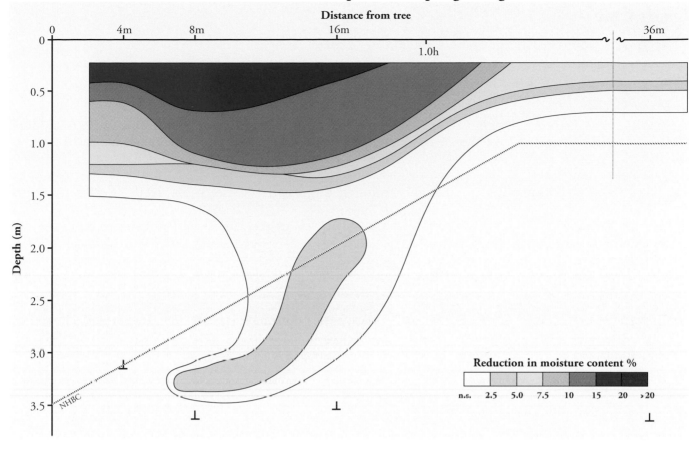

Soil moisture deficit on 25/9/85 compared with spring average

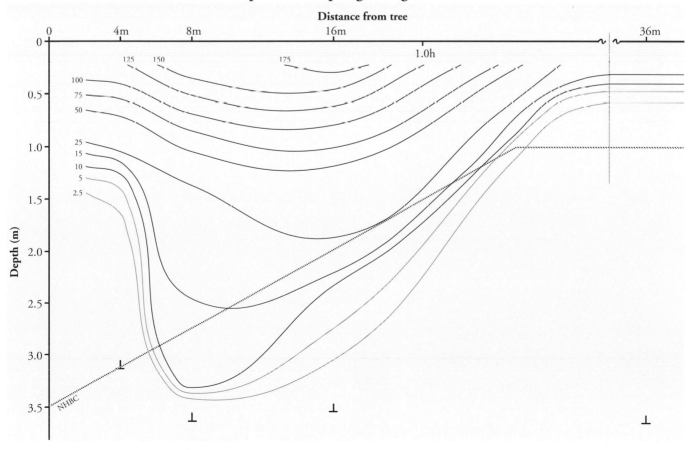

Poplar
Gault Clay

Location: Pembroke College Sports Ground, Cambridge   Map ref: TL 437 569

Size: Height :19m (1981); 22m (1989)

Current status: Tree felled in April 1991 (because of excessive drying of adjacent Sports Ground).

Site: Tree part of a double row of poplars (mainly Lombardy) along southern edge of sports ground. Access tubes in close mown grass of playing fields, aligned NNE at right angles to row of trees.

Soil profile:				Distance from tree (m)	4.8	9.5	19.0	28.5	57.0
				x height (in 1981)	0.25	0.5	1.0	1.5	3.0

Soil classification tests:

Distance from tree (m)	9.5	9.5	19.0
Depth (m)	1.0	2.0	1.5
Plastic limit	27	30	30
Liquid limit	66	70	73
Plasticity index	39	40	43
% linear shrinkage	18.6	15.3	12.9

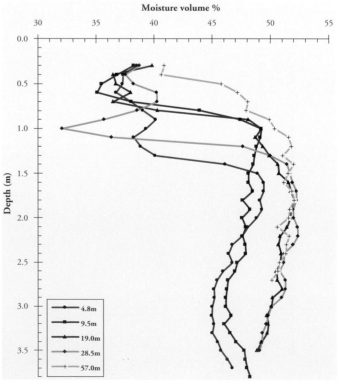

Spring soil moisture content profiles

Comments: A considerable persistent deficit appears to have been present at the start of the project at the two tubes closest to the tree.

Seasonal fluctuations in soil moisture deficit at 1.0m depth

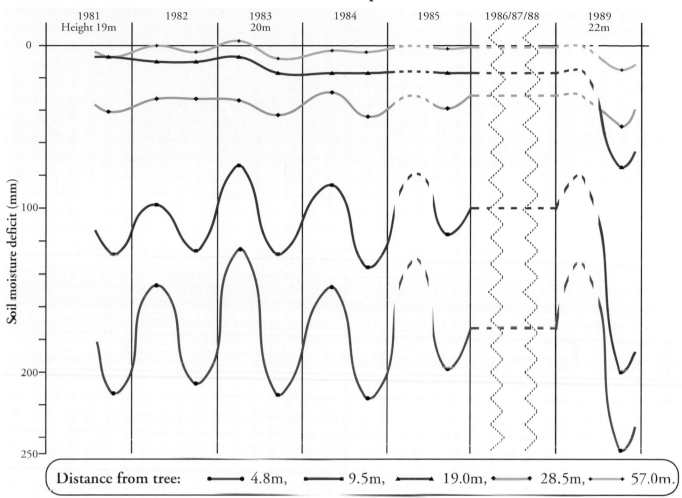

Comments: The two tubes close to the tree show considerable seasonal fluctuation, but no significant long-term change in the persistent deficit. Note the considerable variation in the spring readings as a result of differing amounts of recovery each winter. The other three tubes all show very similar fluctuations indicating negligible influence from the tree, except possibly for slight additional drying in 1989 at the tube 19.0m from the tree.

Maximum soil drying recorded at 4.8m from tree in various years

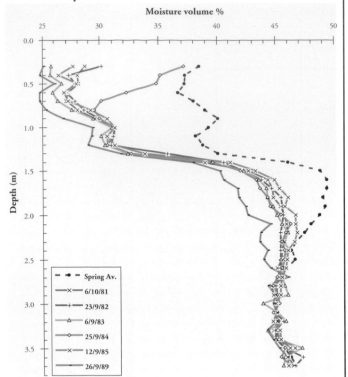

Comments: Profiles very similar each year, except for additional drying in 1989.

Seasonal and persistent deficits 4.8m from tree

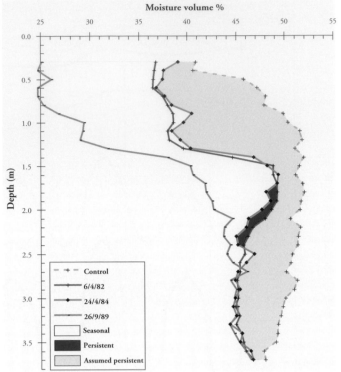

Comments: The spring profiles show the development of a slight persistent deficit. There were no spring readings after 1989 to determine whether the increased deficit of that year was seasonal or persistent.

Seasonal development of soil drying at 4.8m from tree during 1983

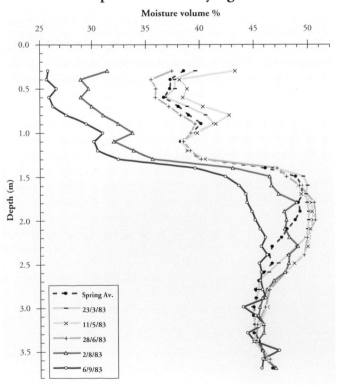

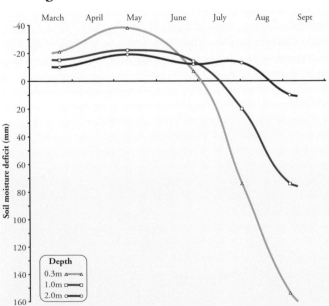

Comments: The readings in March 1983 were wetter than the spring readings in 1982 and 1984, with further recovery by May. Significant drying had only just started by 25/6/83.

Seasonal development of soil drying at 4.8m from tree during 1984

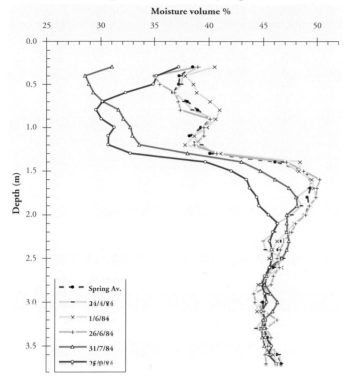

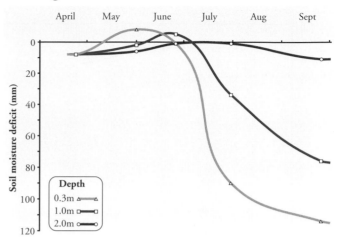

Comments: Compared with 1983 (see opposite), there was still a slight deficit in April, but further recovery through May. On 26/6/84 the only drying was near the surface; at greater depth there had been further recovery.

Seasonal development of soil drying at 9.5m from tree during 1984

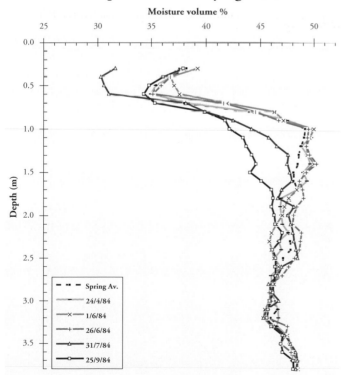

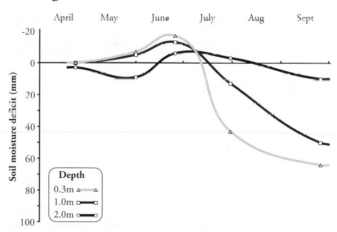

Comments: At this distance from the tree recovery also continues until the readings on 26/6/84.

Seasonal reduction in soil moisture content on 25/9/84 compared with spring average

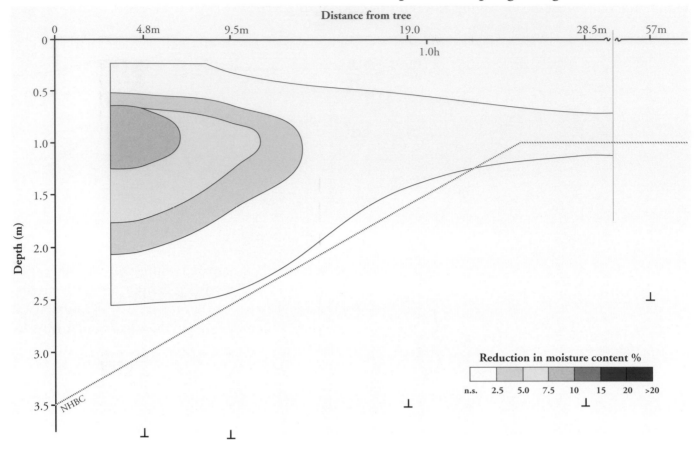

Seasonal soil moisture deficit on 25/9/84 compared with spring average

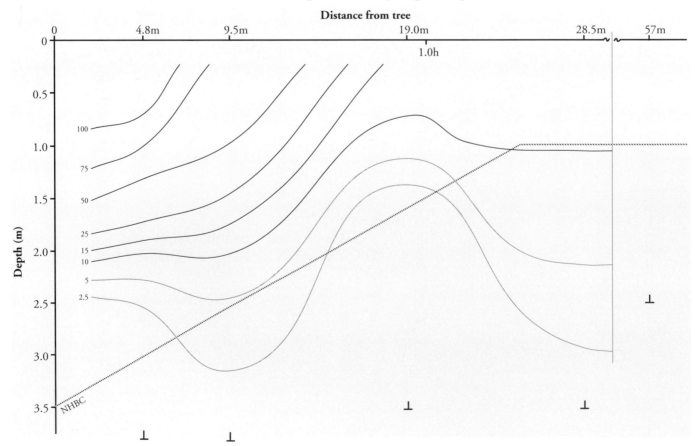

Reduction in soil moisture content on 26/9/89 compared with spring average

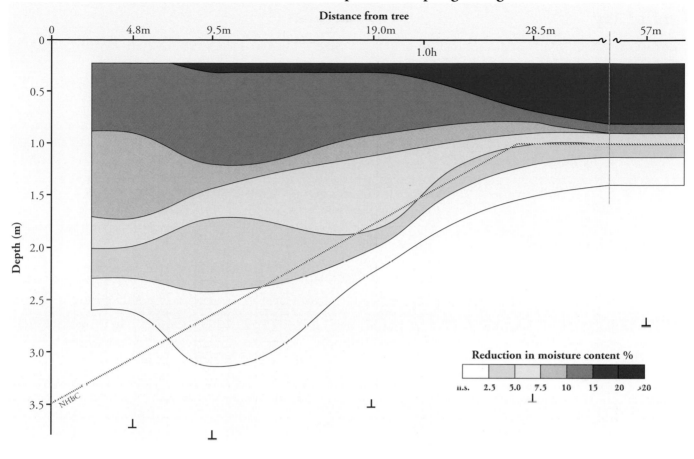

Soil moisture deficit on 26/9/89 compared with spring average

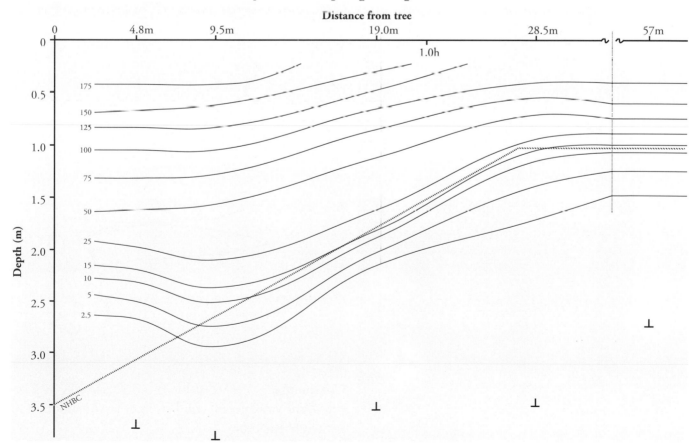

Poplar
Gault Clay

Location: Pembroke College Sports Ground, Cambridge   Map ref: TL 438 569

Size: Height: 17m (1981); 20m (1989)

Current status: Tree felled in April 1991 (because of excessive drying of adjacent Sports Ground).

Site: One of trees in row of poplars along eastern boundary of sports ground. Access tubes sited in the close mown grass of the field in a line NW of the tree.

| **Soil profile:** | Distance from tree (m) | 4.2 | 8.5 | 17.0 | 25.5 | 42.5 |
| | x height (in 1981) | 0.25 | 0.5 | 1.0 | 1.5 | 2.5 |

Soil classification tests:

Distance from tree (m)	8.5	8.5
Depth (m)	2.0	3.0
Plastic limit	-	25
Liquid limit	22	81
Plasticity index	-	56
% linear shrinkage	4.6	-

Spring soil moisture content profiles

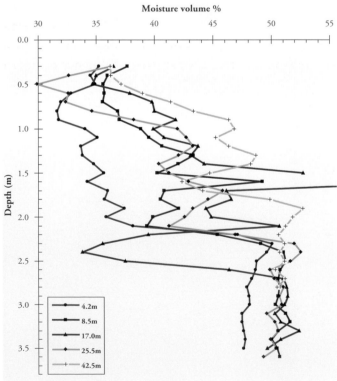

Comments: Very variable profiles, partially as a result of the variable soil conditions down to about 2.0m at each of the tubes.

Seasonal fluctuations in soil moisture deficit at 1.0m depth

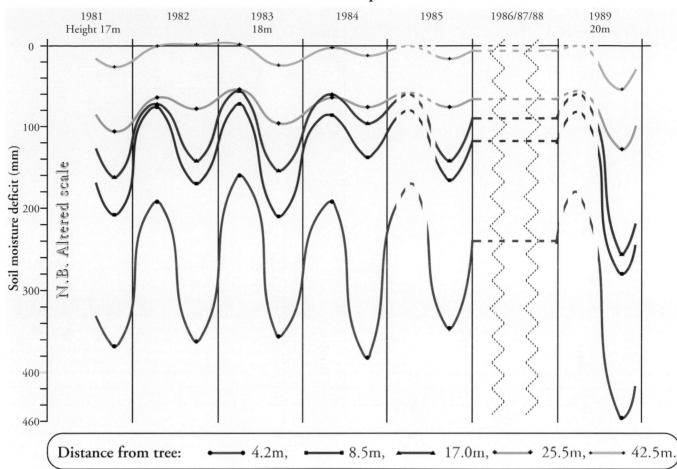

Comments: Massive seasonal fluctuations (note altered vertical scale) of similar amplitude most years, but greater in 1989. The fluctuations are greatest at the tube closest to the tree, but significant effects also at 8.5 and 17.0m from the tree. No apparent influence of the tree at 25.5m.

Maximum soil drying recorded at 4.2m from tree in various years

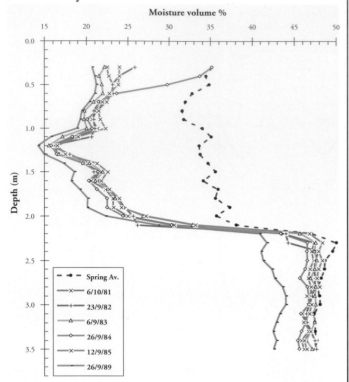

Comments: The profiles prior to 1985 are generally similar, with 1984 marginally the driest. 1989 was considerably drier, particularly below 2.2m.

Seasonal (and persistent) deficits 4.2m from tree

Comments: In the absence of spring readings since 1989, it is not possible to check whether the deficit in that year was persistent (in previous years there was recovery to the base of the access tubes). Assumed deficit above 3.2m probably caused by variable soil conditions.

Seasonal development of soil drying at 8.5m from tree during 1984

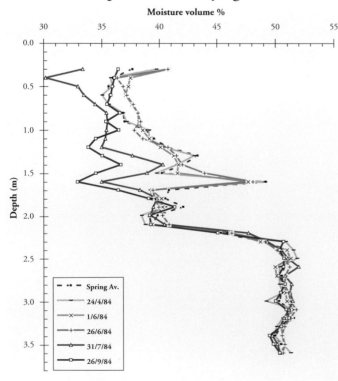

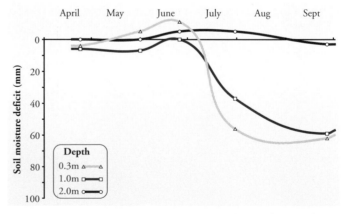

Comments: Recovery continues through until 26/6/84.

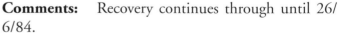

Reduction in soil moisture content on 26/9/89 compared with spring average

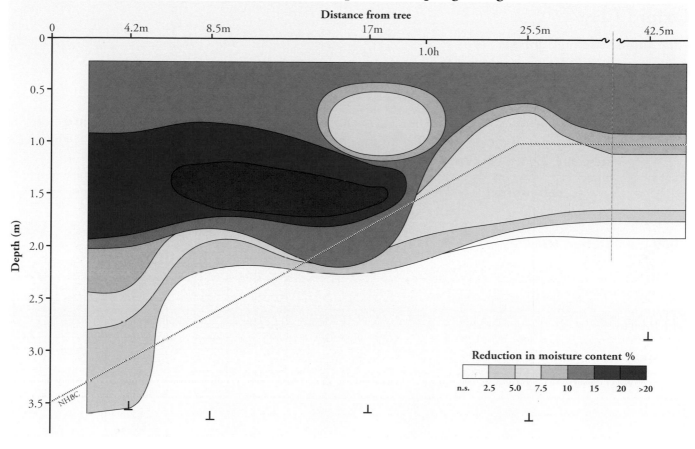

Soil moisture deficit on 26/9/89 compared with spring average

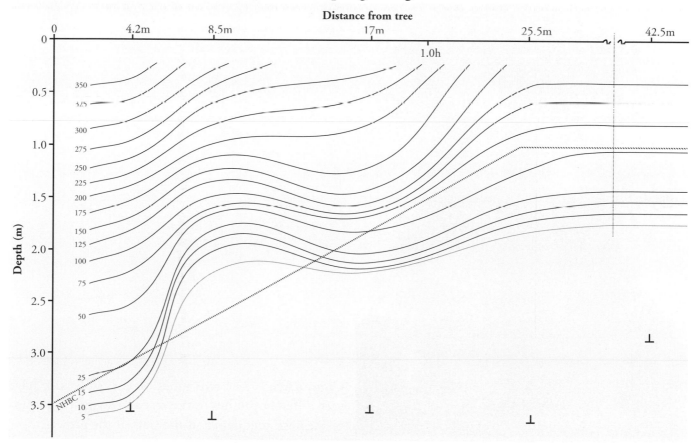

Poplar
Oxford Clay

Location: Merlin Gardens, Bedford   Map ref: TL 053 518

Current status: Routine readings still in progress.

Size: Height: 15m (1981); 22m (1993)
b.h.d.: 76cm (1992).

Site: An isolated tree in the centre of a small area of public open space. The tree is situated near the highest point of the open space, with the ground sloping gently away in all directions. The access tubes are aligned N of tree. The surrounding grass is regularly mown, but not kept short.

| Soil profile: | Distance from tree (m) | 3.75 | 7.5 | 15.0 | 22.5 | 40.2 |
| | x height (in 1981) | 0.25 | 0.5 | 1.0 | 1.5 | 2.7 |

Soil classification tests:

Distance from tree (m)	7.5	7.5	15.0
Depth (m)	1.0	2.0	1.5
Plastic limit	29	27	26
Liquid limit	64	54	57
Plasticity index	35	27	31
% linear shrinkage	14.6	12.1	10.7

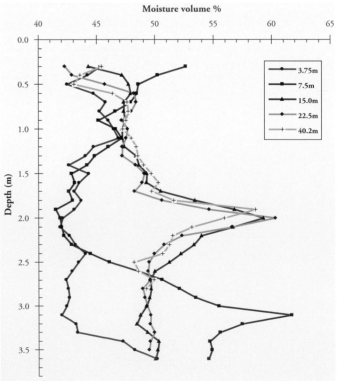

Spring soil moisture content profiles

Comments: The two tubes closest to the tree have very different profiles to the rest and suggest a considerable persistent deficit at the start of the project.

Seasonal fluctuations in soil moisture deficit at 1.0m depth

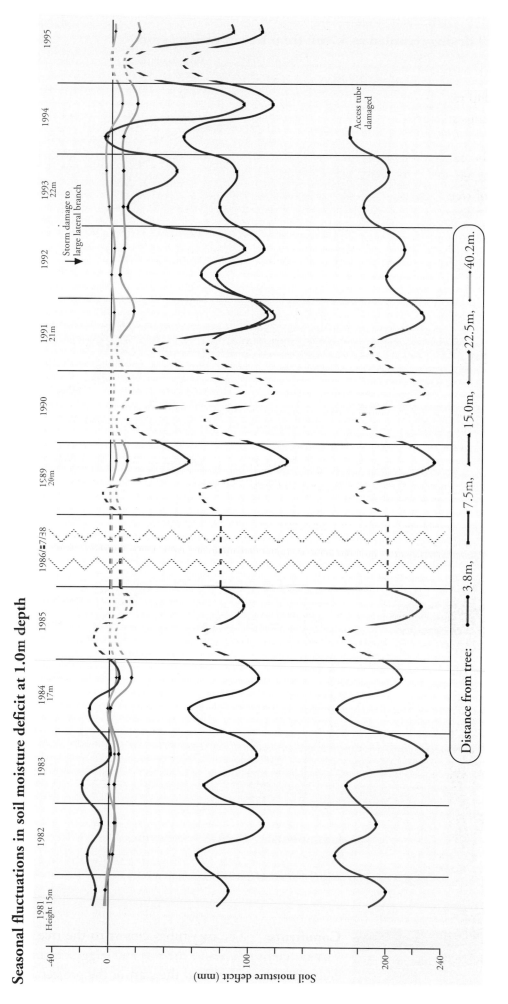

Comments: At the two access tubes closest to the tree the seasonal fluctuations remain very similar, with a slight progressive increase through to 1991 and recovery in subsequent years. At the tube 15.0m from the tree significant seasonal movements start in 1989 and increase considerably in 1991. The persistent deficit which had developed by 1991 had recovered by 1994 (i.e. it was only semi-persistent), but seasonal movements continue at this position.

Maximum soil drying recorded at 3.75m from tree in various years

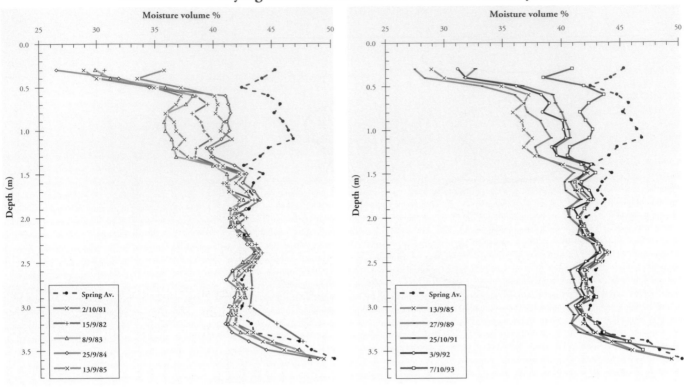

Comments: Profiles generally similar, with 1983 as the driest. The wetter profile in 1982 below 2.6m is difficult to understand.

Comments: Below about 2.0m the driest profiles are those of 1989 and 1991, but suprisingly at shallower depth the driest is 1985.

Seasonal development of soil drying at 3.75m from tree during 1983

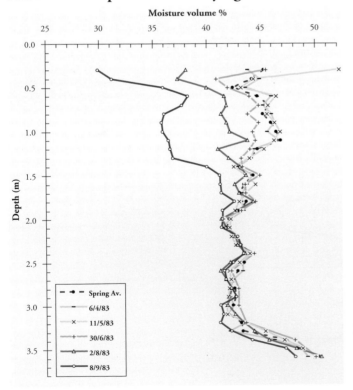

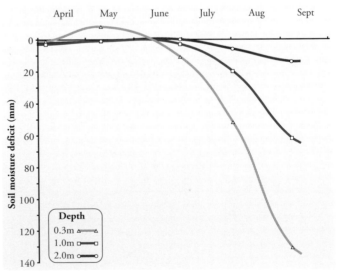

Comments: Recovery continues until May. Readings on 8/9/83 show seasonal drying extending to the base of the access tube.

162

Seasonal development of soil drying at 3.75m from tree during 1984

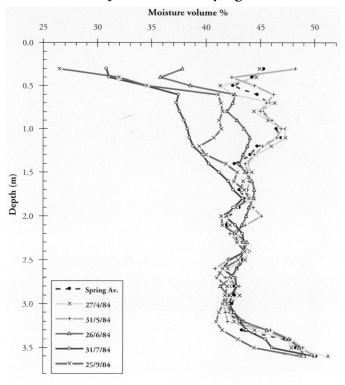

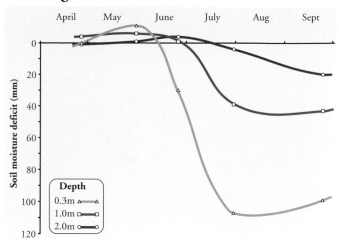

Comments: Very similar results to those of 1983 (see opposite). The readings on 25/9/84 show considerable recovery (down to 1.8m) as a result of the early onset of rain in September.

Seasonal development of soil drying at 7.5m from tree during 1984

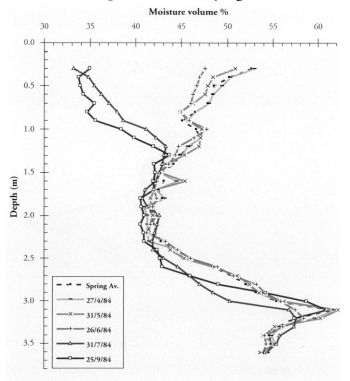

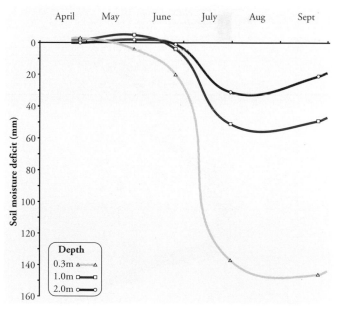

Comments: At this distance from the tree the recovery by 25/9/84 extends to the full depth of seasonal dessication at 3.2m.

Seasonal and persistent deficits

3.8m from tree

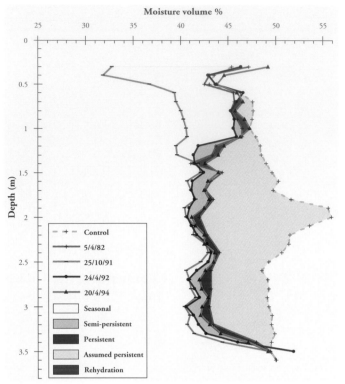

Comments: Development of persistent deficit, in addition to considerable assumed persistent deficit. Seasonal recovery to base of tube, and slight rehydration down to 1.5m.

7.5m from tree

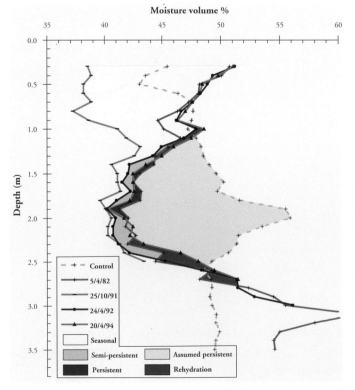

Comments: Slight rehydration below 2.0m, with slight development of persistent deficit at shallower depth.

15.0m from tree

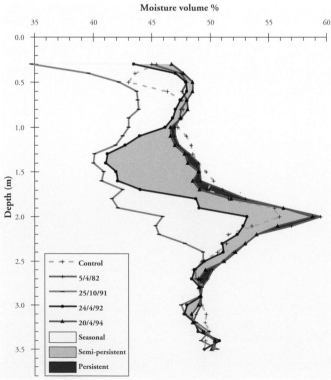

Comments: There has been virtual full recovery from the considerable deficit which developed in 1991, partially in the first winter and partially semi-persistent.

Reduction in soil moisture content on 27/9/89 compared with spring average

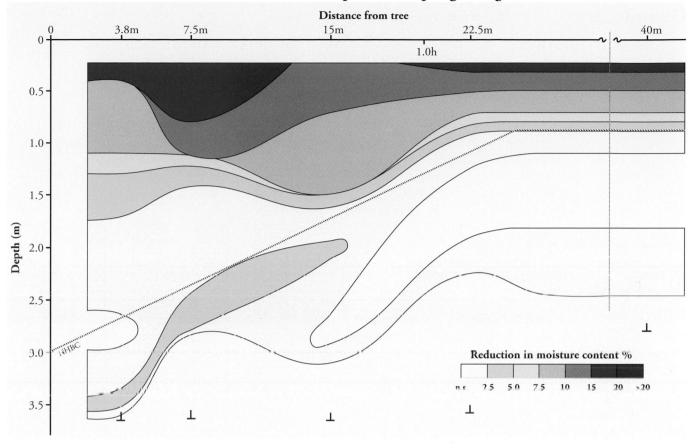

Soil moisture deficit on 27/9/89 compared with spring average

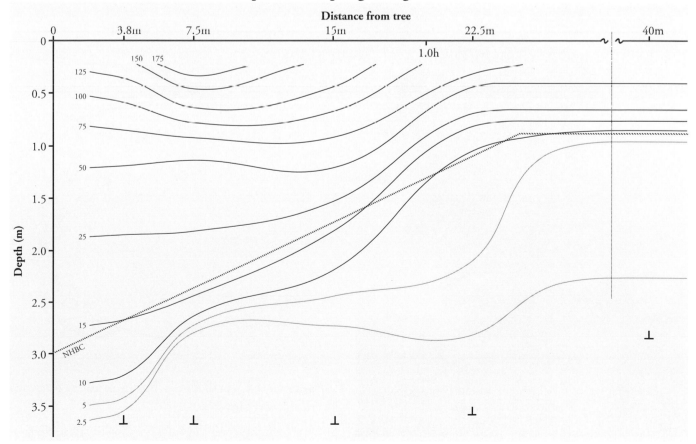

Poplar
Oxford Clay

Location: Putnoe Green,
Bedford   Map ref: TL 068 515

Current status: Routine readings still in progress.

Size: Height: 17m (1981); 22m (1993)
b.h.d.: 80cm (1992).

Site: The south-eastern tree of a well-spaced pair. The access tubes are aligned SSW of the tree in level mown grass. 40m north and NE of the tree, the ground rises sharply by about 10m where boulder clay overlies the Oxford clay.

Soil profile:	Distance from tree (m) x height (in 1981)	4.25 0.25	8.5 0.5	17.0 1.0	25.5 1.5	51.2 3.0

Soil classification tests:

Distance from tree (m)	8.5	8.5	17.0
Depth (m)	1.0	2.0	1.5
Plastic limit	23	27	27
Liquid limit	50	57	59
Plasticity index	27	30	32
% linear shrinkage	13.9	12.3	12.5

Spring soil moisture content profiles

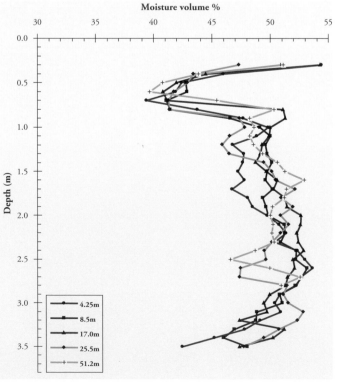

Comments: Overall similarlity in profiles, but with significant variations.

Seasonal fluctuations in soil moisture deficit at 1.0m depth

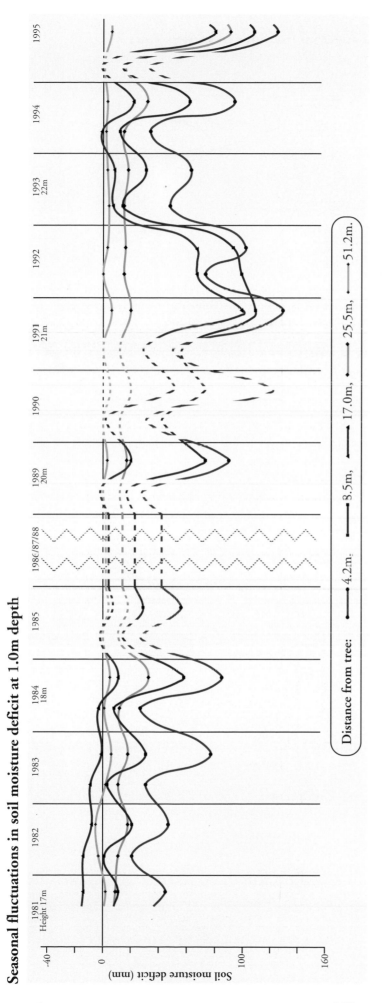

Distance from tree: 4.2m., 8.5m, 17.0m, 25.5m., 51.2m.

Comments: The two access tubes closest to the tree show development of a slight semi-persistent deficit, particularly in the period from 1989 to 1991, with full recovery back to the original deficit by 1994. The tube 17.0m from the tree shows no significant influence by the tree prior to 1989, but a considerable deficit established by 1991, but this also is only semi-persistent with full recovery by spring 1994.

Maximum soil drying recorded at 4.25m from tree in various years

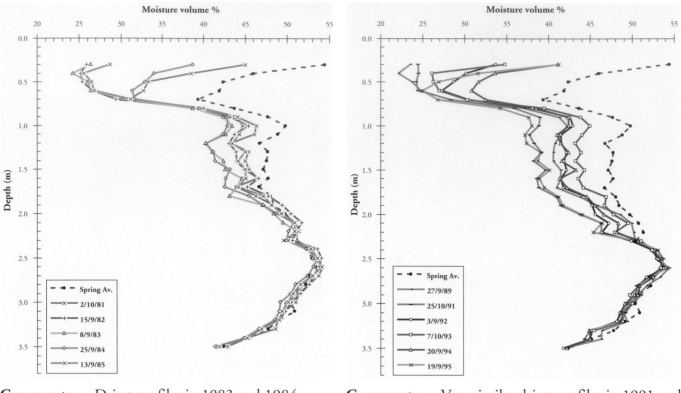

Comments: Driest profiles in 1983 and 1984.

Comments: Very similar driest profiles in 1991 and 1995.

Seasonal development of soil drying at 8.5m from tree during 1984

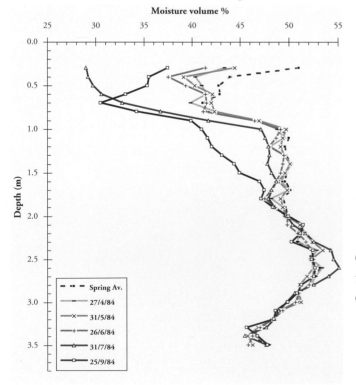

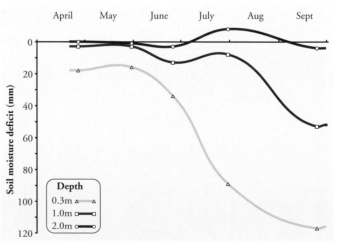

Comments: The soil has become significantly wetter between 2.2m and 2.8m on 31/7/84, despite the dry conditions in 1984.

Seasonal and persistent deficits

4.25m from tree

8.5m from tree

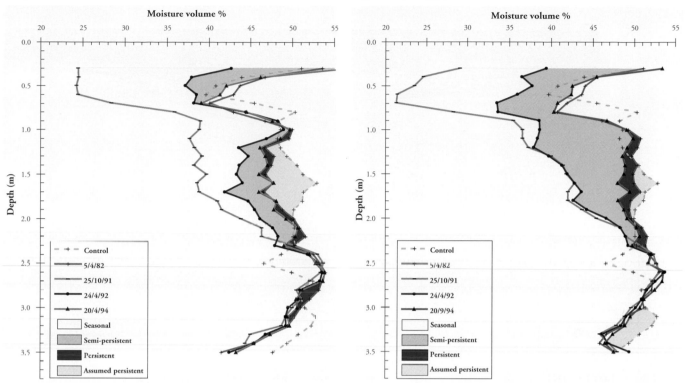

Comments: Close to the tree the effects are primaily seasonal with development of only a slight persistent deficit.

Comments: There was a considerable semi-persistent deficit in 1992, but only a slight persistent deficit by 1994.

17.0m from tree

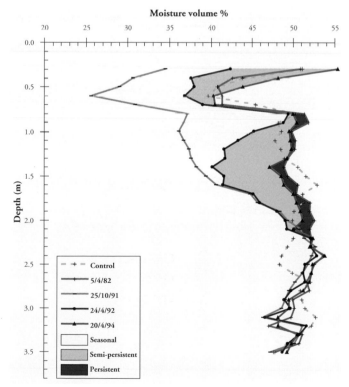

Comments: At this distance the deficit is largely semi-persistent, and does not extend as deep as at the closer tubes.

Reduction in soil moisture content on 27/9/89 compared with spring average

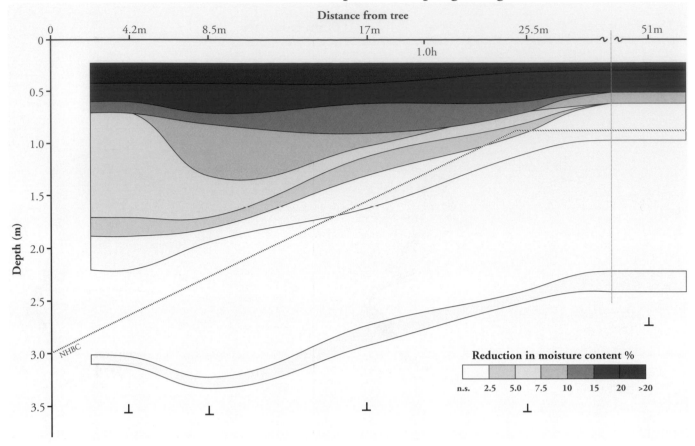

Soil moisture deficit on 27/9/89 compared with spring average

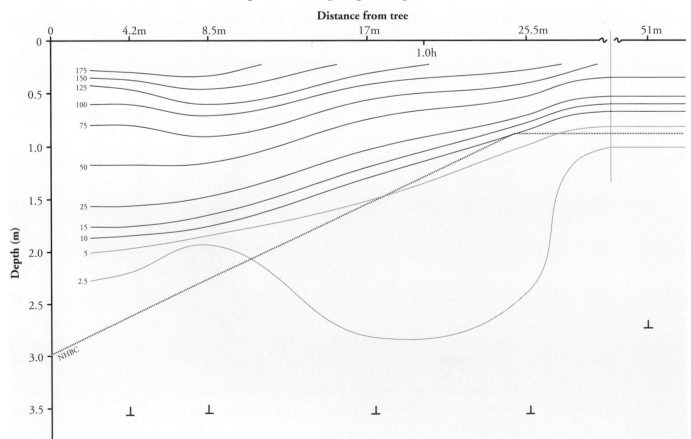

Reduction in soil moisture content on 25/10/91 compared with spring average

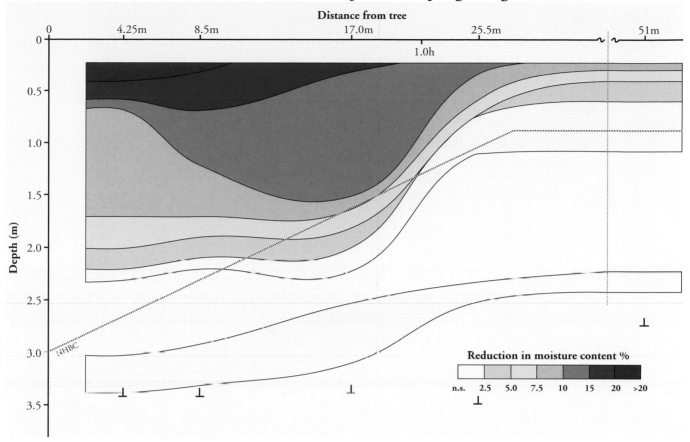

Soil moisture deficit on 25/10/91 compared with spring average

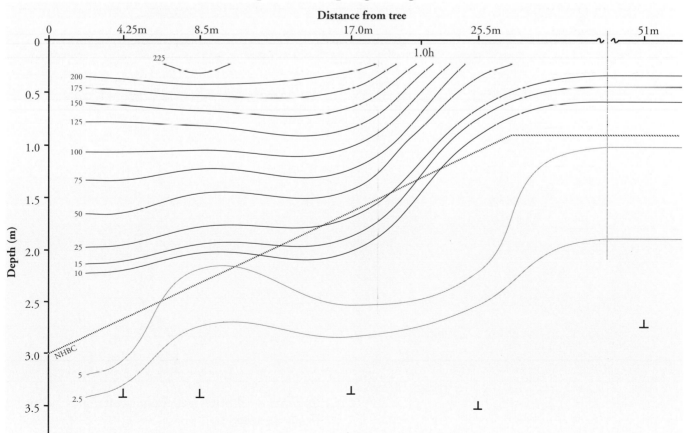

Poplar
Boulder Clay

Tree 32

Location: Rickley Park, Bletchley   Map ref: SP 859 338

Size: Height: 17m (1979); 18m (1985)

Current status: Tree felled 1985 (photo taken in 1984, after pollarding).

Site: Single hybrid black poplar in row of Lombardy poplars along east boundary of park, with rear gardens to east of tree. Access tubes in playing fields of mown grass, oriented to NW of trees. Site previously occupied by war-time buildings, and buried remains of old foundations slabs still present.

Soil profile:	Distance from tree (m)	3.0	6.6	10.2	13.2	33.8
	x height (in 1979)	0.2	0.4	0.6	0.8	2.0

Soil classification tests:

Distance from tree (m)	6.6	6.6
Depth (m)	1.5	2.0
Plastic limit	18	17
Liquid limit	36	34
Plasticity index	18	17
% linear shrinkage	8.4	7.2

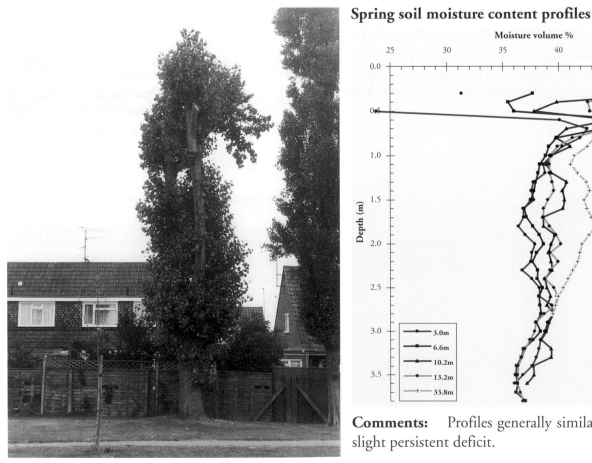

Spring soil moisture content profiles

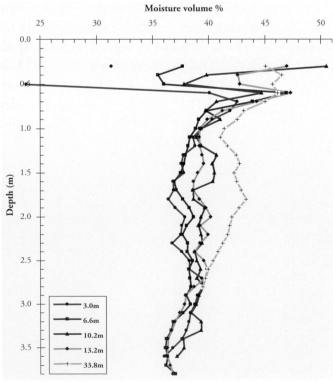

Comments: Profiles generally similar and suggest a slight persistent deficit.

172

Seasonal fluctuations in soil moisture deficit at 1.0m depth

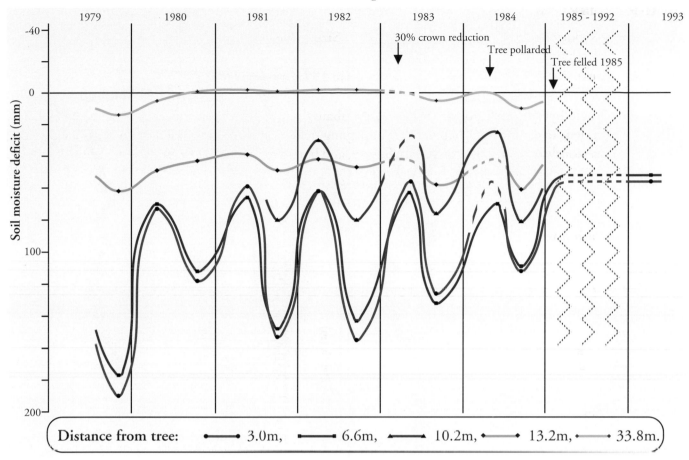

Comments: From 1979 to 1982 there was considerable seasonal fluctuation, particularly in 1979. In spring 1983 the crown was reduced by about 30%, and at the beginning of 1984 the tree was pollarded, removing virtually all of the branch structure (photo opposite taken in autumn 1984, after one season of regrowth). The seasonal fluctuations diminish progressively during this period. The tree was then completely felled in early 1985. No further readings were taken until 1993, but during this period recovery was no greater than the normal seasonal recovery. As there has been no recovery during this period it is reasonable to deduce that recovery is complete, and the soil has returned to field capacity. Any assumption that there was a persistent deficit at the start of the project would therefore be incorrect.

Maximum soil drying recorded at 3.0m from tree in various years

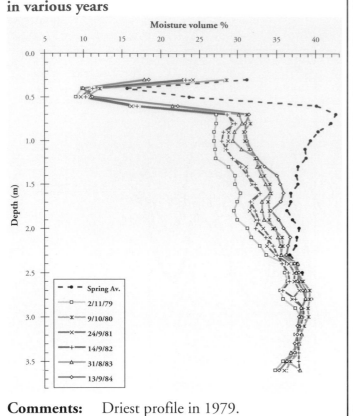

Comments: Driest profile in 1979.

Seasonal and persistent deficits 3.0m from tree

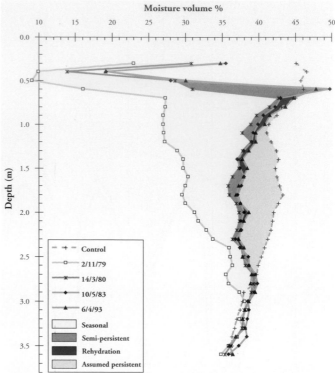

Comments: Slight rehydration of a semi-persistent deficit by spring 1983, but negligible further rehydration after the tree was pollarded and then felled.

Seasonal development of soil drying at 3.0m from tree during 1980

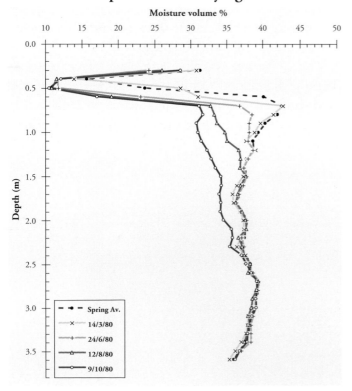

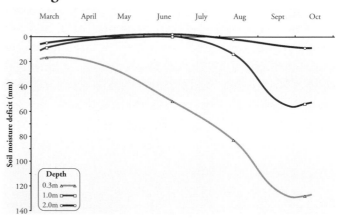

Comments: Recovery continues through to the readings on 24/6/80.

Seasonal development of soil drying at 6.6m from tree during 1980

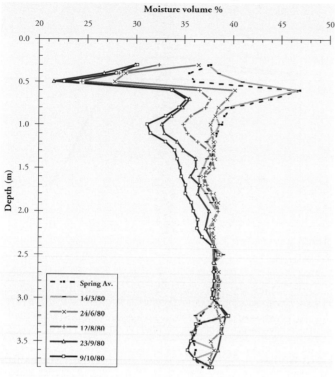

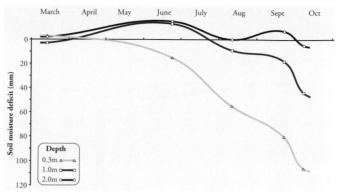

Comments: The extent of the deficit fluctuates through the summer as a result of wet spells, with the peak deficit on 9th October.

Seasonal development of soil drying at 3.0m from tree during 1981

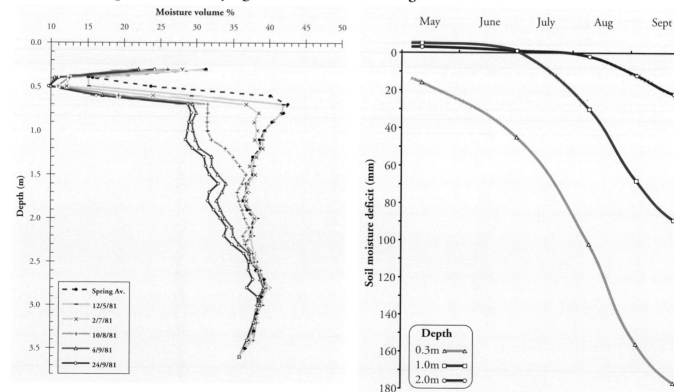

Comments: Below 1.0m, the deficit does not start to develop until after 2nd July.

175

Seasonal development of soil drying at 3.0m from tree during 1983

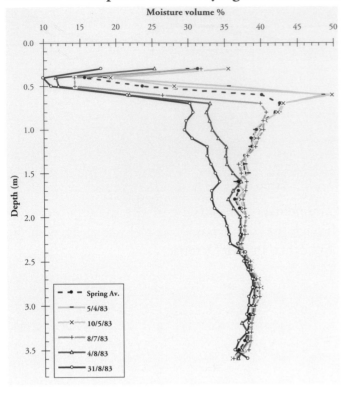

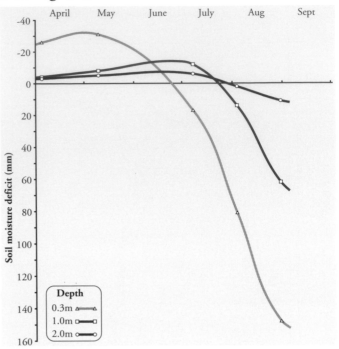

Comments: At 0.3m soil drying does not start until after 10th May, but at 1.0 and 2.0m not until after 8th July.

Seasonal development of soil drying at 6.6m from tree during 1984

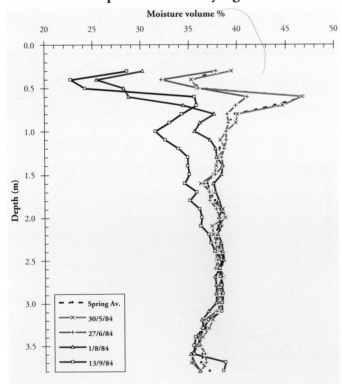

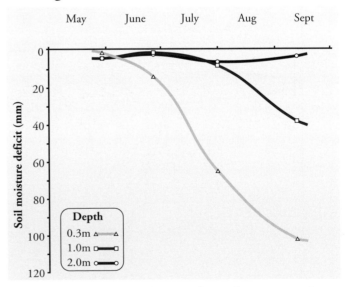

Comments: At this distance from the tree significant drying at 1.0m depth does not start until after 1st August, and there was negligible drying below 2.0m.

Reduction in soil moisture content on 2/11/79 compared with spring average

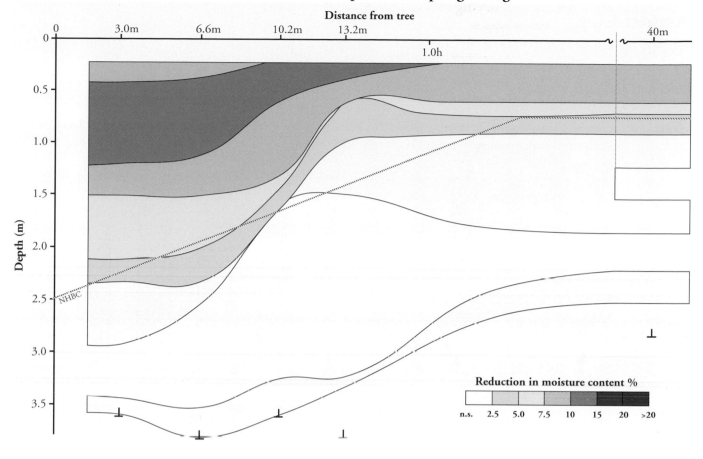

Soil moisture deficit on 2/11/79 compared with spring average

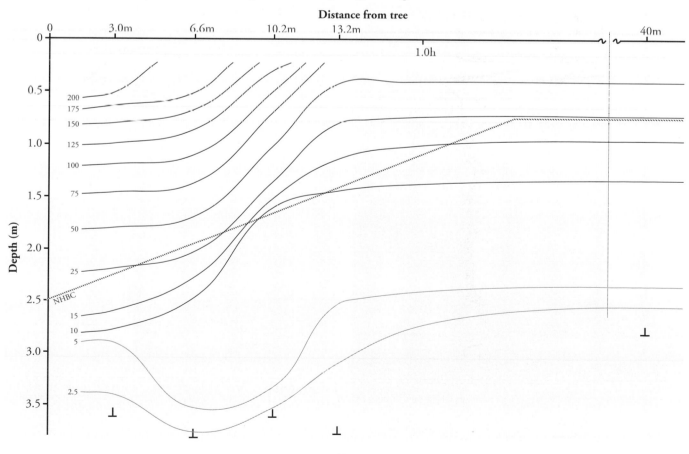

Poplar
Boulder Clay

Location: Rickley Park,
Bletchley   Map ref: SP 859 339

Size: Height: 20m (1981); 25m (1990)
b.h.d.: 84cm (1990).

Current status: Tree felled in 1990; occasional readings still in progress.

Site: One of a line of similar poplars along the northern boundary of the Park. All holes are in the short grass of the sports area. Tree 32 is closely adjacent to the SE. The access holes are aligned SSW of the tree.

Soil profile:	Distance from tree (m)	5.0	10.0	20.0	30.0	60.0
	x height (in 1981)	0.25	0.5	1.0	1.5	3.0

Soil classification tests:

Distance from tree (m)	10.0
Depth (m)	2.0
Plastic limit	19
Liquid limit	47
Plasticity index	28
% linear shrinkage	13.2

Spring soil moisture content profiles

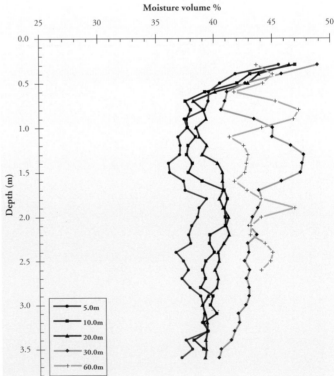

Comments: Variable profiles, with profiles at 30.0m and 60.0m considerably wetter than profiles close to the tree.

Seasonal fluctuations in soil moisture deficit at 1.0m depth

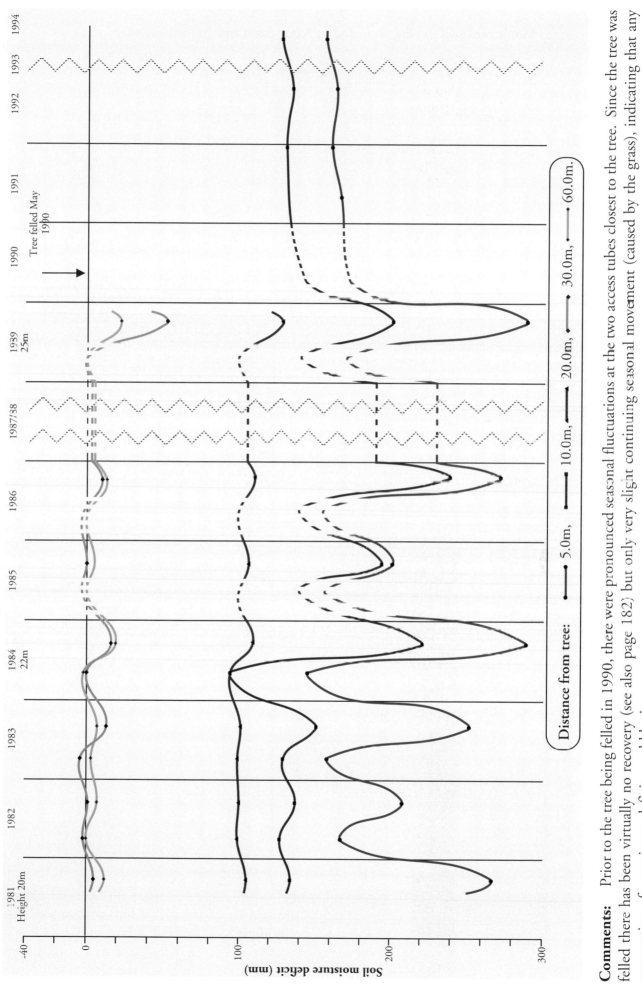

Soil moisture deficit (mm)

Distance from tree: •—— 5.0m, •—— 10.0m, •—— 20.0m, •—— 30.0m, •—— 60.0m.

Comments: Prior to the tree being felled in 1990, there were pronounced seasonal fluctuations at the two access tubes closest to the tree. Since the tree was felled there has been virtually no recovery (see also page 182) but only very slight continuing seasonal movement (caused by the grass), indicating that any assumption of a persistent deficit would be incorrect.

Maximum soil drying recorded at 5.0m from tree in various years

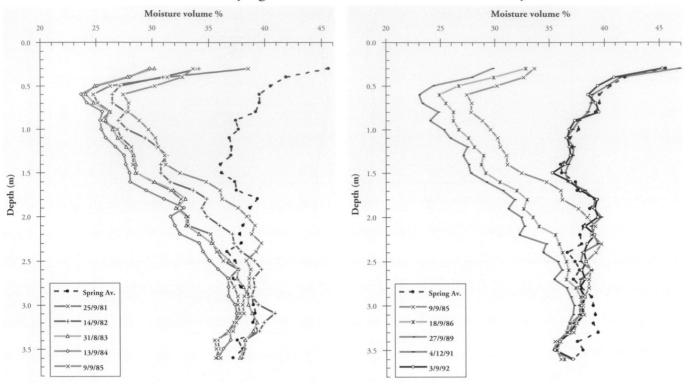

Comments: Driest profile in 1984, but some unusual results with the profiles in 1982 and 1985 wetter than the spring average below 2.0m.

Comments: Driest profile in 1989, and profiles since the tree was felled in 1990 remain virtually identical.

Seasonal development of soil drying at 5.0m from tree during 1983

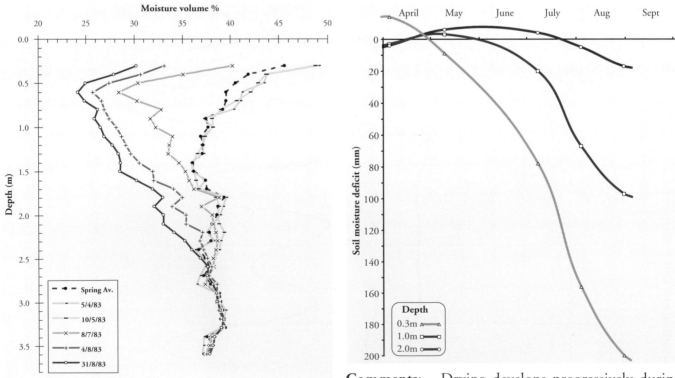

Comments: Drying develops progressively during the summer to a depth of 2.5m.

Seasonal development of soil drying at 5.0m from tree during 1984

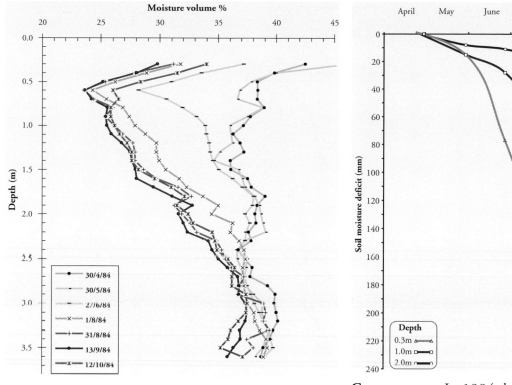

Comments: In 1984 drying develops to the base of the access tube at 3.6m. Significant drying had started by 16th May.

Seasonal development of soil drying at 10.0m from tree during 1984

Comments: At 10.0m from the tree, drying also develops to the base of the access tube.

Seasonal and persistent deficits 5.0m from tree

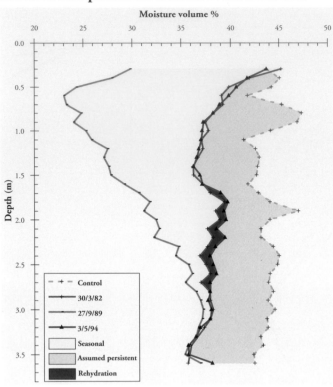

Comments: In 1989 seasonal considerable seasonal drying extended to 3.3m. Rehydration since the tree was felled has been negligible and appears to be complete. Assumptions of a persistent deficit, although shown, would be incorrect.

Seasonal and persistent deficits 10.0m from tree

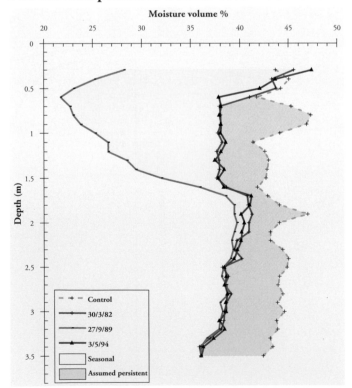

Comments: Deficit entirely seasonal, with no further rehydration since the tree was felled. Assumptions of a persistent deficit, although shown, would be incorrect.

182

Reduction in soil moisture content on 27/9/89 compared with spring average

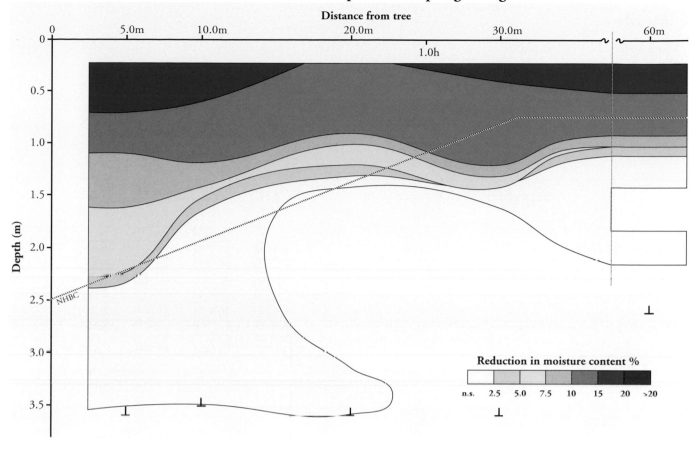

Soil moisture deficit on 27/9/89 compared with spring average

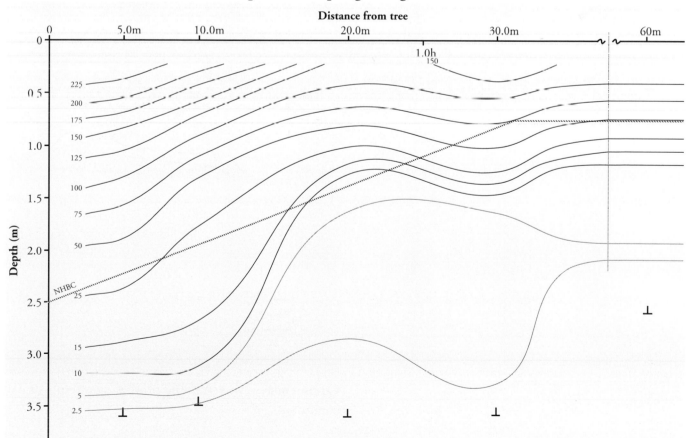

Poplar
Clay silt

Tree 34

Location: Barn Elm Park,   **Size:**   Height: 23m (1981); 23m (1984)
Barnes,   Map ref: TQ 225 764
Current status: Readings discontinued since 1984.

Site: One of a long row of trees (mainly London planes) running along the western edge of the playing fields. The holes are positioned in the short grass of the pitches in a line east of the tree.

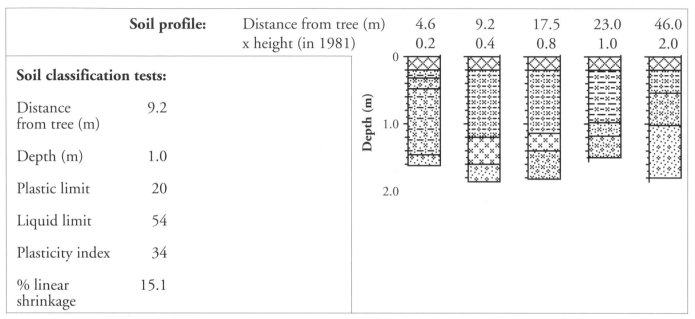

| Soil profile: | Distance from tree (m) | 4.6 | 9.2 | 17.5 | 23.0 | 46.0 |
| | x height (in 1981) | 0.2 | 0.4 | 0.8 | 1.0 | 2.0 |

Soil classification tests:

Distance from tree (m)	9.2
Depth (m)	1.0
Plastic limit	20
Liquid limit	54
Plasticity index	34
% linear shrinkage	15.1

Spring soil moisture content profiles

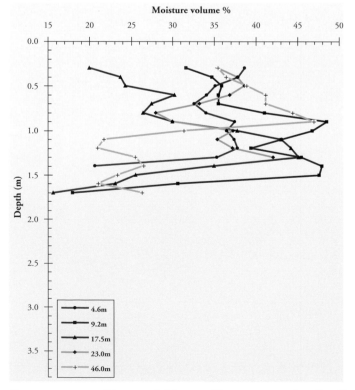

Comments: Very variable profiles as a result of soil conditions.

Seasonal fluctuations in soil moisture deficit at 1.0m depth

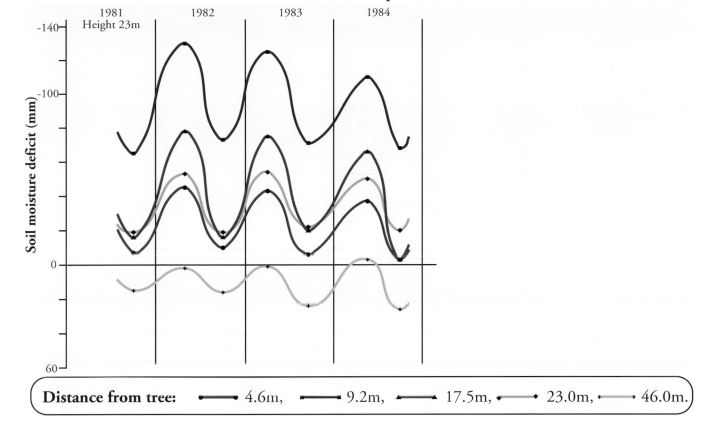

Comments: Considerable seasonal fluctuation at all tubes, including the control.

Maximum soil drying recorded at 4.6m from tree in various years

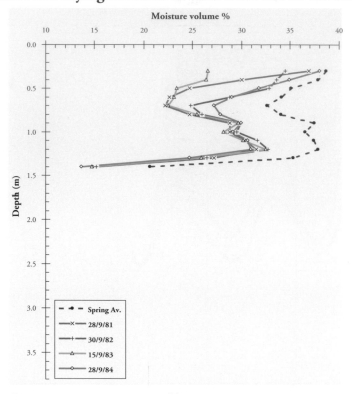

Comments: Driest profile in 1983; extensive recovery had occurred by the time readings taken in 1984.

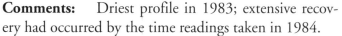

Seasonal and persistent deficits 4.6m from tree

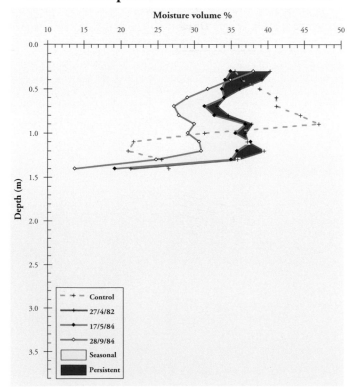

Comments: Although a persistent deficit is shown, it is probably only because the spring 1984 readings were taken after soil drying had started.

Reduction in soil moisture content on 15/9/83 compared with spring average

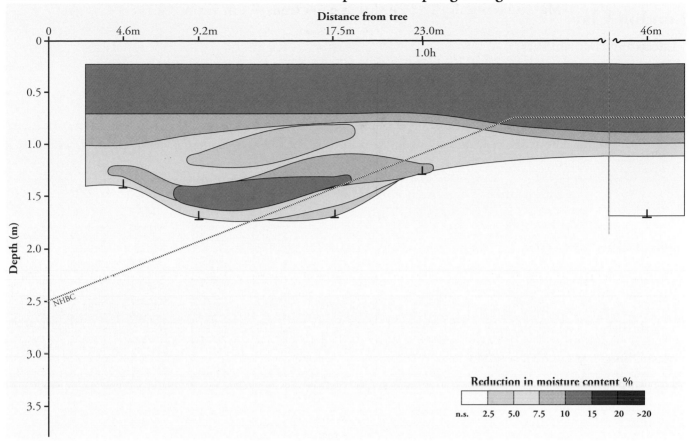

Soil moisture deficit on 15/9/83 compared with spring average

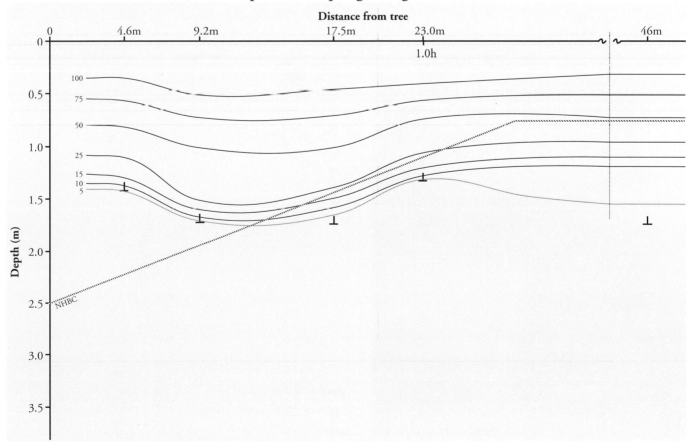

Silver birch
London Clay

Location: Barham Park,
Wembley   Map ref: TQ 172 852

Size: Height: 9m (1981); 11m (1993)
b.h.d.: 27cm (1992).

Current status: Routine readings still in progress.

Site: The tree is the last of a line of silver birches along the grass verge on the western side of a park access road. The access holes are aligned to the north of the tree, across a large well-kept lawn, with a park access road between 3 and 5m away from the holes.

Soil profile:	Distance from tree (m)	1.8	3.6	5.4	7.2	18.0
	x height (in 1981)	0.2	0.4	0.6	0.8	2.0

Soil classification tests:

Distance from tree (m)	1.8
Depth (m)	1.0
Plastic limit	31
Liquid limit	96
Plasticity index	65
% linear shrinkage	18.9

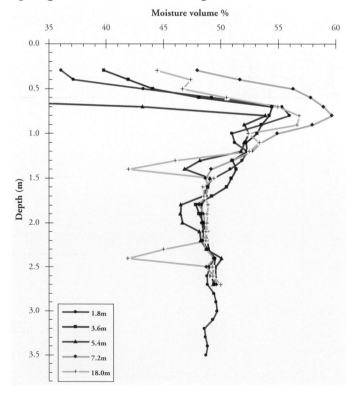

Spring soil moisture content profile

Comments: Similar profiles below 1.0m, apart from influence of bands of sand on the control.

Seasonal development of soil drying at 1.8m from tree during 1983

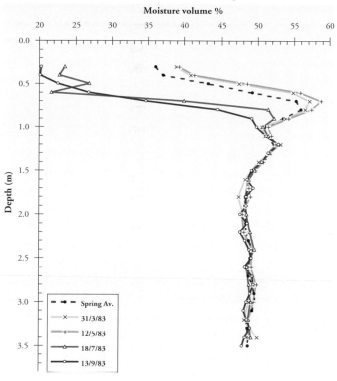

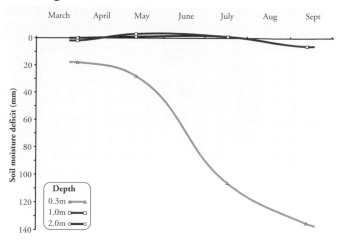

Comments: Deficit at 0.3m depth develops gradually through the season, with negligible drying below 1.0m.

Seasonal development of soil drying at 1.8m from tree during 1984

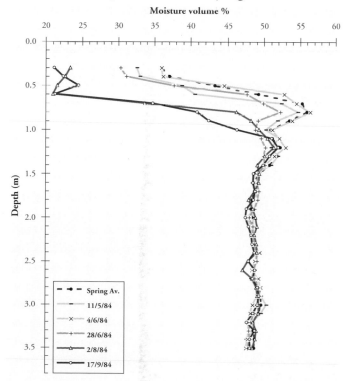

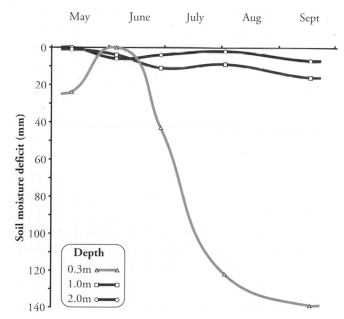

Comments: Deficit at 0.3m depth develops very rapidly during July, with negligible further change and with negligible drying below 1.0m.

Reduction in soil moisture content on 29/10/91 compared with spring average

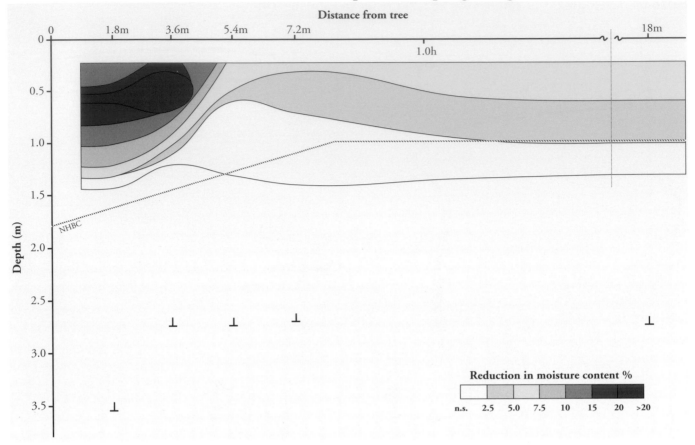

Soil moisture deficit on 29/10/91 compared with spring average

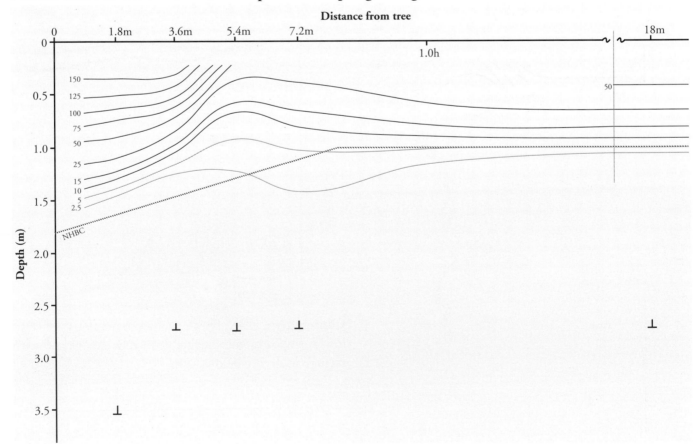

Seasonal reduction in soil moisture content on 16/9/94 compared with spring average

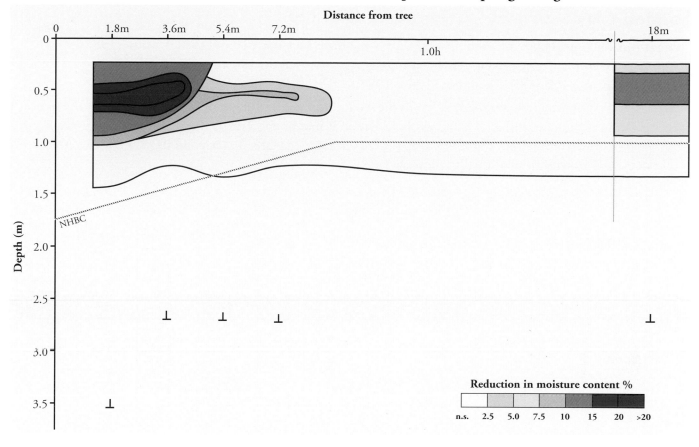

Seasonal soil moisture deficit on 16/9/94 compared with spring average

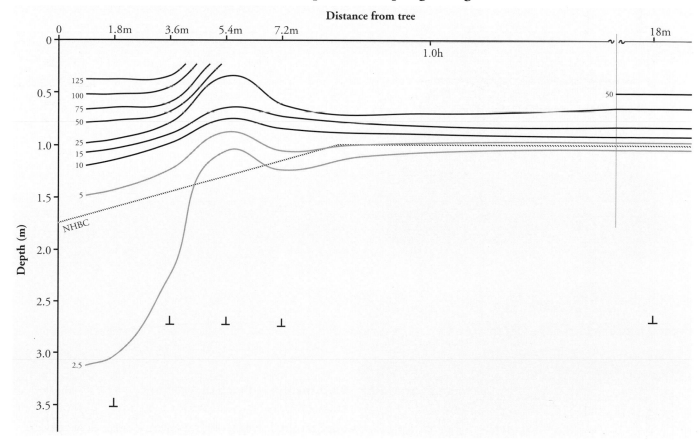

Silver birch
London Clay

Location: Fryent Regional Open Space,   **Size:**   Height: 10m (1981); 10m (1985)
Wembley   Map ref: TQ 197 877   b.h.d.: 26cm (1981).

Current status: Readings discontinued after 1985.

Site: Fryent Way (a main road) is 5m to the west of the tree and there is a footpath between the tree and nearest access tube. The access holes are in a line to the NE of the tree in tussocky rough grass (mown annually). There is a deep ditch 10m from the tree, just beyond the 8.0m access hole, with the control in poor quality meadow land.

Soil profile:	Distance from tree (m)	2.0	4.0	6.0	8.0	20.0
	x height (in 1981)	0.2	0.4	0.6	0.8	2.0

Soil classification tests:

Distance from tree (m)	2.0
Depth (m)	2.0
Plastic limit	26
Liquid limit	85
Plasticity index	59
% linear shrinkage	14.6

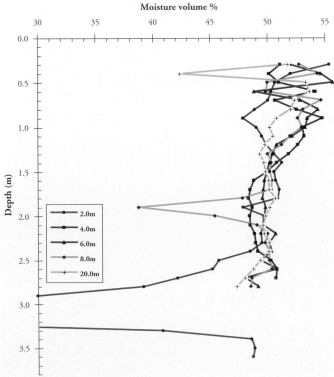

Spring soil moisture content profiles

Comments: Band of sand and gravel near base of closest access tube has major influence on profile, and appears shallower than indicated by soil description.

Seasonal fluctuations in soil moisture deficit at 1.0m depth

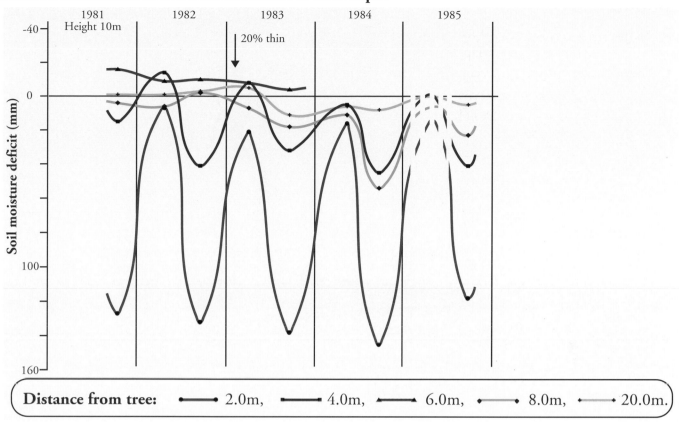

Comments: Considerable seasonal movement at closest access tube, and minor seasonal changes to 4.0m. The The branches were thinned by 20% in spring 1983, but this appears to have made no difference to subsequent seasonal movement.

Maximum soil drying recorded at 2.0m from tree in various years

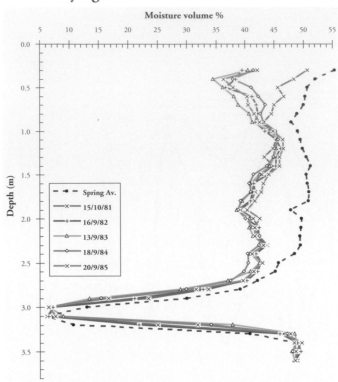

Comments: Below 1.0m the seasonal changes each year are almost identical, possibly influenced by drainage into sand and gravel below 3.0m.

Seasonal and persistent deficits

2.0m from tree

4.0m from tree

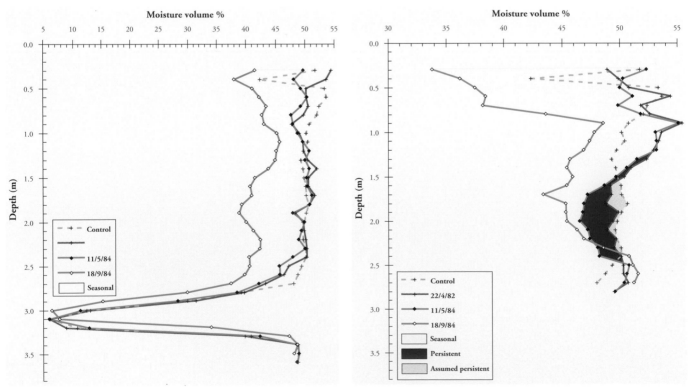

Comments: Extensive seasonal drying extending down to the sand and gravel below 3.0m.

Comments: Seasonal changes extending to 2.3m, possibly associated with gravel below base of access tube. Slight persistent deficit appears to have established.

Reduction in soil moisture content on 13/9/83 compared with spring average

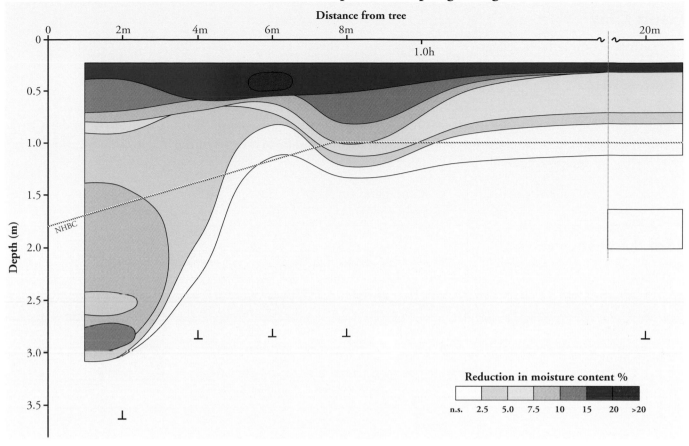

Soil moisture deficit on 13/9/83 compared with spring average

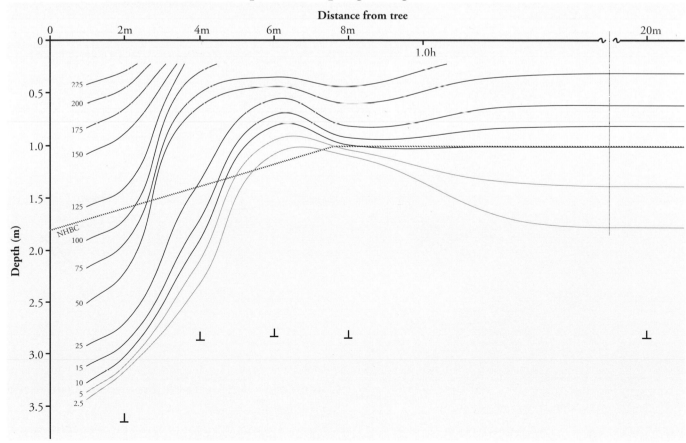

Silver birch
Gault Clay

Location: Emmanuel College,
            Cambridge   Map ref: TL 435 589

Size: Height: 12m (1981); 12m (1984)

Current status: Readings discontinued after 1984.

Site: Single tree situated in corner of playing field. There is a small mixed elm and thorn boundary hedge about 1.5m to the south west. Access holes are aligned to the east of the tree in the close mown grass of the playing field.

Soil profile:	Distance from tree (m)	3.0	4.8	7.2	9.6	24.0
	x height (in 1981)	0.25	0.4	0.6	0.8	2.0

Soil classification tests:

Distance from tree (m)	4.8	7.2
Depth (m)	2.0	1.5
Plastic limit	21	21
Liquid limit	52	38
Plasticity index	31	17
% linear shrinkage	-	9.4

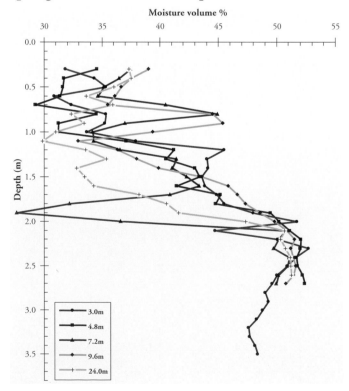

Spring soil moisture content profiles

Comments: Very variable profiles associated with bands of sand.

Seasonal fluctuations in soil moisture deficit at 1.0m depth

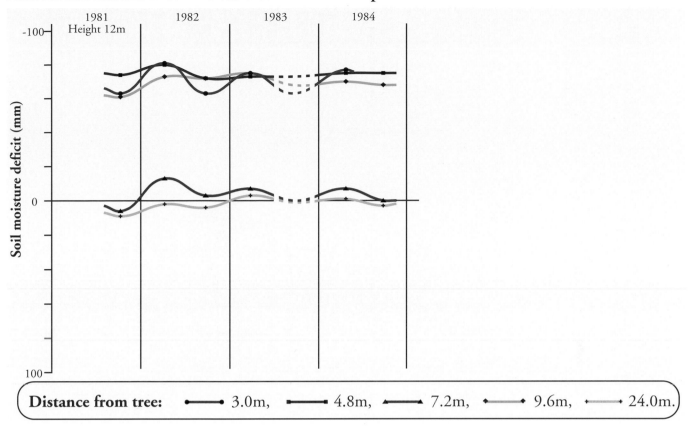

Comments: Negligible change below 1.0m.

Maximum soil drying recorded at 3.0m from tree in various years

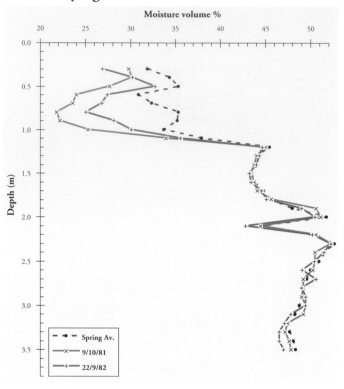

Comments: Similar profiles both years.

Seasonal deficit 3.0m from tree

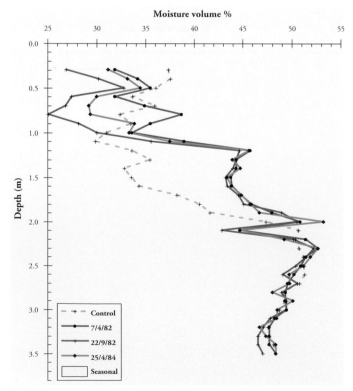

Comments: Seasonal changes only extend to 1.2m.

Reduction in soil moisture content on 9/10/81 compared with spring average

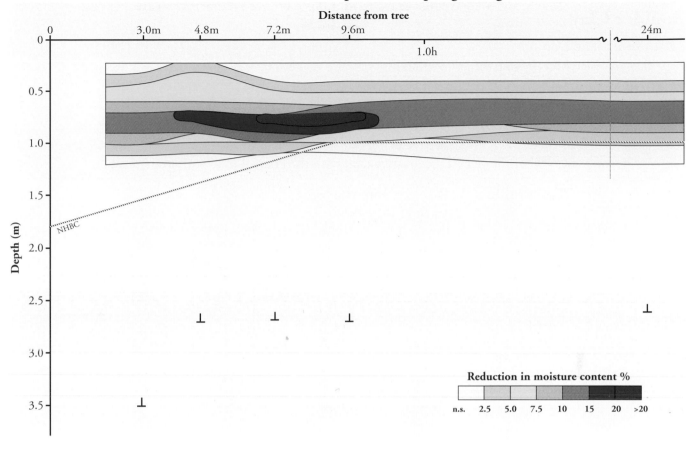

Soil moisture deficit on 9/10/81 compared with spring average

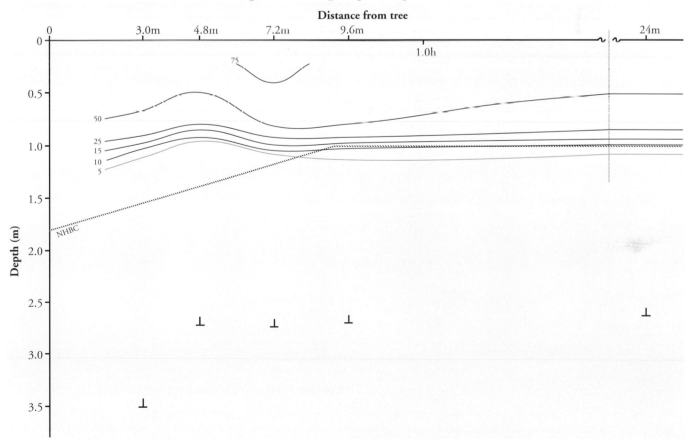

Silver birch
Boulder Clay

Location: The Don,
Bletchley   Map ref: SP 849 342

Size: Height:8 m (1981); 9m (1985)
b.h.d.: 22cm (1981).

Current status: Readings discontinued after 1985.

Site: The tree is situated in a grassed area between a double row of houses. There are paths on all four sides of the grassed area, the tree being 3m NE of the nearest of them. The four closest holes are aligned NW of the tree in the grassed area, with the control in a worn grass slope.

Soil profile:	Distance from tree (m)	1.5	3.1	4.7	6.3	16.0
	x height (in 1981)	0.2	0.4	0.6	0.8	2.0

Soil classification tests:

Distance from tree (m)	1.5
Depth (m)	1.0
Plastic limit	17
Liquid limit	38
Plasticity index	21
% linear shrinkage	12.4

Spring soil moisture content profiles

Legend:
- 1.5m
- 3.1m
- 4.7m
- 6.3m
- 16.0m

Comments: Variable profiles in Boulder Clay soil.

Seasonal fluctuations in soil moisture deficit at 1.0m depth

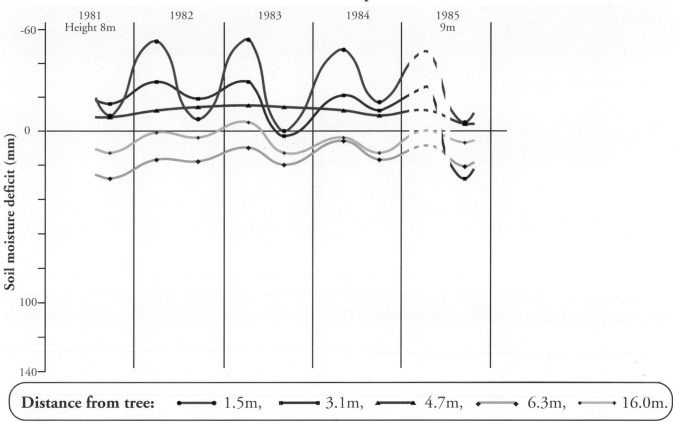

Distance from tree: ●————● 1.5m, ■————■ 3.1m, ▲————▲ 4.7m, ◆————◆ 6.3m, +————+ 16.0m.

Comments: Slight seasonal changes at the two closest access tubes, with other tubes similar to the control.

Maximum soil drying recorded at 1.5m from tree in various years

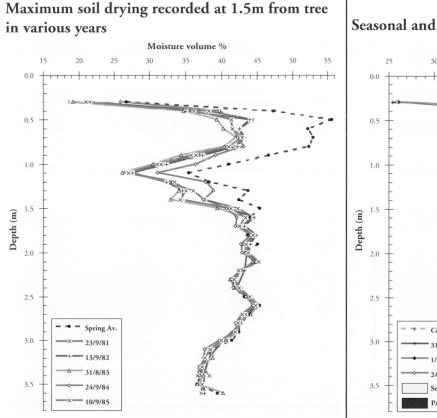

Comments: Similar variation each year extending to 1.6m depth.

Seasonal and persistent deficits 1.5m from tree

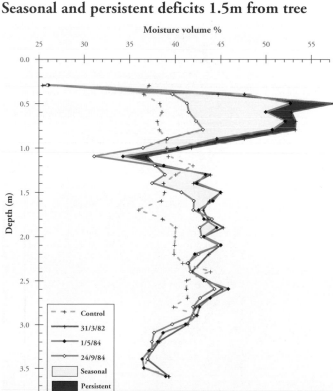

Comments: Soil drying by grass prior to readings in March 1982 is the probable explanation for apparent persistent deficit.

Seasonal development of soil drying at 1.5m from tree during 1983

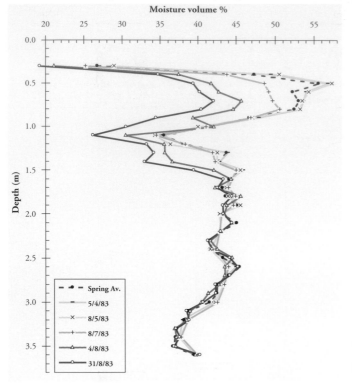

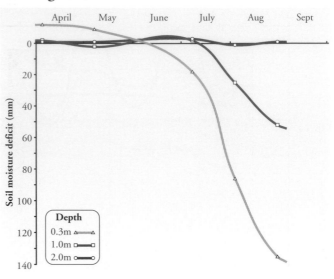

Comments: In this year, the soil drying develops progressively from May through to August.

Seasonal development of soil drying at 1.5m from tree during 1984

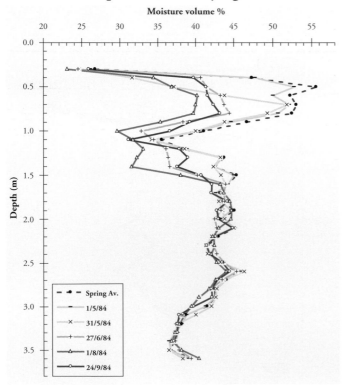

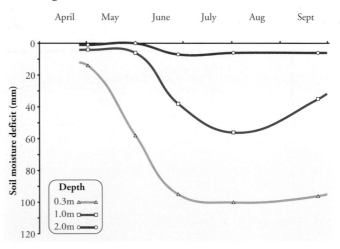

Comments: In 1984, in contrast to 1983, negligible further drying after end of June, and partial recovery by September.

Reduction in soil moisture content on 31/8/83 compared with spring average

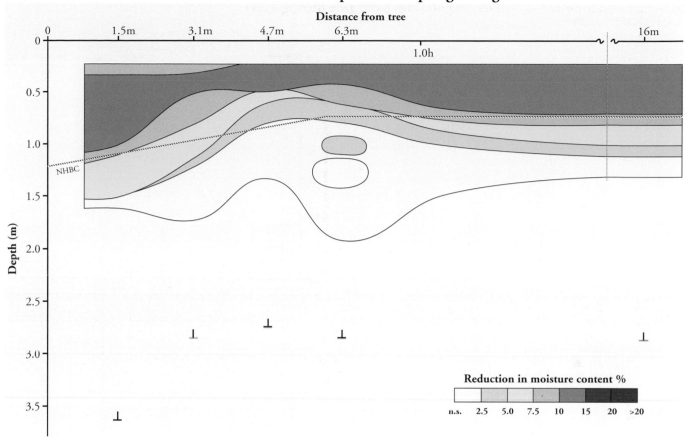

Soil moisture deficit on 31/8/83 compared with spring average

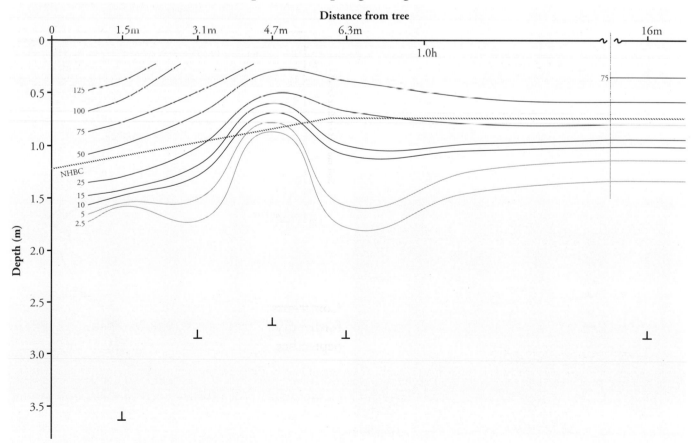

Whitebeam
London Clay

Location: Preston Park,
North Wembley   Map ref: TQ 177 873

Size: Height: 7m (1983); 8m (1991)
b.h.d.:   18cm (1984).

Current status: Readings discontinued after 1991.

Site: One of a small group of trees situated on the northern boundary of the park. The access tubes are sited in close mown grass, and aligned roughly parallel to the park fence to the east of the tree.

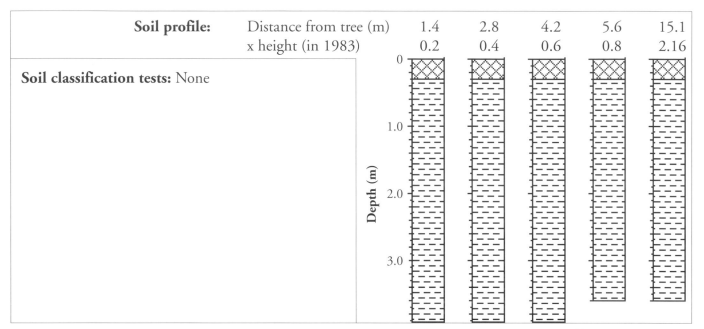

Soil profile:	Distance from tree (m)	1.4	2.8	4.2	5.6	15.1
	x height (in 1983)	0.2	0.4	0.6	0.8	2.16

Soil classification tests: None

Spring soil moisture content profiles

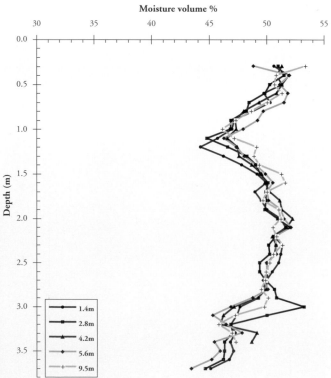

Comments: All profiles fairly similar, but varying with depth.

Seasonal fluctuations in soil moisture deficit at 1.0m depth

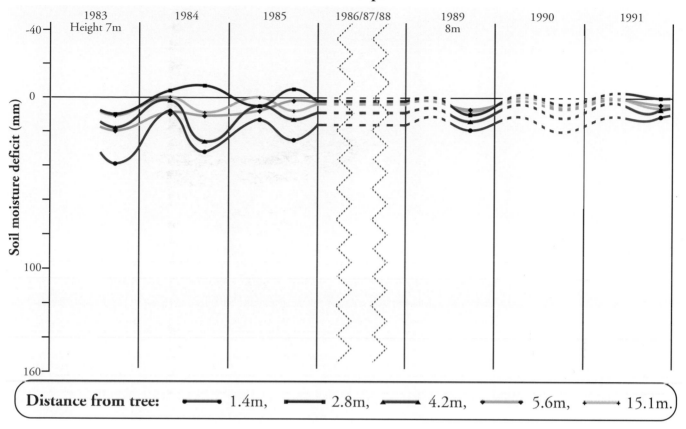

Comments: Slight seasonal changes in 1983 and 1985 at the three closest access tubes. Negligible drying recorded in 1989 and 1991, probably because readings were taken too late, allowing partial recovery. Likewise, recovery was complete by time readings taken in 1984 at access tube 2.8m from tree.

Maximum soil drying recorded at 1.4m from tree in various years

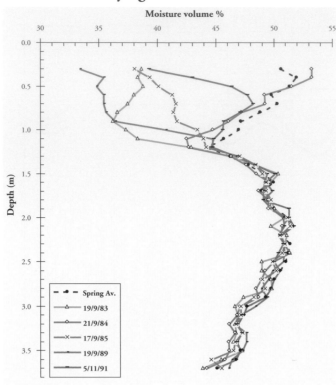

Comments: Considerable variation between the different years, with recovery almost complete by the time readings taken in 1984.

Seasonal deficit 1.4m from tree

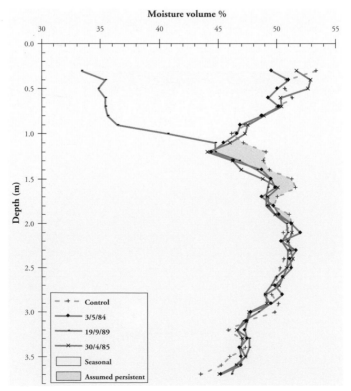

Comments: Seasonal drying only extending to 1.2m depth.

Reduction in soil moisture content on 19/9/83 compared with spring average

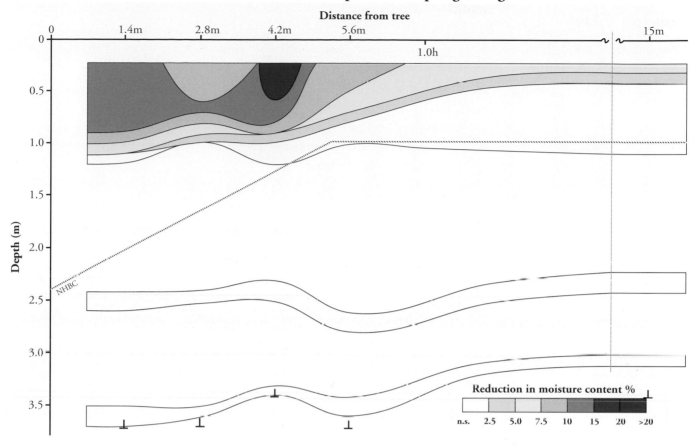

Soil moisture deficit on 19/9/83 compared with spring average

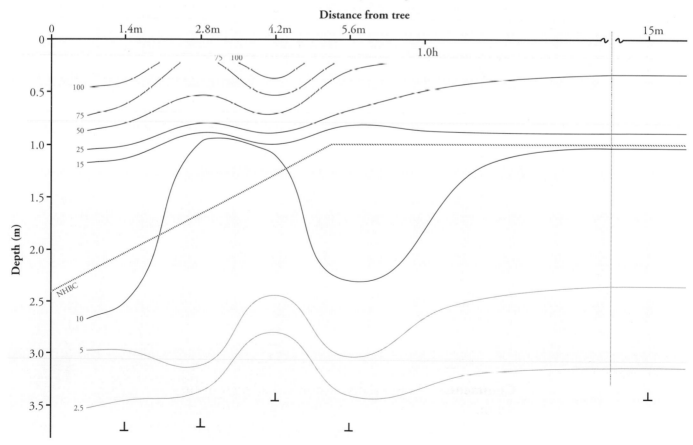

Whitebeam
London Clay

Location: Canons Park, **Size:** Height: 10m (1983); 10 m (1985)
  East Harrow Map ref: TQ 182 919 b.h.d.: 22 cm (1983).
Current status: Readings discontinued after 1985.

Site: One of a row of trees alongside a footpath leading to the northern end of the King George V Memorial Gardens which are situated within the park. The access tubes are located in the mown grass of the park in an easterly direction from the tree.

Soil profile:	Distance from tree (m)	2.0	4.0	6.0	8.0	20.0
	x height (in 1983)	0.2	0.4	0.6	0.8	2.0

Soil classification tests: None

Spring soil moisture content profiles

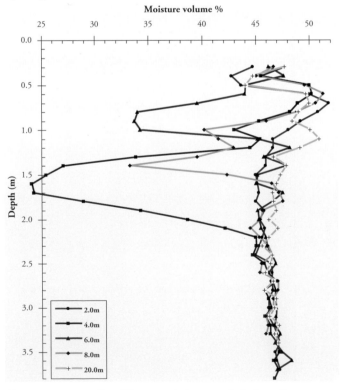

Comments: Profiles at 4.0m and 8.0m from tree greatly influenced by localised bands of clayey gravel.

210

Seasonal fluctuations in soil moisture deficit at 1.0m depth

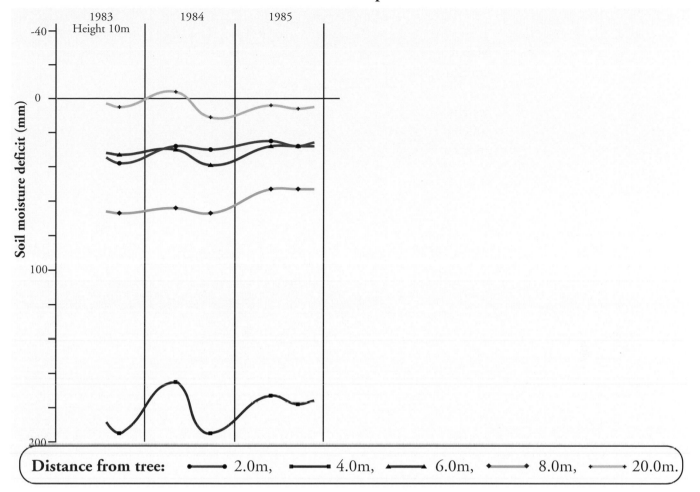

Comments: Negligible seasonal changes, except in the band of gravel at access tube 4.0m from tree.

Maximum soil drying recorded at 2.0m from tree in various years

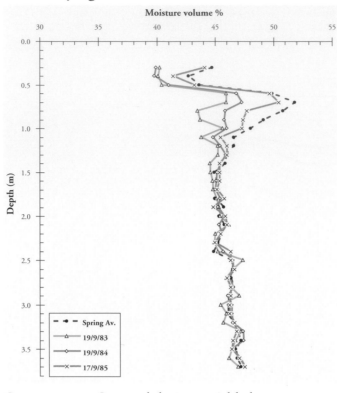

Comments: Seasonal drying variable between years.

Seasonal (and persistent) deficits

2.0m from tree

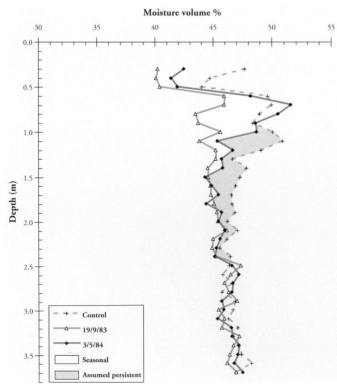

Comments: Seasonal drying extending to 1.5m.

4.0m from tree

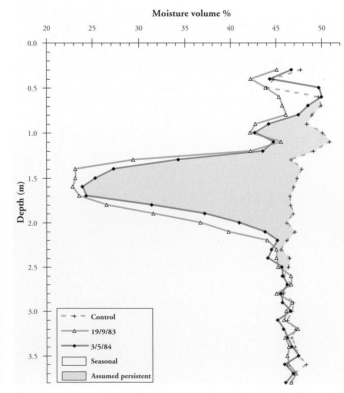

Comments: Massive assumed persistent deficit due to band of gravel. Seasonal drying to base of gravel.

Reduction in soil moisture content on 19/9/83 compared with spring average

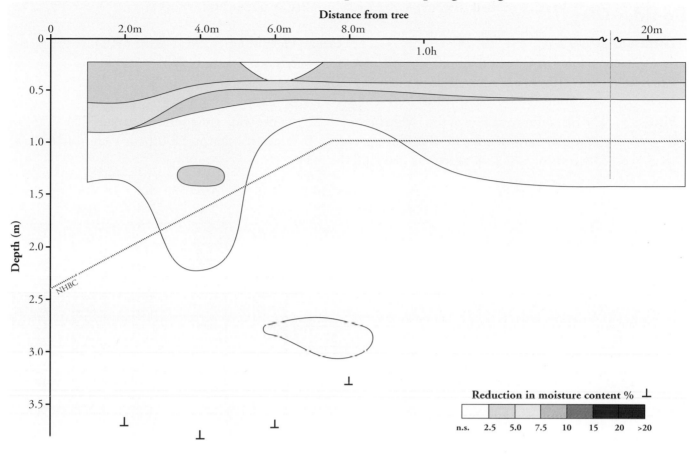

Soil moisture deficit on 19/9/83 compared with spring average

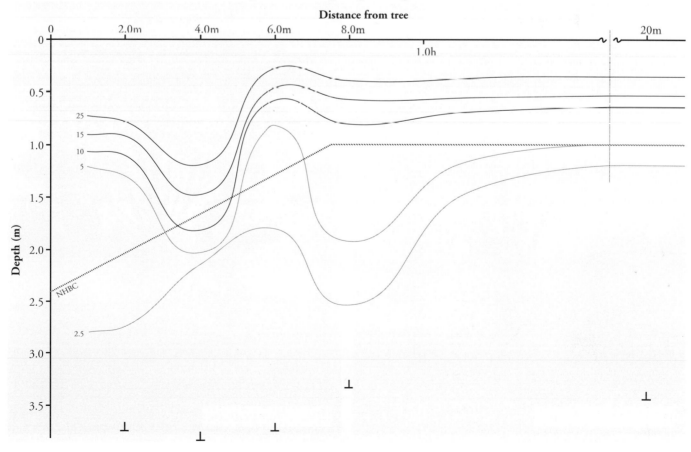

Whitebeam
Boulder Clay

Location: Chequers,
Welwyn Garden City   Map ref: TL 240 118

Current status: Routine readings still in progress.

Size: Height: 8m (1983); 7m (1993)
b.h.d.: 39cm (1992).

Site: The tree is one of a row of four whitebeam growing in the wide grass verge of a road. The tubes are in the close mown grass in a line due west of the tree towards a tarmac footpath 13m from the tree. The control tube is between the path and the road.

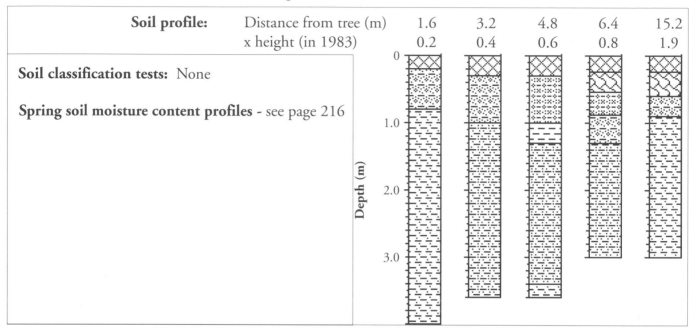

| Soil profile: Distance from tree (m) | 1.6 | 3.2 | 4.8 | 6.4 | 15.2 |
| x height (in 1983) | 0.2 | 0.4 | 0.6 | 0.8 | 1.9 |

Soil classification tests: None

Spring soil moisture content profiles - see page 216

1992 - before pruning

1992 - after pruning

Seasonal fluctuations in soil moisture deficit at 1.0m depth

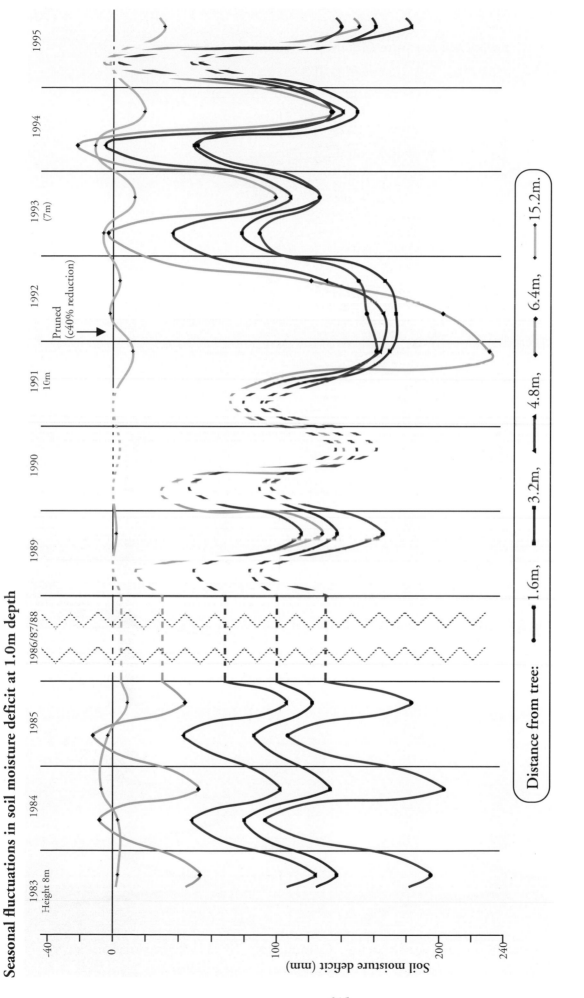

Distance from tree: 1.6m, 3.2m, 4.8m, 6.4m, 15.2m.

Comments: Large seasonal fluctuations during period from 1983 - 1989, with massive increase in amplitude at tube 6.4m from tree. The low rainfall in winter 1991/92 resulted in virtually no recovery during the winter, but the heavy crown reduction in early 1992 allowed some recovery during that summer (see page 220). By spring 1994 the reduced water uptake had allowed some rehydration of a pre-existing persistent deficit (see page 221). By 1995, seasonal drying was almost back to the situation prior to pruning.

Spring soil moisture content profiles

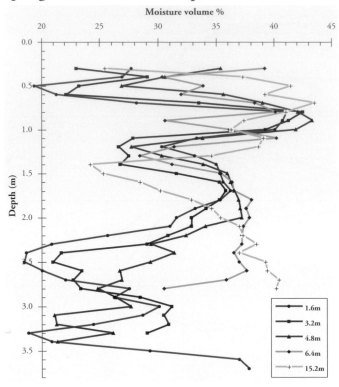

Comments: Very variable profiles in Boulder Clay.

Maximum soil drying recorded at 1.6m from tree in various years

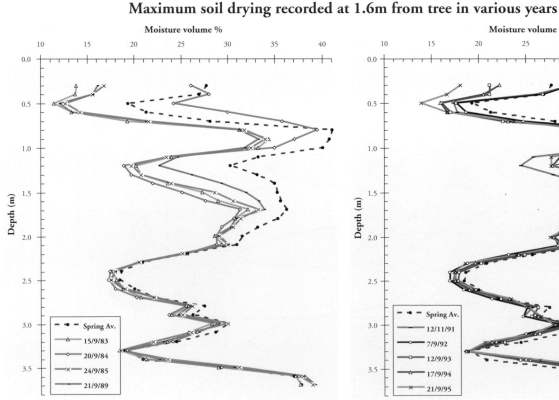

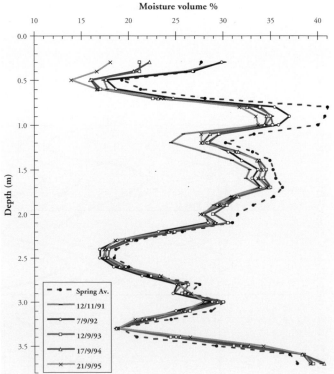

Comments: Slight variation between years, extending to 2.2m depth.

Comments: Similar slight variation between years, with driest profile in 1991.

Seasonal and Persistent deficits

1.6m from tree

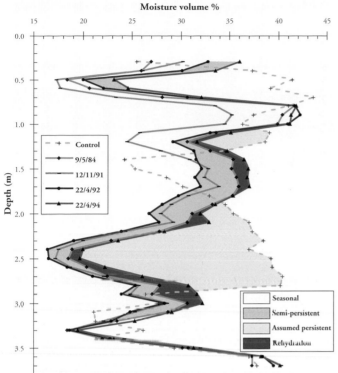

3.2m from tree

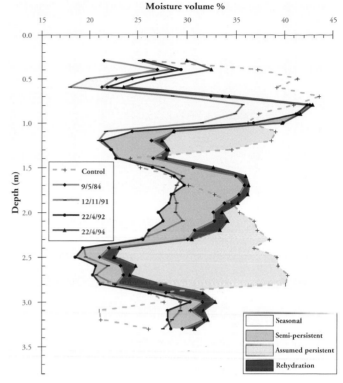

Comments: Recovery from semi-persistent deficit and additional rehydration of pre-existing persistent deficit after tree pruned early in 1992.

Comments: Even greater recovery than at 1.6m from tree.

4.8m from tree

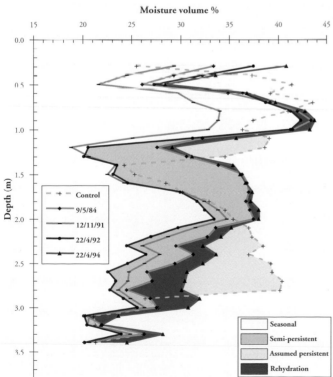

6.4m from tree

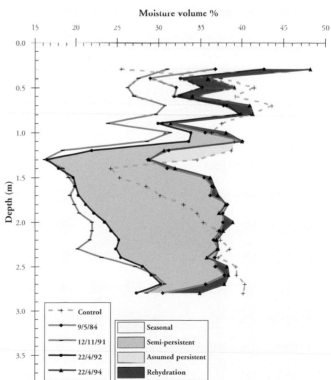

Comments: Even greater recovery than at 1.6m and 3.2m from tree.

Comments: Massive recovery of moisture after the tree was pruned.

Reduction in soil moisture content on 20/9/84 compared with spring average

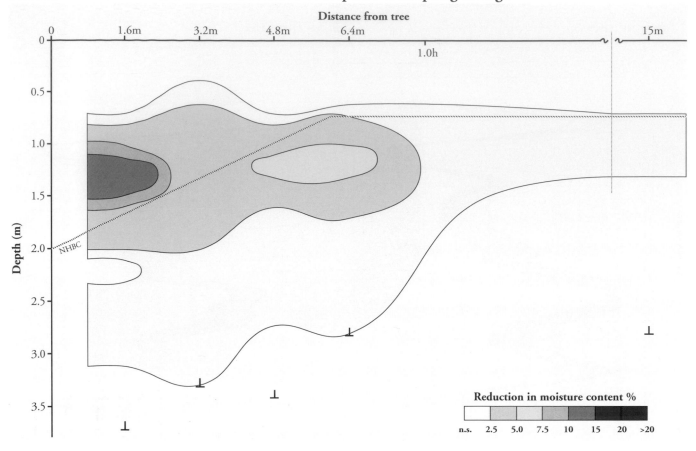

Soil moisture deficit on 20/9/84 compared with spring average

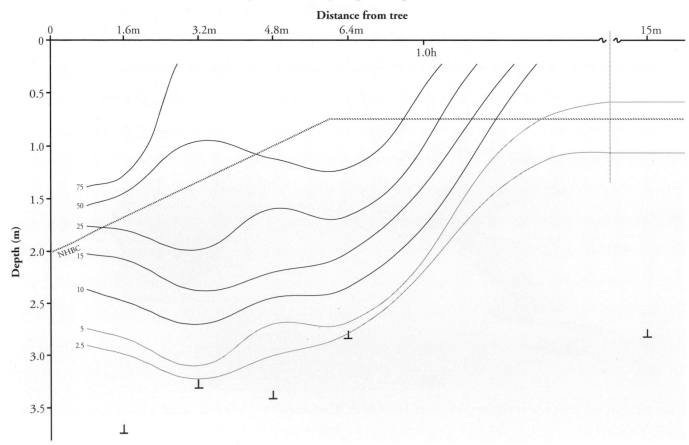

Reduction in soil moisture content on 12/11/91 compared with spring average

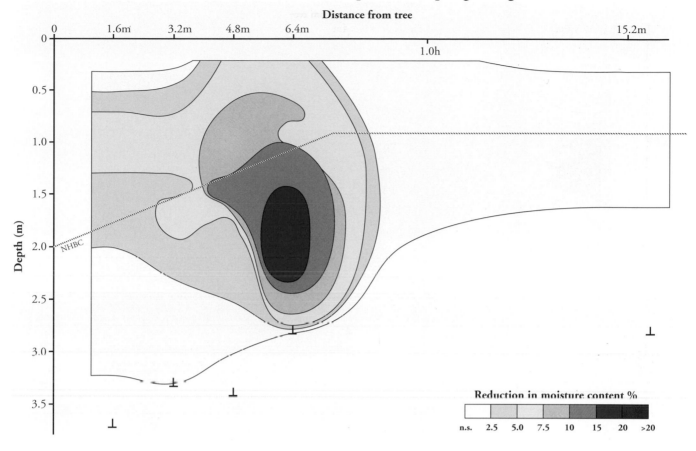

Soil moisture deficit on 12/11/91 compared with spring average

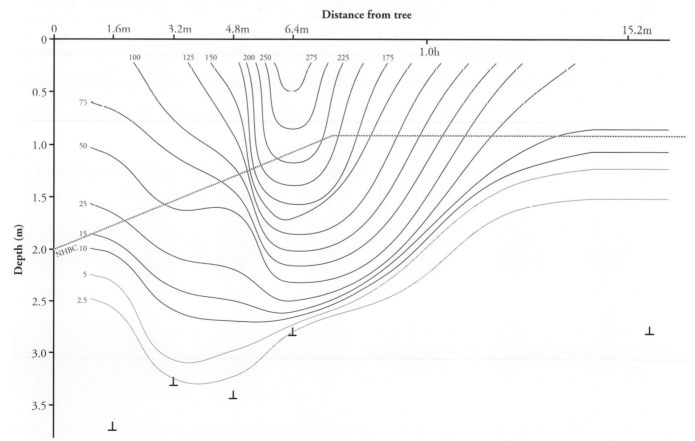

Changes soil moisture content between 22/4/92 and 7/9/92 (i.e. during summer after pruning)

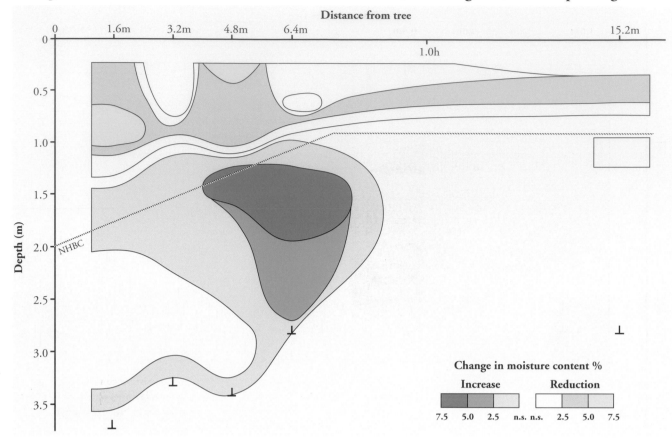

Changes in soil moisture deficit between 22/4/92 and 7/9/92 (i.e. during summer after pruning)

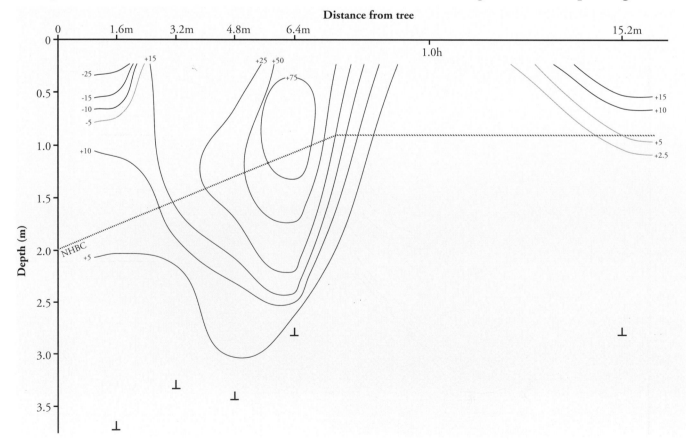

Increase in soil moisture content between 22/4/92 and 22/4/94 (recovery from persistent deficit)

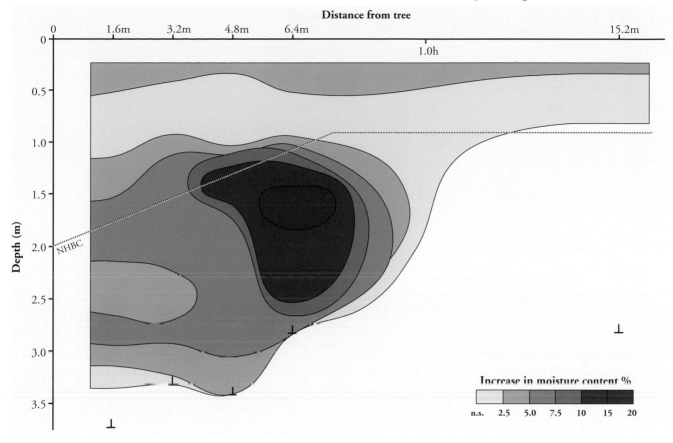

Rehydration on 22/4/94 compared with 22/4/92 (recovery from persistent deficit)

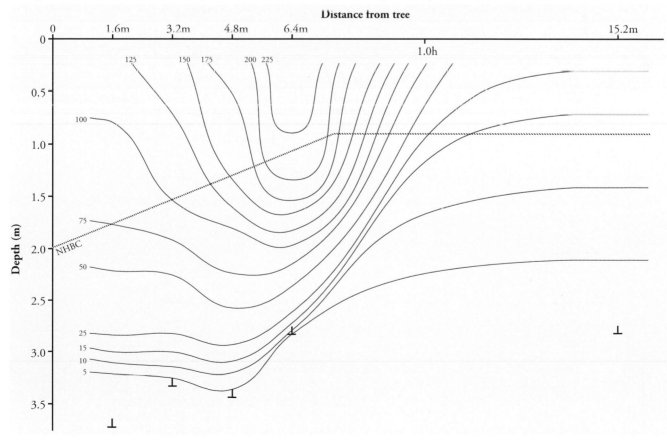

Whitebeam
Boulder Clay

Location: Russellcroft,   **Size:**   Height: 10m (1983);
       Welwyn Garden City   Map ref: TL 236 130

Current status: Tree felled prior to readings in April 1985.

Site: The tree was one of a row of four whitebeam growing along the edge of an ornamental grassed area bordered on two sides by Parkway and Russellcroft. The access tubes run in a northerly direction, parallel with Parkway.

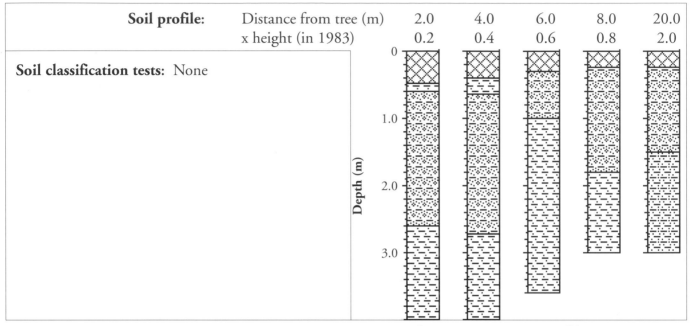

Soil profile:	Distance from tree (m)	2.0	4.0	6.0	8.0	20.0
	x height (in 1983)	0.2	0.4	0.6	0.8	2.0

Soil classification tests: None

Spring soil moisture content profiles

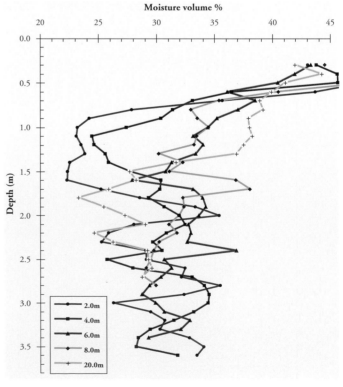

Comments: Very variable profiles.

Seasonal fluctuations in soil moisture deficit at 1.0m depth

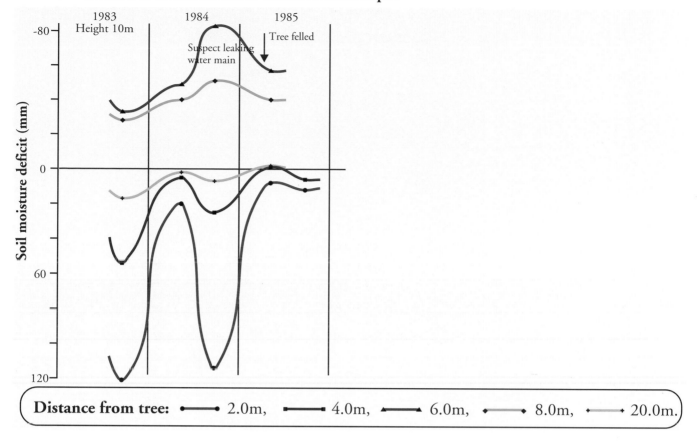

Distance from tree: 2.0m, 4.0m, 6.0m, 8.0m, 20.0m.

Comments: Considerable seasonal fluctuation at access tube closest to tree. No further recovery after tree was felled, thus indicating that no persistent deficit had been present.

Maximum soil drying recorded at 2.0m from tree in various years

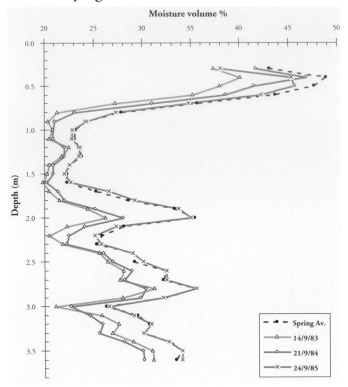

Comments: Very similar profiles in both years prior to felling of tree.

Seasonal deficit 2.0m from tree

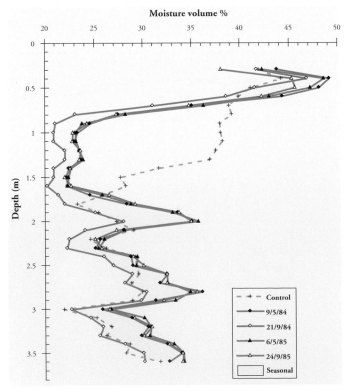

Comments: Seasonal changes extend to base of access tube at 3.6m depth. No significant rehydration after tree was felled.

Reduction in soil moisture content on 14/9/83 compared with spring average

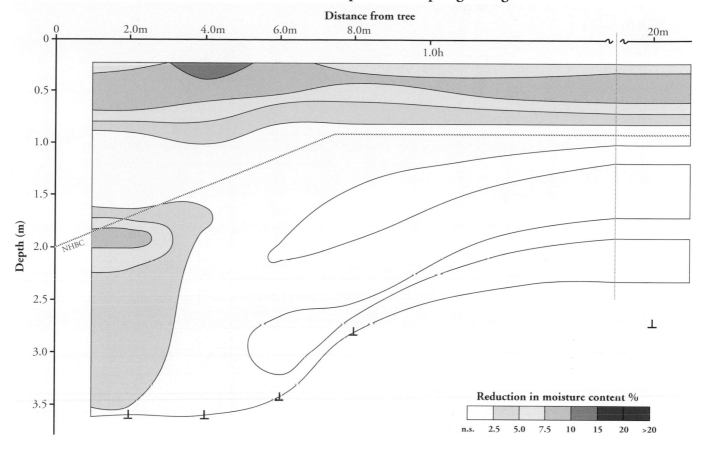

Soil moisture deficit on 14/9/83 compared with spring average

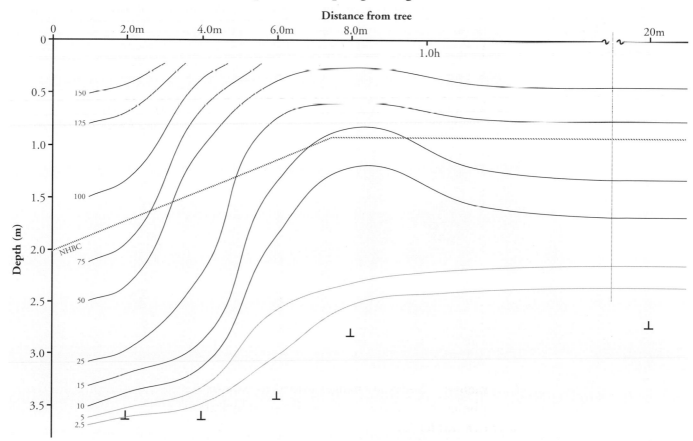

Leyland cypress
London Clay

Tree 43

Location: Eton Grove Recreation Ground, Wembley   Map ref: TQ196 897

Size: Height: 12m (1981); 16m (1993); b.h.d.: 46cm (1992).

Current status: Occasional readings still in progress.

Site: The westernmost of a group of 4 trees growing in a wide shrub border, with footpath curving in front of it. The two closest tubes are east of the tree in the hard-packed bare earth of the shrub bed. The other 3 tubes are in a line south west of the tree, in the mown grass of the recreation ground.

Soil profile:	Distance from tree (m)	1.8	3.6	6.0	9.0	24.0
	x height (in 1981)	0.15	0.3	0.5	0.75	2.0

Soil classification tests:

Distance from tree (m)	3.6	6.0
Depth (m)	2.0	1.5
Plastic limit	24	24
Liquid limit	70	56
Plasticity index	46	32
% linear shrinkage	13.9	14.3

Spring soil moisture content profiles

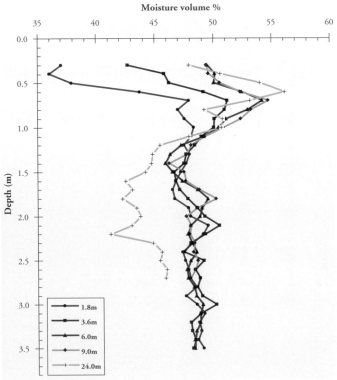

Comments: Similar profiles, apart from control tube which is considerably drier.

226

Seasonal fluctuations in soil moisture deficit at 1.0m depth

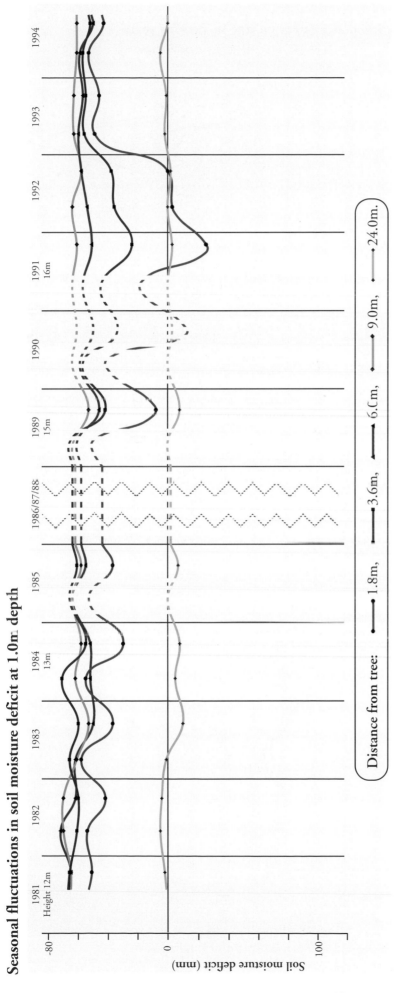

Distance from tree: 1.8m, 3.6m, 6.0m, 9.0m, 24.0m.

Comments: Two access tubes closest to tree show slight seasonal fluctuation which increases during dry period from 1989 - 1990, but deficit is only semi-persistent, and reverts to minor seasonal movements by 1993.

Maximum soil drying recorded at 1.8m from tree in various years

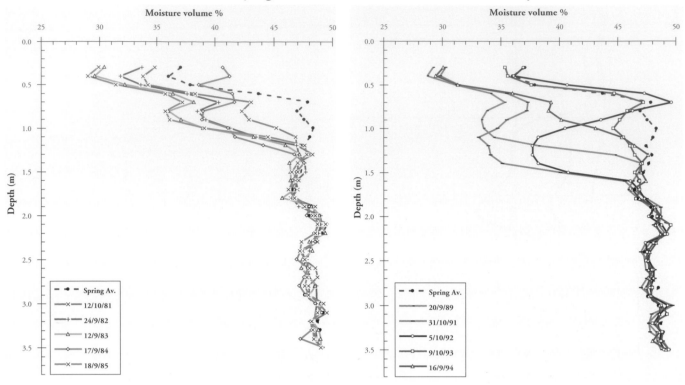

Comments: Variable extent of drying each year, only extending to 1.3m depth.

Comments: Very variable extent of drying each year, extending to 1.6m depth.

Seasonal and persistent deficits 1.8m from tree

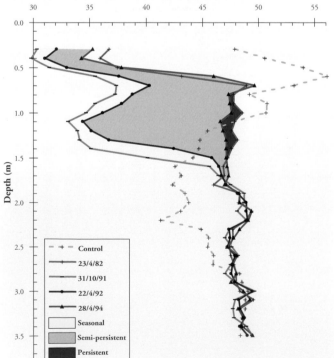

Comments: Massive semi-persistent deficit in 1992, but recovery near-complete by 1994, leaving only a small persistent deficit.

Reduction in soil moisture content on 31/10/91 compared with spring average

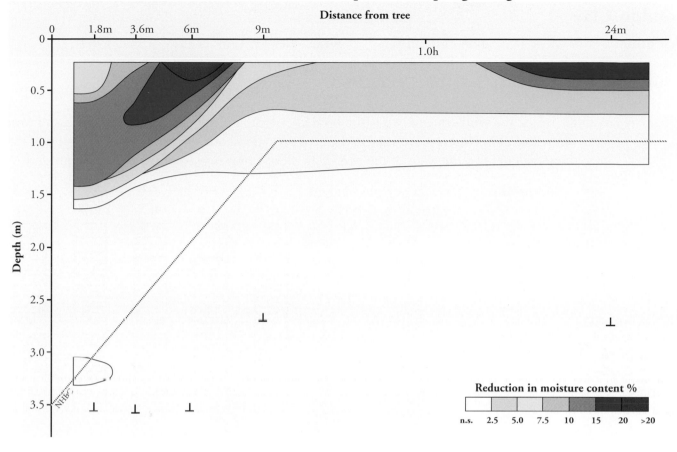

Soil moisture deficit on 31/10/91 compared with spring average

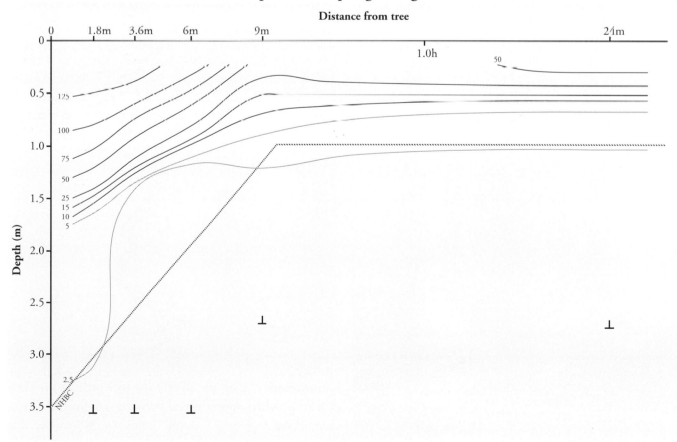

Leyland cypress
London Clay

Tree 44

Location: Eton Grove Recreation Ground,
Wembley   Map ref: TQ 196 896

Size: Height: 12m (1981); 15m (1989)
b.h.d.: 36cm (1981).

Current status: Blown down in storms, January 1990.

Site: A single tree at the southern end of a shrub border. A footpath curved close to the south and west sides of the tree. The closest access tube in the hard packed soil of a shrub border to the south of the tree; the remainder in a line west of the tree in the closely mown grass of the recreation ground.

Soil profile:	Distance from tree (m)	1.7	3.6	6.0	9.0	24.0
	x height (in 1981)	0.14	0.3	0.5	0.75	2.0

Soil classification tests:

Distance from tree (m)	3.6
Depth (m)	2.0
Plastic limit	31
Liquid limit	82
Plasticity index	51
% linear shrinkage	17.0

Spring soil moisture content profiles

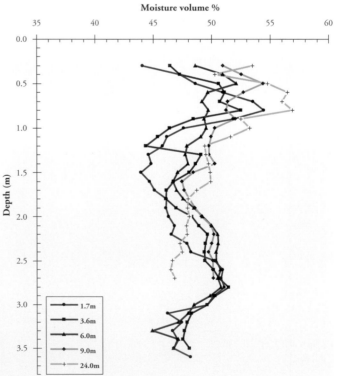

Comments: Comparatively variable profiles for London Clay, with suggestion of persistent deficit at closest access tube.

230

Seasonal fluctuations in soil moisture deficit at 1.0m depth

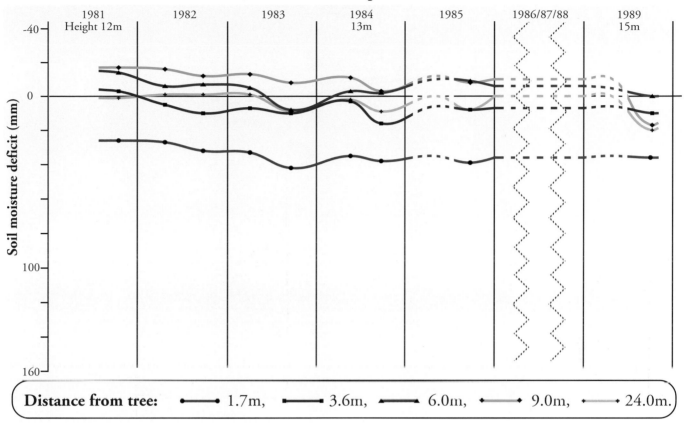

Distance from tree: ●——● 1.7m, ■——■ 3.6m, ▲——▲ 6.0m, ◆——◆ 9.0m, •——• 24.0m.

Comments: Only very slight seasonal fluctuation.

Seasonal and persistent deficits 1.7m from tree

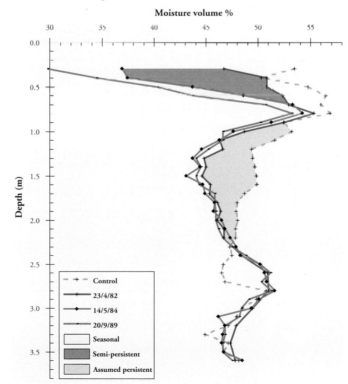

Comments: Seasonal and semi-persistent drying only extending to 1.0m depth.

Maximum soil drying recorded at 1.7m from tree in various years

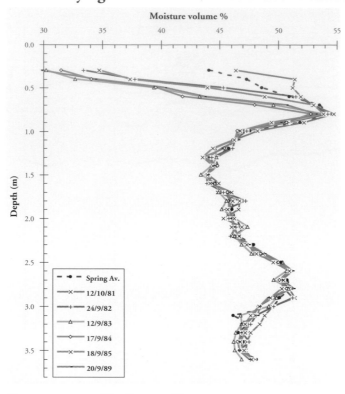

Comments: Similar profiles most years.

Seasonal development of soil drying at 1.7m from tree during 1984

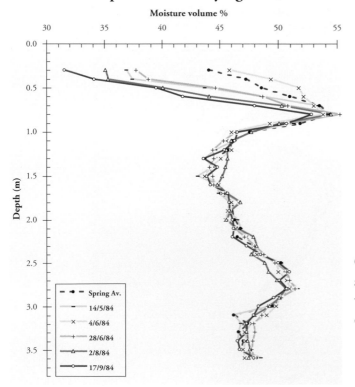

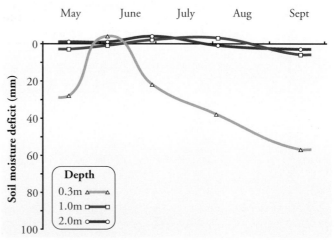

Comments: Although the tree is an evergreen, the soil was still recovering until June, with progressive development of deficit at 0.3m depth throughout the rest of the summer.

Reduction in soil moisture content on 20/9/89 compared with spring average

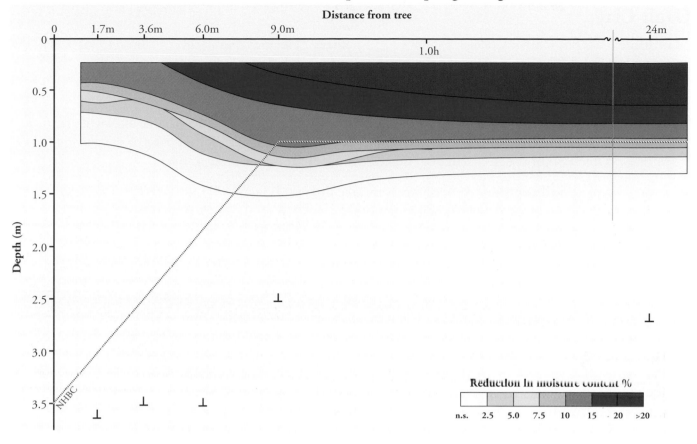

Soil moisture deficit on 20/9/89 compared with spring average

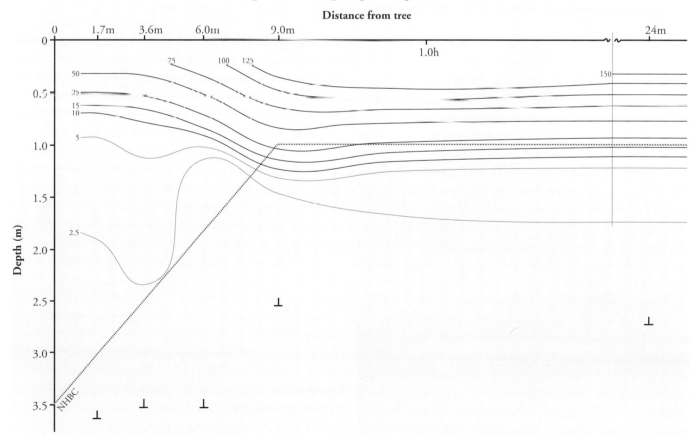

Leyland cypress
Gault Clay

Tree 45

Location: Corpus Christi College,
Cambridge Map ref: TL 435 580

Size: Height: 10m (1981); 18m (1995)
b.h.d.: 47cm (1992).

Current status: Routine readings still in progress.

Site: Tree is at southern end of a row of close-planted cypresses along western edge of playing field (part of same row as tree 46). The access holes are situated in the lush mown grass of the playing field in a line ESE of the tree. 2m deep drainage ditch 8m to west of row of trees.

| Soil profile: | Distance from tree (m) | 1.5 | 3.0 | 5.0 | 7.5 | 20.0 |
| | x height (in 1981) | 0.15 | 0.3 | 0.5 | 0.75 | 2.0 |

Soil classification tests:

Distance from tree (m)	3.0	5.0
Depth (m)	100	150
Plastic limit	29	29
Liquid limit	71	73
Plasticity index	42	44
% linear shrinkage	15.4	10.9

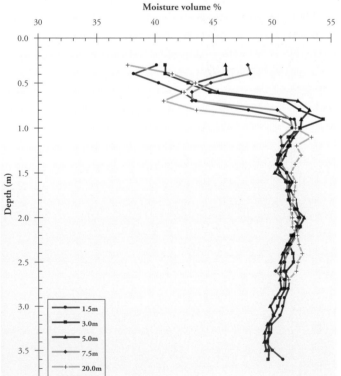

Spring soil moisture content profiles

Comments: Very similar profiles at all tubes below the surface layers of sandy soil.

Tree 45. Leyland cypress, Gault Clay

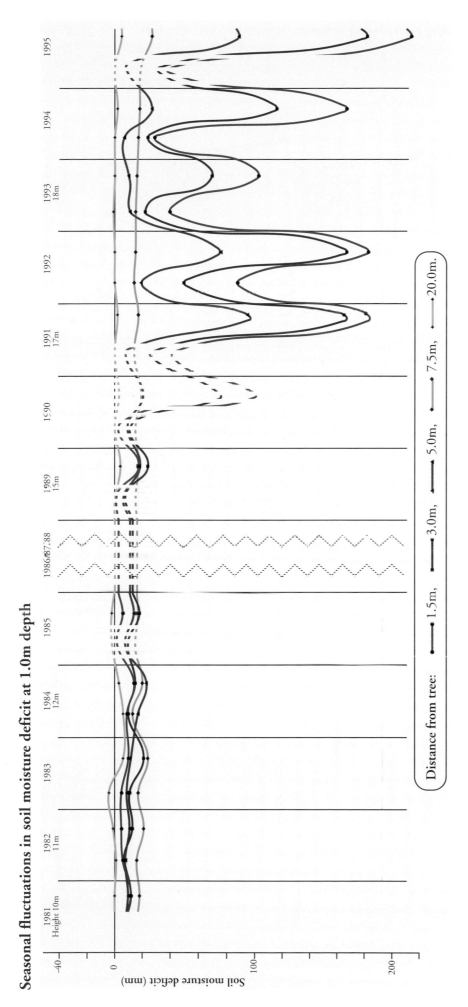

Seasonal fluctuations in soil moisture deficit at 1.0m depth

Distance from tree: ●—— 1.5m,   ■—— 3.0m,   ——— 5.0m,   ◆—— 7.5m,   ◆—— 20.0m.

Comments: Negligible soil drying at any of the tubes from 1981 through to 1989, but major soil moisture deficit had developed by 1991 (associated soil shrinkage sufficient to leave the top of the two access tubes closest to the tree projecting above ground level!). Considerable recovery at all of the access tubes during winter 1991/92 leaving only a slight semi-persistent deficit (contrast with tree 46, page 241), and almost full recovery by spring 1994. Soil moisture deficit in 1995 greater than previous years.

235

Maximum soil drying recorded at 1.5m from tree in various years

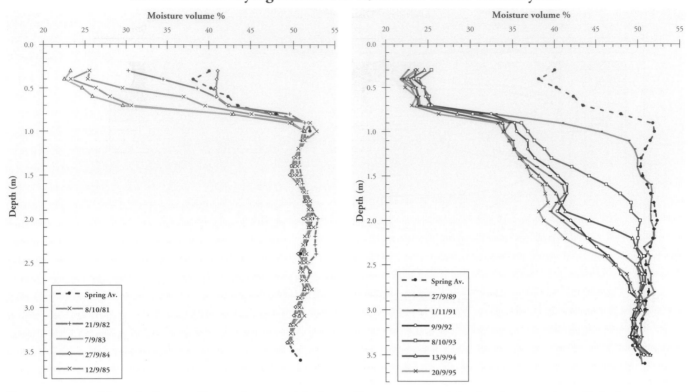

Comments: Very similar profiles each year with drying only extending to 0.9m.

Comments: Massive increase in soil drying extending to 3.5m, particularly in 1991 and 1995 but less so in 1993.

Seasonal and persistent deficits

1.5m from tree

3.0m from tree

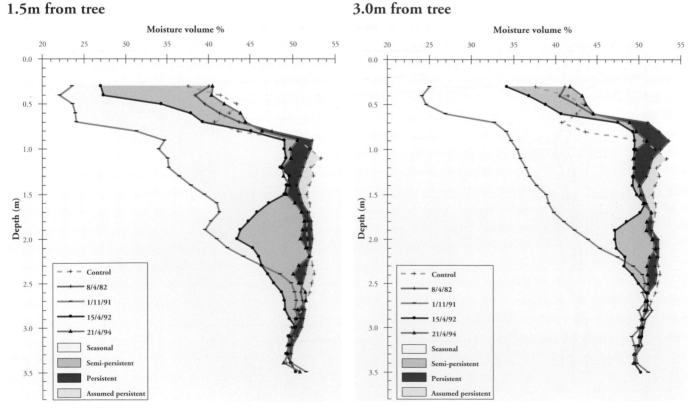

Comments: Despite increase in soil drying, only a very slight persistent deficit has developed.

Comments: Pattern of soil drying very similar to that at 1.5m from tree (contrast with tree 46, page 242).

Reduction in soil moisture content on 27/9/89 compared with spring average

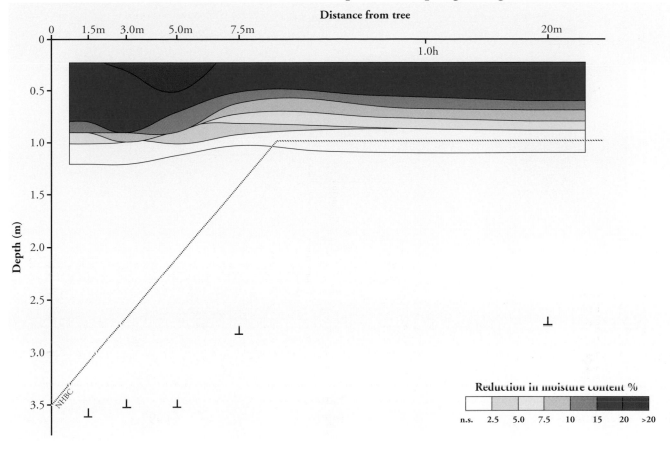

Soil moisture deficit on 27/9/89 compared with spring average

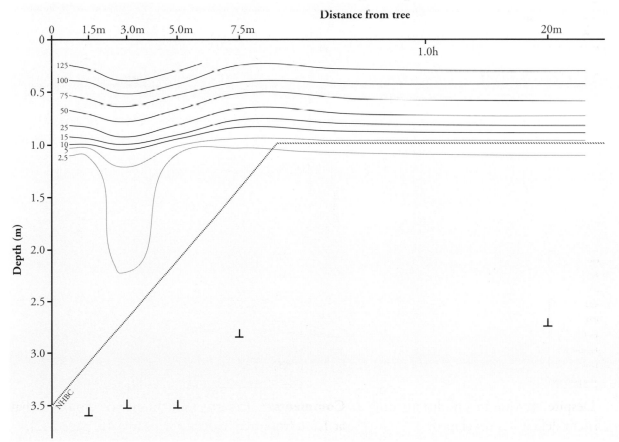

Reduction in soil moisture content on 1/11/91 compared with spring average

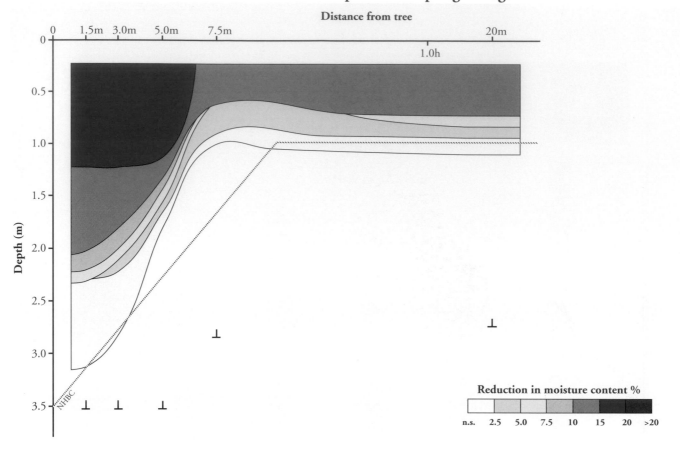

Soil moisture deficit on 1/11/91 compared with spring average

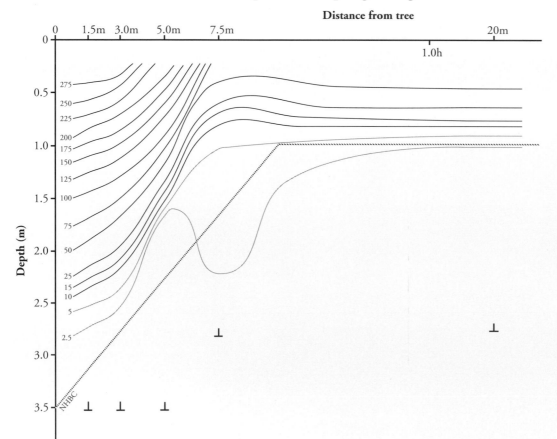

Reduction in soil moisture content on 20/9/95 compared with spring average

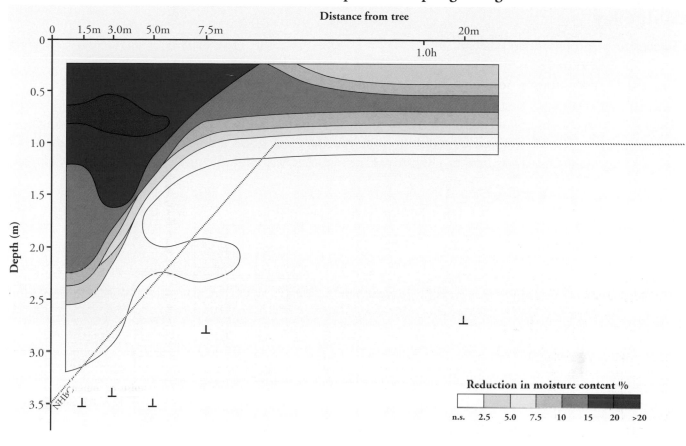

Soil moisture deficit on 20/9/95 compared with spring average

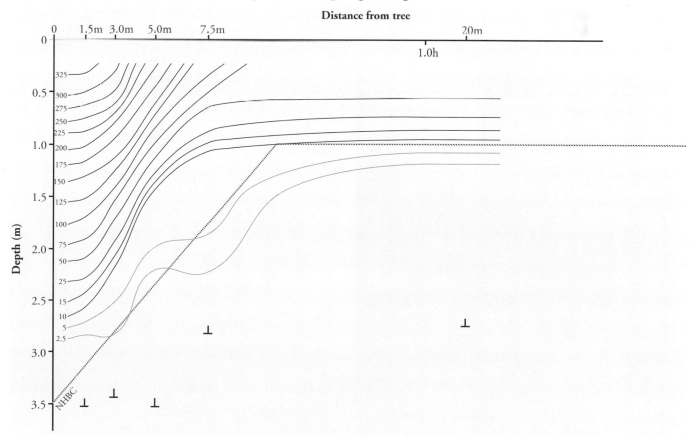

Leyland cypress
Gault Clay

Location: Corpus Christi College,
Cambridge   Map ref:TL 435 580

Size: Height: 12m (1981); 17m (1995)
b.h.d.: 53cm (1992).

Current status: Routine readings still in progress.

Site: Tree is a dominant specimen in a row of close-planted cypresses along western edge of playing field (part of same row and 20m distant from tree 46). The access holes are situated in the lush mown grass of the playing field in a line east of the tree. 2m deep drainage ditch 8m to west of row of trees.

Soil profile:	Distance from tree (m)	1.8	3.6	6.0	9.0	24.0
	x height (in 1981)	0.15	0.3	0.5	0.75	2.0

Soil classification tests:

Distance from tree (m)	3.6	6.0
Depth (m)	100	150
Plastic limit	26	32
Liquid limit	82	70
Plasticity index	56	38
% linear shrinkage	16.4	12.4

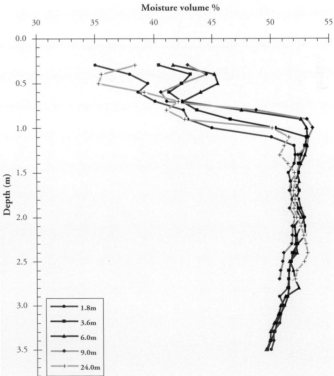

Spring soil moisture content profiles

Comments: Very similar profiles at all tubes below the surface layers of sandy soil.

Tree 46. Leyland cypress, Gault Clay

Seasonal fluctuations in soil moisture deficit at 1.0m depth

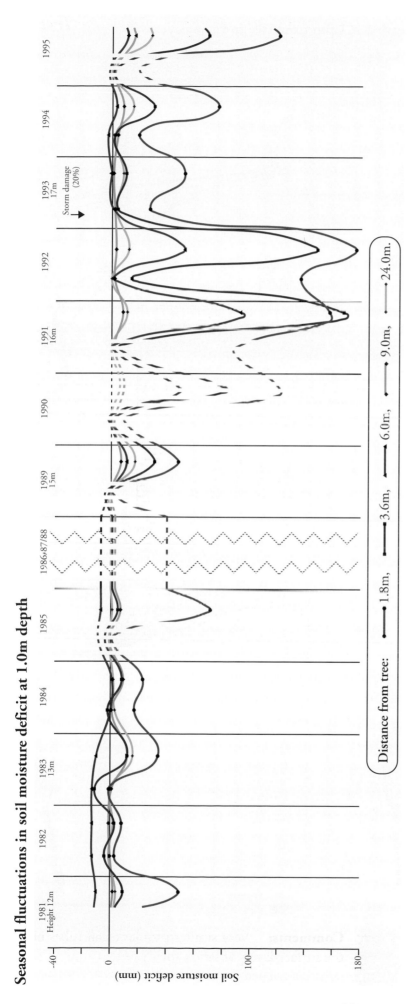

Distance from tree: ●—— 1.8m, ——— 3.6m, ——— 6.0m, ——— 9.0m, ◆——— 24.0m.

Comments: Slight soil drying at closest of the tubes but none at other tubes from 1981 through to 1989. In 1991 a major soil moisture deficit had developed, extending at least 6m from tree. During the winter 1991/92 the two closest access tubes show very different amount of recovery despite their close proximity to each other (negligible recovery at 1.8m from tree, but nearly complete at 3.6m). By contrast, in the following winter 1992/93, there was almost full recovery at both of these access tubes. Storm damage in 1993 broke one of the main stems, removing about 20% of the foliage. Drying in 1993 and 1994 was considerably less than in previous years. It increase in 1995, but was still less than in 1991 and 1992 (contrast with tree 45, page 235).

241

Maximum soil drying recorded at 1.8m from tree in various years

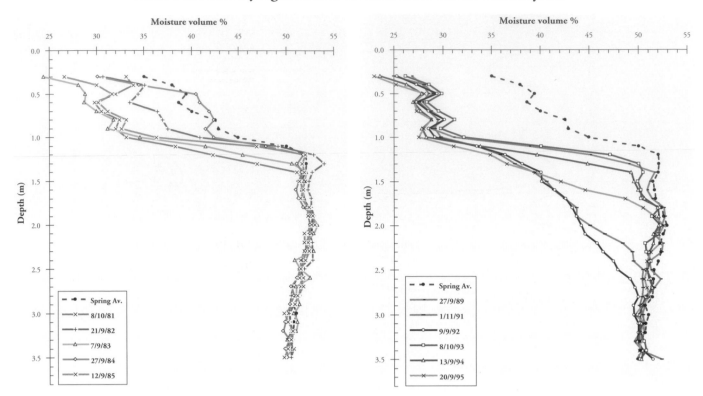

Comments: Very similar profiles each year, with 1981 as the driest, but only extending to 1.4m depth.

Comments: Considerable increase in depth and intensity of drying. Maximum effects in 1992, extending to 3.0m, and significantly less in subsequent years.

Seasonal and persistent deficits

1.8m from tree.

3.6m from tree.

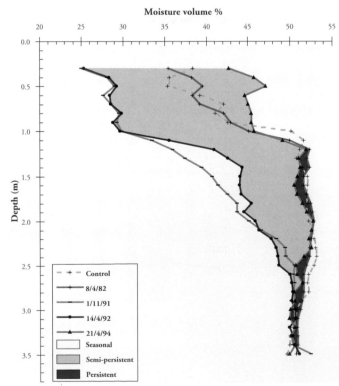

Comments: At this distance, massive semi-persistent deficit remains in spring 1992, but almost full recovery by spring 1994.

Comments: At this distance, there is almost full recovery in winter 1991/92, with only a limited semi-persistent deficit.

Seasonal development of soil drying at 1.8m from tree during 1983

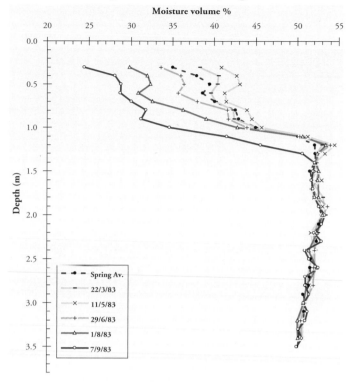

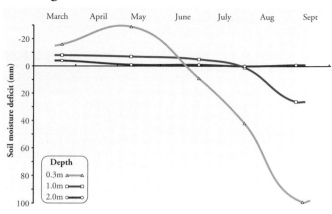

Comments: Drying does not start until May, and continues through to September.

Seasonal development of soil drying at 1.8m from tree during 1984

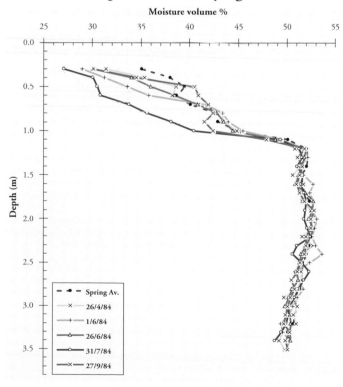

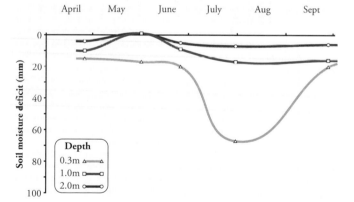

Comments: Drying does not start until May, but, in contrast to 1993, rain in September is sufficient to allow almost full recovery.

Reduction in soil moisture content on 27/9/89 compared with spring average

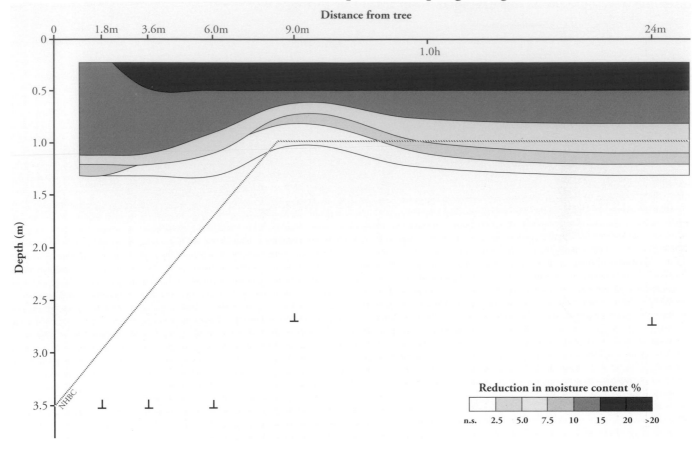

Soil moisture deficit on 27/9/89 compared with spring average

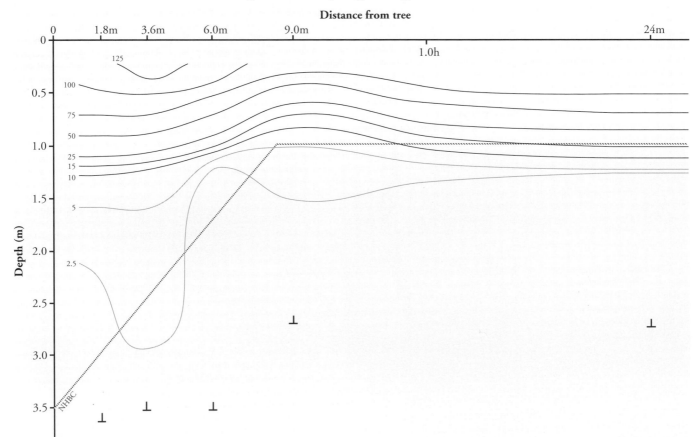

Reduction in soil moisture content on 1/11/91 compared with spring average

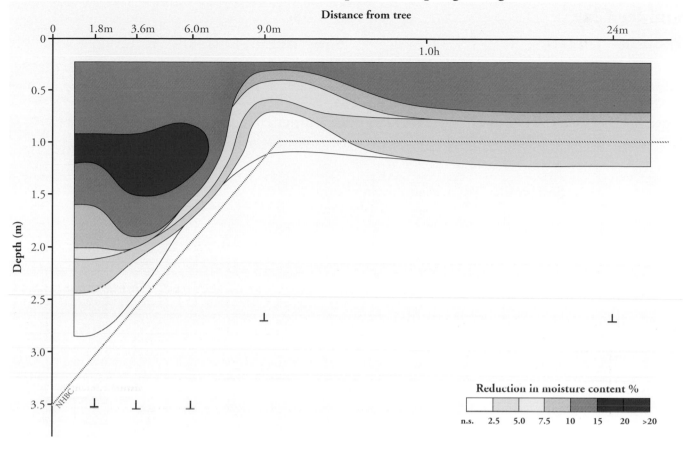

Soil moisture deficit on 1/11/91 compared with spring average

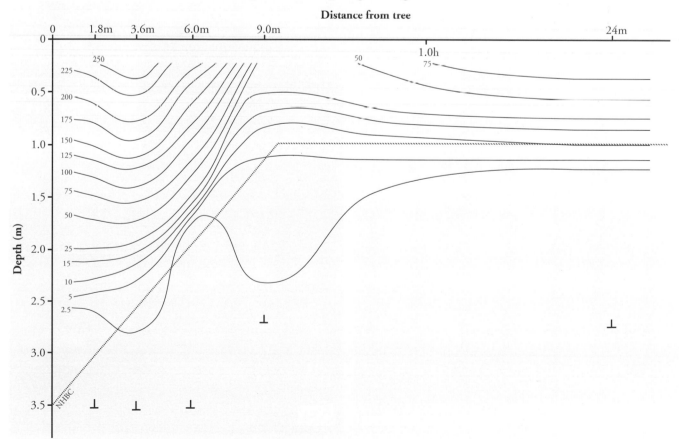

Leyland cypress
Boulder Clay

Location: The Leys,
Bletchley   Map ref: SP 864 346

Size: Height: 9m (1981); 7m (1994)
b.h.d.: 32cm (1992).

Current status: Intermittent readings still in progress.

Site: Western end of a row of cypresses in a private garden. The access holes are in a line to the NW of the tree in a 2m wide grass verge between the garden and a roadway.

Soil profile:	Distance from tree (m)	1.35	2.7	5.4	6.75	30.0
	x height (in 1981)	0.15	0.3	0.6	0.7	3.3

Soil classification tests:

Distance from tree (m)	2.7
Depth (m)	1.0
Plastic limit	19
Liquid limit	46.6
Plasticity index	28
% linear shrinkage	13.1

1981

1991

246

Seasonal fluctuations in soil moisture deficit at 1.0m depth

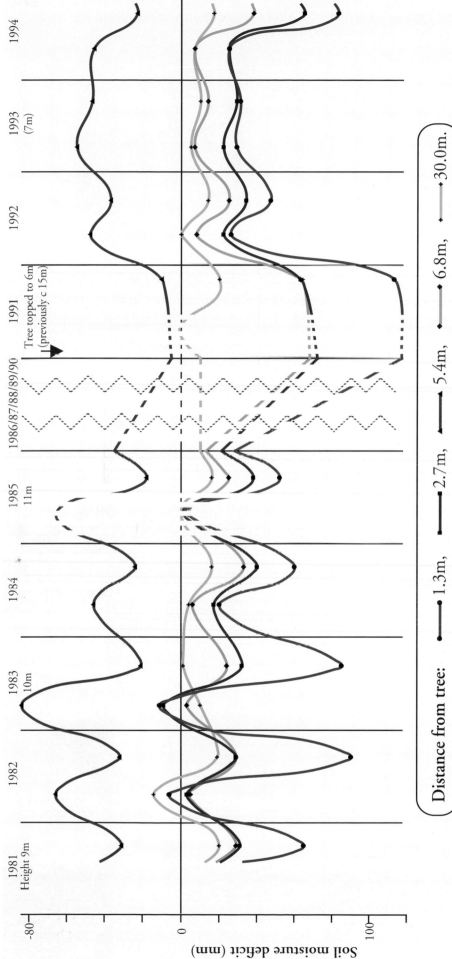

Distance from tree: ●— 1.3m, ■— 2.7m, ◆— 5.4m, ◆— 6.8m, ▲— 30.0m.

Comments: Considerable seasonal fluctuation at access tubes closest to the tree from 1981 to 1985. Absence of data in spring 1991 prevents detailed assessment of effects of topping the tree. However, the profiles on page 248 imply that a persistent deficit had established between 1985 and 1991, and it was this, rather than seasonal drying after the tree had been topped, which accounts for the soil moisture deficit in autumn 1991. Seasonal effects in the two years after topping (1992 and 1993) are considerably less, but fluctuations resume in 1994.

Maximum soil drying recorded at 1.35m from tree in various years

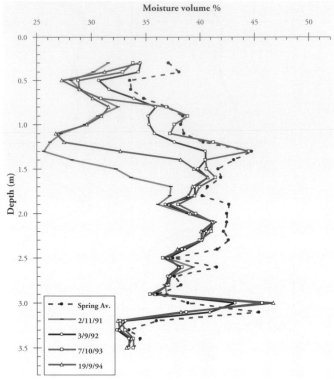

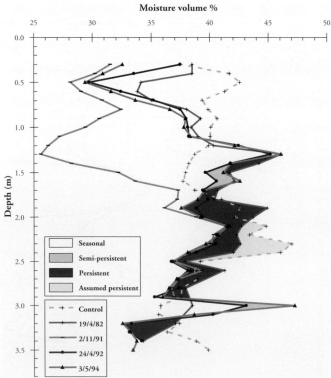

Comments: The anomalous reading at 1.9m depth in 1985 was confirmed as accurate; it may have been produced by an animal in close proximity to the tube.

Comments: Driest profile in 1991, but changes compared with the spring average suggest that a persistent deficit established between 1985 and 1991.

Spring soil moisture content profiles

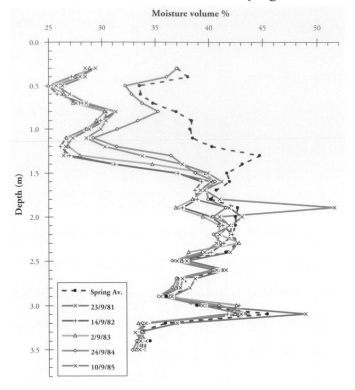

Comments: Considerable variation between the profiles.

Seasonal and persistent deficits 1.35m from tree

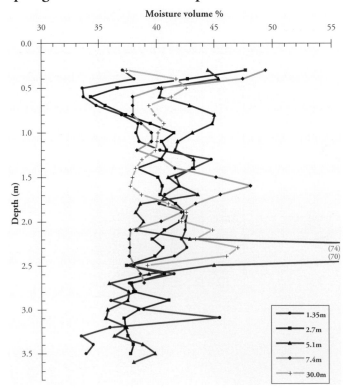

Comments: A considerably greater persistent deficit may have been present prior to the tree being topped.

Reduction in soil moisture content on 2/11/91 compared with spring average

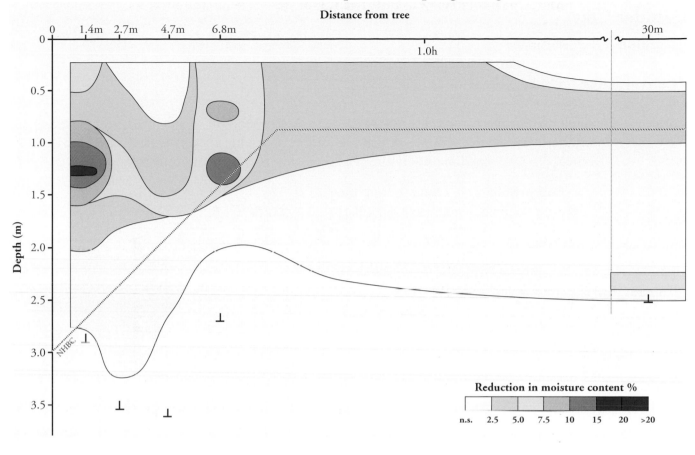

Soil moisture deficit on 2/11/91 compared with spring average

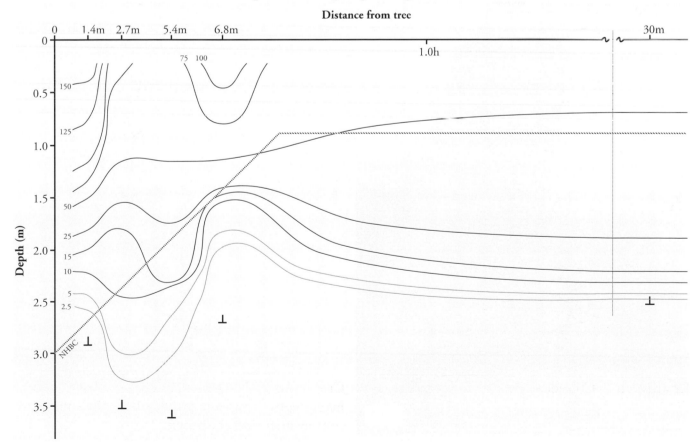

Leyland cypress
Boulder Clay

Location: Rickley Park,
Bletchley   Map ref: SP 858 337

Size: Height: 9m (1981); 7m (1991)

Current status: Readings discontinued since 1991

Site: A single tree in the corner of a private garden. Access tubes in a wide grass verge between the boundary fence and the kerb of a car park. The three closest holes are in a line north of the tree with the most distant access hole also in the grass verge, but is to the east of the tree.

Soil profile:	Distance from tree (m)	2.2	4.5	6.8	13.6
	x height (in 1981)	0.25	0.5	0.75	1.5

Soil classification tests:

Distance from tree (m)	2.2
Depth (m)	2.0
Plastic limit	19
Liquid limit	45
Plasticity index	26
% linear shrinkage	11.2

Spring soil moisture content profiles

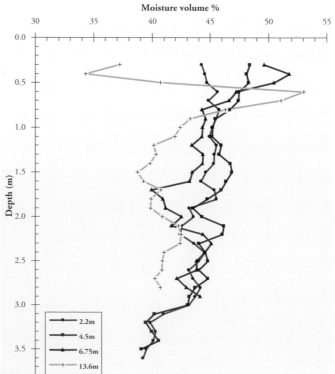

Comments: Variable profiles, with the control noticeably drier than the others.

Seasonal fluctuations in soil moisture deficit at 1.0m depth

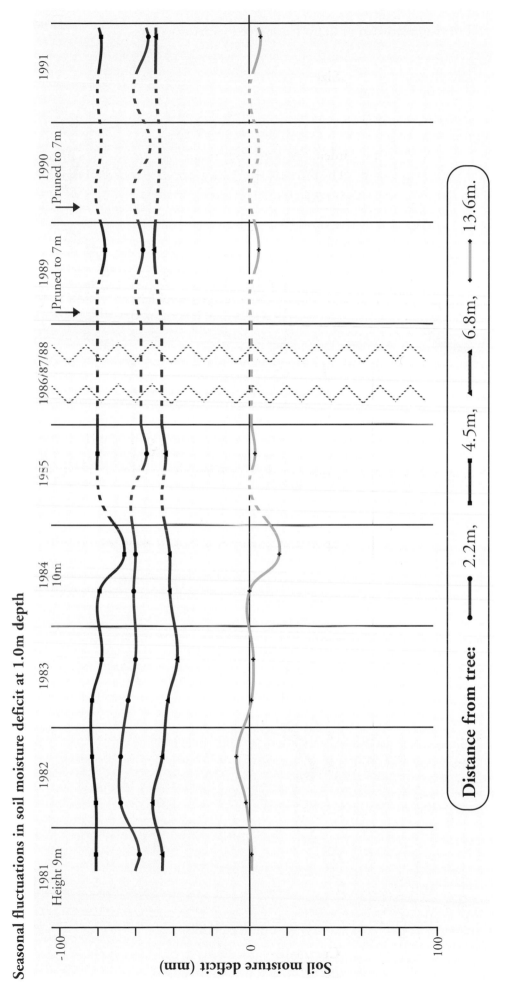

Distance from tree: •—— 2.2m, ■—— 4.5m, ▲—— 6.8m, +—— 13.6m.

Comments: Negligible seasonal drying from 1981 - 1985. In 1989 the owner topped the tree to 7m, and repeated this treatment in 1990. Readings in 1989 and 1991 confirmed that the extent of drying was still negligible.

Maximum soil drying recorded at 2.2m from tree in various years

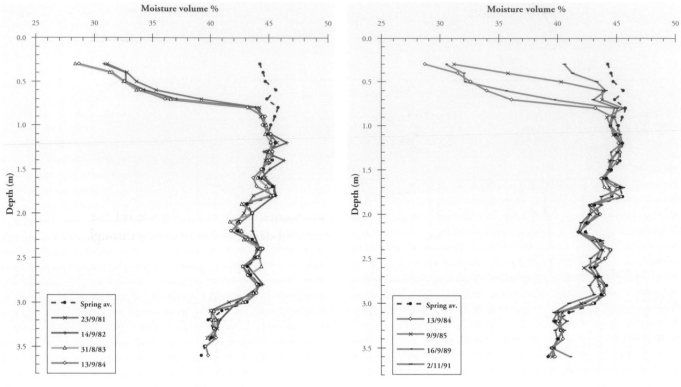

Comments: Very similar profiles each year.

Comments: Greater variation in profiles, probably because of partial recovery in autumn before readings taken.

Seasonal and persistent deficits 2.2m from tree

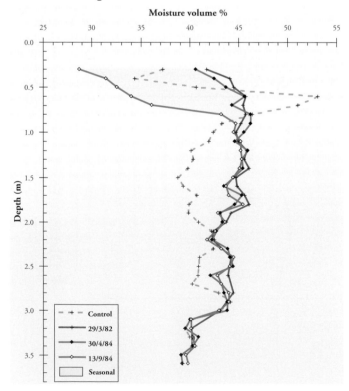

Comments: Slight seasonal drying, only extending to 1.1m.

Seasonal development of soil drying at 2.2m from tree during 1983

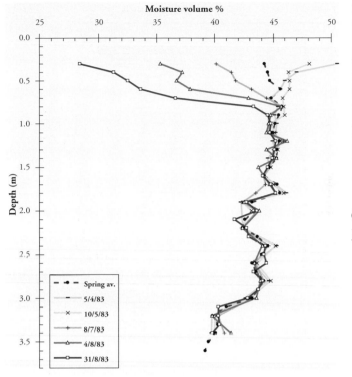

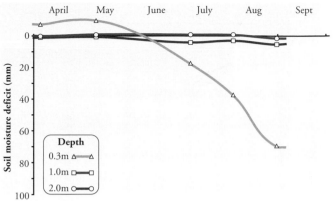

Comments: Drying in surface 1m does not start until May, and develops progressively through the summer

Seasonal development of soil drying at 2.2m from tree during 1984

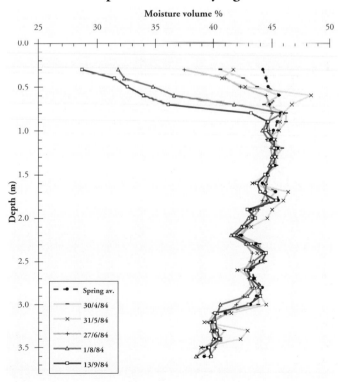

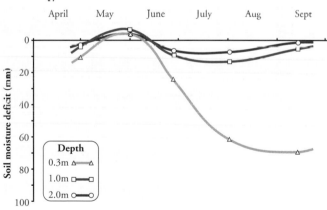

Comments: Similar development to 1983.

Reduction in soil moisture content on 13/9/84 compared with spring average

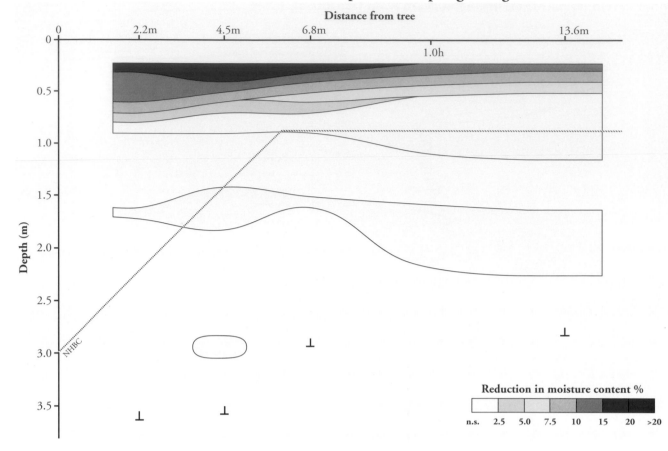

Reduction in moisture content %

n.s.   2.5   5.0   7.5   10   15   20   >20

Soil moisture deficit on 13/9/84 compared with spring average

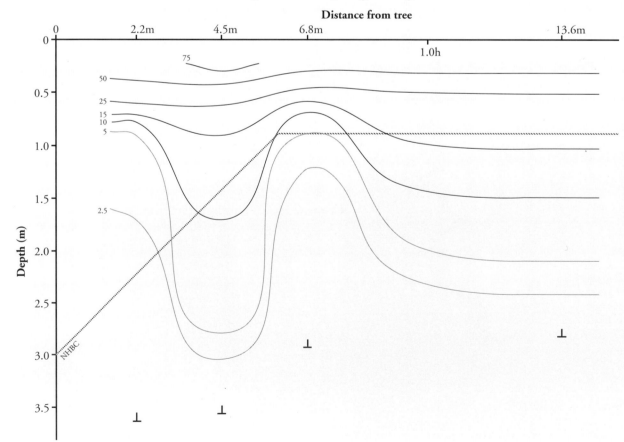

Plane
London Clay
Pruning experiment

Location: Cottenham Park,
Merton,   Map ref: TQ 227 698

Size: Heights - various.

Introduction.   12 plane trees on this site were used to observe the effects of differing pruning regimes on the patterns of soil drying.   The objective was to apply three differing pruning regimes plus an unpruned control, i.e. four treatments, with three replicates of each.

The ideal site for this purpose would have had 12 near identical trees, growing in uniform conditions on a suitable clay, sufficiently far apart so as not to interfere with each other, and which could be pruned as required. Perhaps not surprisingly a letter to all local authorities in London failed to identify such a site, but the London Borough of Merton were able to offer a site at Cottenham Park which met most of the requirements.

Tree location.   This site has a row of 7 similar trees near the southern edge of the Park, growing beside a peripheral path around the edge of a playing field (used for cricket and football), with the trees about 10m apart (Figure 15). The trees which, which had all been kept regularly pollarded in the past to a height of 5m, had been allowed to develop a larger crown and were each about 15 - 16m high in 1983. Adjacent pairs of these trees were pruned in similar fashion,

with the seventh tree heavily pruned and used as a spacer between the moderate and heavy pruning regimes. These trees are numbered 51 - 56. The two untreated control trees (numbered 49 and 50) are located on the north side of the park, in an area of mown grass between the peripheral path and a hard tennis court. They had a similar history of previous pollarding and regrowth, but had not regrown to quite the same size (height 13m). The restricted space prevented the use of a control access tube for these two trees.

The other four trees were located in the south east corner of the Park. The trees along the eastern boundary back onto the rear gardens of an adjacent terrace of housing, and as a result the trees had not been allowed to grow to the same size as trees 49 - 56. They had previously been kept heavily pollarded to a height of about 5m, but prior to 1983 had been allowed to grow to a height of 10 - 11m. Four of these trees were used with different treatments, with the intervening trees pruned in similar fashion; they are numbered 57 - 60.

The location of all of these trees is shown in the plan in Figure 16.

Figure 15
Part of row of plane trees along southern edge of Cottenham Park. Photograph taken just after start of pruning work.

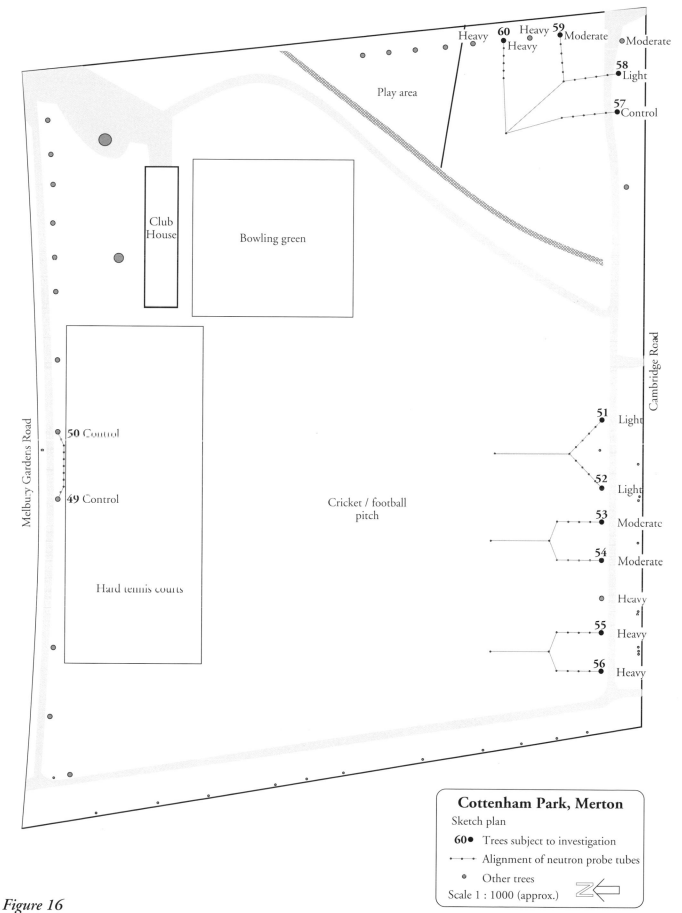

Figure 16

Location of trees and alignment of neutron probe access tubes in Cottenham Park

Access tubes. As there are so many trees in a small area, it was unnecessary for each to have its own control access tube. The four trees in the south east corner shared a single control tube; each of the three pairs along the southern boundary had a single control tube shared between the two adjacent trees. There was insufficient space for a control tube for trees 49 and 50. With this number of control tubes, the available funding allowed the insertion of additional tubes close to the trees, so that each tree had 5 tubes at varying distance in the close proximity. The most distant of these were shared between the adjacent trees along the southern boundary, and also shared for trees 49/50 and 58/59.

As the trees were going to be subject to varying intensity of pruning, the spacing of the access tubes was not related to the initial height of the trees (as applies to all of the other tree species). Instead, fixed spacing was used. For most of the trees, the five closest tubes are 3.0m apart (i.e. at 3, 6, 9, 12, and 15m from the tree), with the control 30m from the tree. This was reduced for those trees which would be subject to the heaviest pruning regime. For this reason they are 2.5m apart for trees 51/52 as it was anticipated that these would be subject to the heavy pruning; however, after installing the tubes it was requested that the heavy pruning should be applied to trees 55 and 56 at the other end of the row. The tubes are 2.5m apart for tree 59 (moderate pruning) and 2.0m apart for tree 60 (heavy). Lack of space dictated that they would be only 2.0m apart for the control trees 49/50.

The alignment and location of the access tubes is shown in Figure 16.

Soil conditions. The geological survey map correctly identifies that the subsoil in the locality should be London Clay. However, in this area of London, the clay tends to have a high sand content, and these conditions were encountered on this site, particularly near the surface. The deeper clay also tended to have a higher sand content than is typically encountered at the other sites on London Clay, which are generally in the north west suburbs.

Diagrams showing the soil conditions at the access tubes for all of the trees are shown on pages 266 to 267.

No soil classification tests were undertaken.

Soil moisture deficits at commencement.

The neutron probe tubes were inserted in the late summer of 1983, and readings were taken with the neutron probes at all of these tubes in September. It was subsequently discovered that one of the probes had a fault, and that all of

the readings taken with that instrument were unreliable. All of these erroneous readings are omitted in the results which are presented. This prevents the inclusion of diagrams showing the spatial pattern of soil drying in 1983. However, results obtained with the other instrument allow calculation of the soil moisture deficit at some of the locations, and these are included in the diagrams showing the seasonal fluctuations in soil moisture deficit.

Pruning of trees.

The pruning of the trees to the varying degrees of intensity was carried out during the first half of March 1984. The four treatments of control, light, moderate and heavy pruning correspond to approximately 0, 25%, 50% and 75% reduction in the crown of the trees. It involved lowering the height and spread of the branches; they were also thinned to reduce the density of shoots and to promote the correct future development of the crown. The work was carried out by a skilled tree surgeon, and should correspond to the standards of craftsmanship which can normally be achieved by a competent tree surgery crew.

The material which was cut from each tree was sub-divided into two categories:

a) young growth, up to 15mm diameter, which included approximately the 1-3 year old shoots.

b) larger branchwood (all wood greater than 15mm).

The amount of wood in each category for each tree was weighed; Figures 18 and 19 illustrate the categories of wood during this operation. The weight of prunings for each tree is shown in Figure 17.

Tree No.	Severity of pruning	Young growth	Branch wood
51	Light	40	63
52		38	64
53	Moderate	85	127
54		88	174
55	Heavy	208	578
56		198	633
58	Light	40	68
59	Moderate	102	147
60	Heavy	138	165

Figure 17

Weight of wood (kg) removed from trees during pruning.

Trees 49, 50 and 57 were the controls, which were untreated.

Figure 19

Some of the branchwood removed from tree 55 during pruning, ready for weighing.

Figure 18

Some of the young growth removed from tree 55 during pruning, bundled together and being weighed.

These results indicate a ratio of about 1:2:4 for the amount of both young growth and branch wood removed from the larger trees which were subject to the light:moderate:heavy regimes. On the smaller trees the amount of wood removed under the heavy regime (tree 60) appears to be disproportionately small, but the amount of branchwood remaining appeared to be appropriate for heavy pruning.

The 12 trees were photographed to illustrate their appearance before and after pruning; these photographs are included in the top two rows on pages 262 to 265. Photographs taken before pruning include a pole being held adjacent to the tree; this pole was 6.1m long, and helps to provide a scale for the pictures. The photographs taken after the pruning show the trees just as the buds were bursting; this helps to show the amount of active shoot growth which was developing.

The trees were allowed to regrow for two years; i.e. through the summers of 1984 and 1985. They were again all photographed just as they were coming into leaf in 1985. These photographs are included in the bottom row on pages 262 to 265, to show the amount of regrowth which had occurred during 1984.

Second cycle of pruning.

In spring 1986 the trees were again pruned. In this case the percentage of thinning/reduction was approximately 20%, 40% and 60%, for the light, moderate and heavy pruning regimes. No record was made of the amount of wood tissue removed.

Subsequent tree management.

After 1986 the trees in the south east corner of the Park (trees 57 to 60 and the adjacent trees outside the experiment) were becoming the subject of complaints about shading by adjacent residents. All of the trees were heavily pruned by a similar amount, destroying the differential which had been developing. Further monitoring in proximity to these trees was therefore discontinued.

The trees 51 to 56 along the southern boundary of the park were all reduced by about 25% at the beginning of 1992.

The two control trees (49 and 50) were completely pollarded at the beginning of 1994, removing all of the branches back to the trunk at the original pollard point at 5m (Figure 20, page 298).

Monitoring readings.

Readings (at all of the access tubes for the tree) were taken:-

i) for all of the trees in autumn 1983, prior to any pruning. As previously noted, one of the neutron probes was faulty, giving erroneous readings for all of the access tubes for which it was used.

ii) for all of the trees (49 to 60) in the spring of 1984 and 1985, and in the autumn of 1984, 1985 and 1986.

ii) on trees 49 to 56 in the autumn of 1989.

This finished monitoring of the effects of pruning. However the readings were continued on trees 51 and 52, in autumn 1991, and in spring and autumn of 1992, 1993, and 1994, to determine any long-term changes in a manner similar to all of the other tree species.

On trees 49 and 50, readings were taken in autumn 1994 after they had been pollarded.

Presentation of results.

The following information is presented on subsequent pages: **Pages**

Trees 51 and 52.
    Although subject to light pruning, these trees are used to present general details on plane trees, similar to that presented for all of the other species in Volume 2. This includes:

Trees 49 to 56. Effects of pruning.

Trees 57 to 60. Effects of pruning.

Tree 49 (control)   Tree 50 (control)   Tree 51 (light)

1984, before pruning

1984, bud burst after pruning

1985, bud burst

Tree 52 (light)   **Tree 53 (moderate)**   **Tree 54 (moderate)**

1984, before pruning

1984, bud burst after pruning

1985, bud burst

Tree 55 (heavy)	Tree 56 (heavy)	Tree 57 (control)

1984, before pruning

1984, bud burst after pruning

1985, bud burst

Tree 58 (light) **Tree 59 (moderate)** **Tree 60 (heavy)**

1984, before pruning

1984, bud burst after pruning

1985, bud burst

Plane trees - Soil profiles

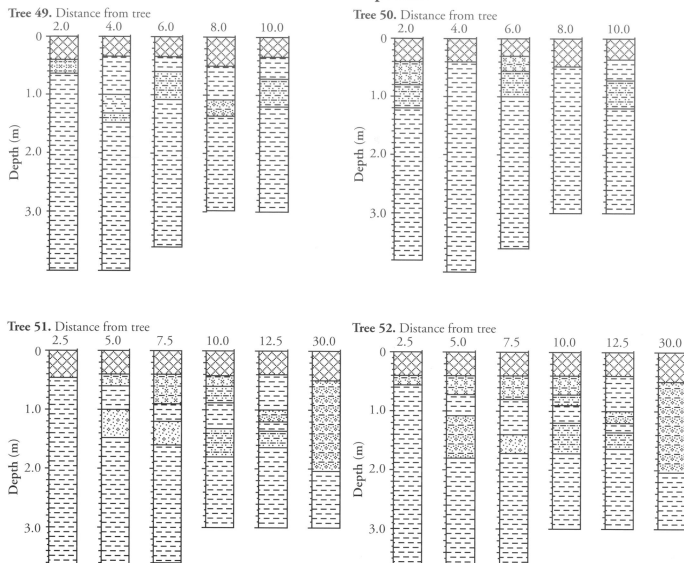

Tree 49. Distance from tree

2.0   4.0   6.0   8.0   10.0

Depth (m)

Tree 50. Distance from tree

2.0   4.0   6.0   8.0   10.0

Depth (m)

Tree 51. Distance from tree

2.5   5.0   7.5   10.0   12.5   30.0

Depth (m)

Tree 52. Distance from tree

2.5   5.0   7.5   10.0   12.5   30.0

Depth (m)

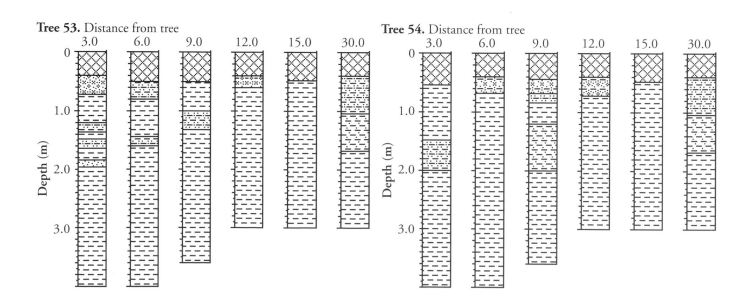

Tree 53. Distance from tree

3.0   6.0   9.0   12.0   15.0   30.0

Depth (m)

Tree 54. Distance from tree

3.0   6.0   9.0   12.0   15.0   30.0

Depth (m)

Plane trees - Soil profiles

Tree 55. Distance from tree

Tree 56. Distance from tree

Tree 57. Distance from tree

Tree 58. Distance from tree

Tree 59. Distance from tree

Tree 60. Distance from tree

Plane
London Clay

Spring soil moisture content profiles

Seasonal (and persistent) deficits 2.5m from tree

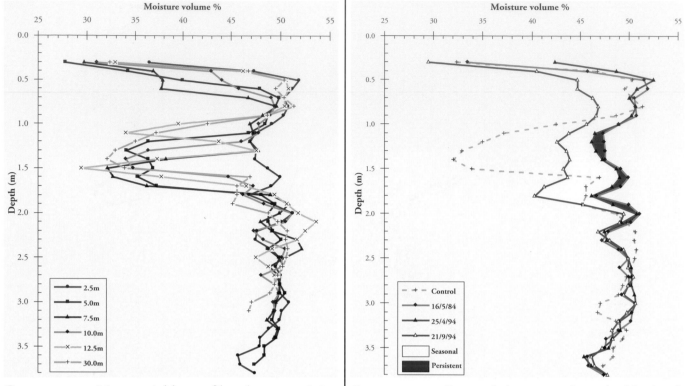

Comments: Very variable profiles down to 2.0m depth in the sandy clay.

Comments: Seasonal drying, with negligible development of a persistent deficit.

Maximum soil drying recorded at 2.5m from tree in various years

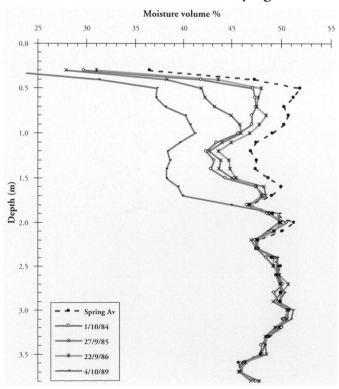

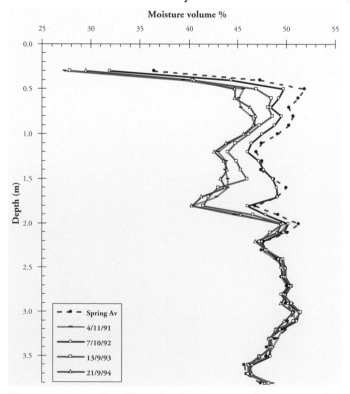

Comments: Variable profiles, with least drying in 1984 and 1986, i.e. after light pruning.

Comments: Profiles similar, except for 1992 after pruning and to a lesser extent 1993.

Plane
London Clay

Spring soil moisture content profiles

Seasonal (and persistent) deficits 2.5m from tree

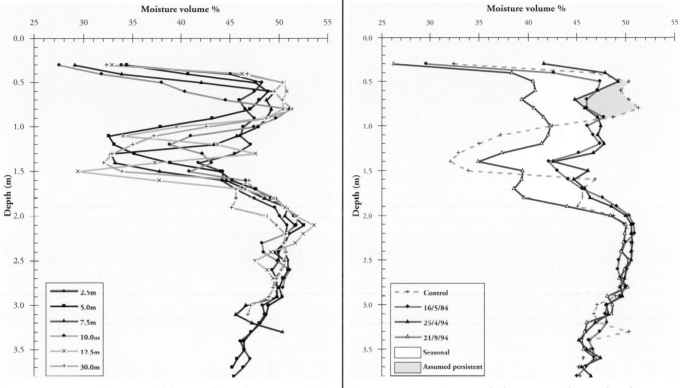

Comments: Very variable profiles down to 1.7m depth in the sandy clay.

Comments: Seasonal drying, with no development of a persistent deficit.

Maximum soil drying recorded at 2.5m from tree in various years

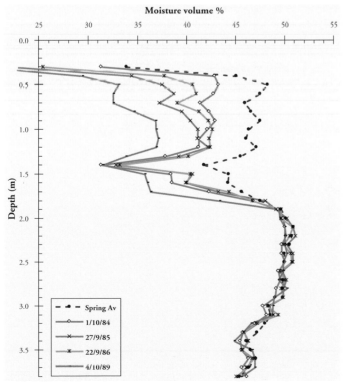

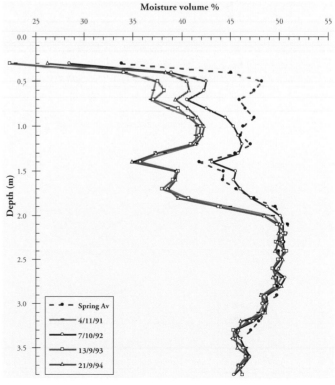

Comments: Variable profiles, with least drying in 1984 and 1986, i.e. after light pruning.

Comments: Profiles similar, except for 1992 after pruning.

Seasonal fluctuations in soil moisture deficit at 1.0m depth

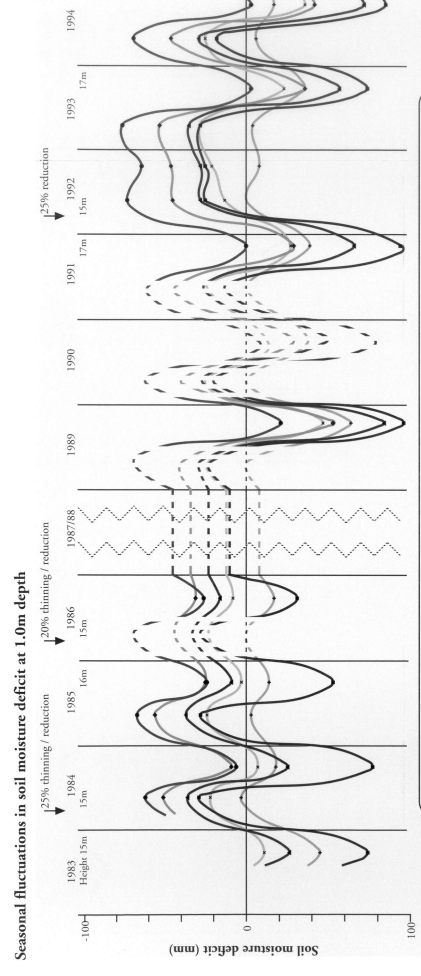

Distance from tree: 2.5m, 5.0m, 7.5m, 10.0m, × 12.5m, 30.0m.

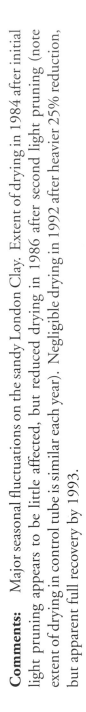

Tree 51
Plane
London Clay

Comments: Major seasonal fluctuations on the sandy London Clay. Extent of drying in 1984 after initial light pruning appears to be little affected, but reduced drying in 1986 after second light pruning (note extent of drying in control tube is similar each year). Negligible drying in 1992 after heavier 25% reduction, but apparent full recovery by 1993.

Tree 52
Plane
London Clay

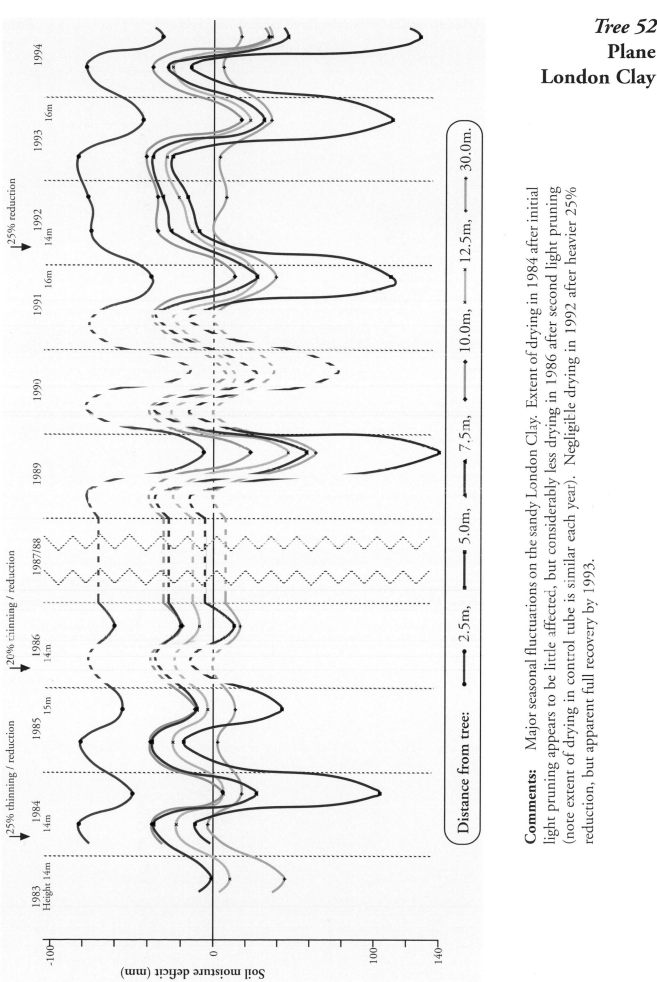

Seasonal fluctuations in soil moisture deficit at 1.0m depth

Distance from tree: 2.5m, 5.0m, 7.5m, 10.0m, 12.5m, 30.0m.

Comments: Major seasonal fluctuations on the sandy London Clay. Extent of drying in 1984 after initial light pruning appears to be little affected, but considerably less drying in 1986 after second light pruning (note extent of drying in control tube is similar each year). Negligible drying in 1992 after heavier 25% reduction, but apparent full recovery by 1993.

Reduction in soil moisture content on 21/9/94 compared with spring average

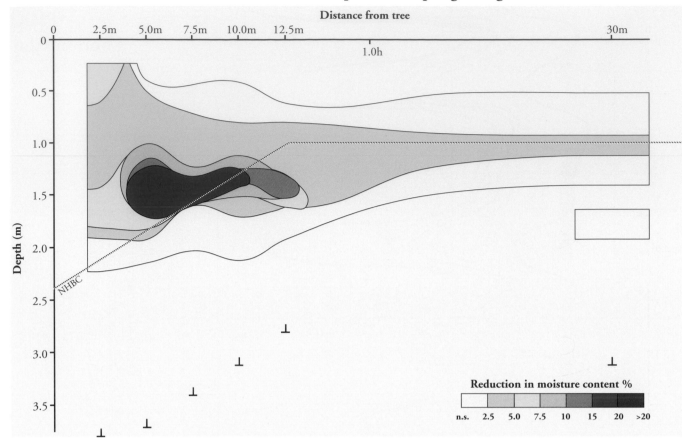

Soil moisture deficit on 21/9/94 compared with spring average

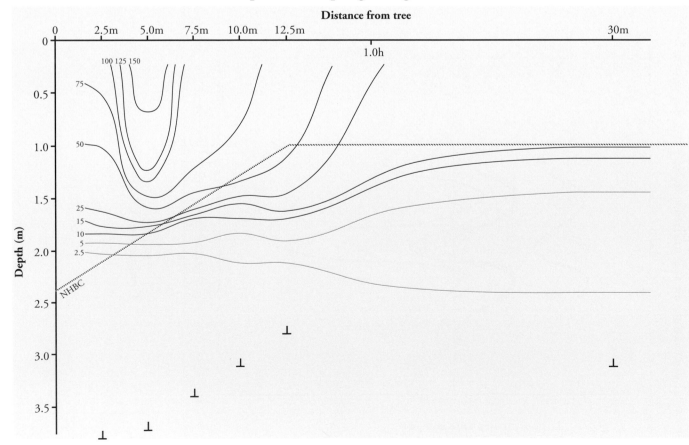

Reduction in soil moisture content on 21/9/94 compared with spring average

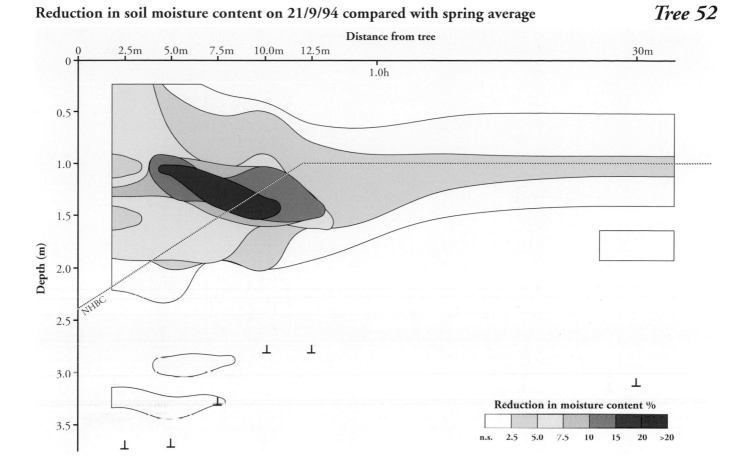

Soil moisture deficit on 21/9/94 compared with spring average

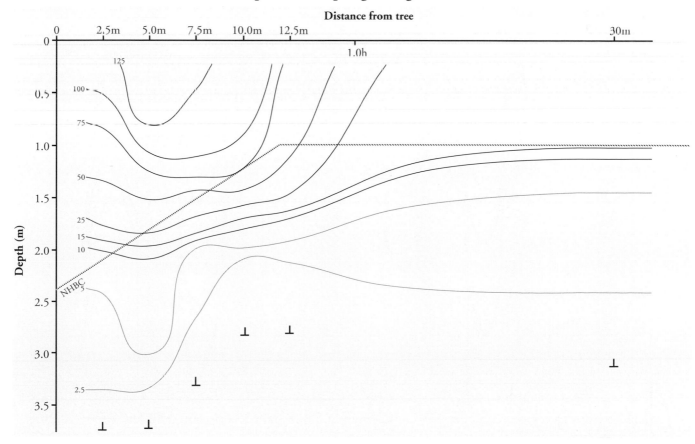

Seasonal fluctuations in soil moisture deficit at 1.0m depth

Control (Trees 49/50)

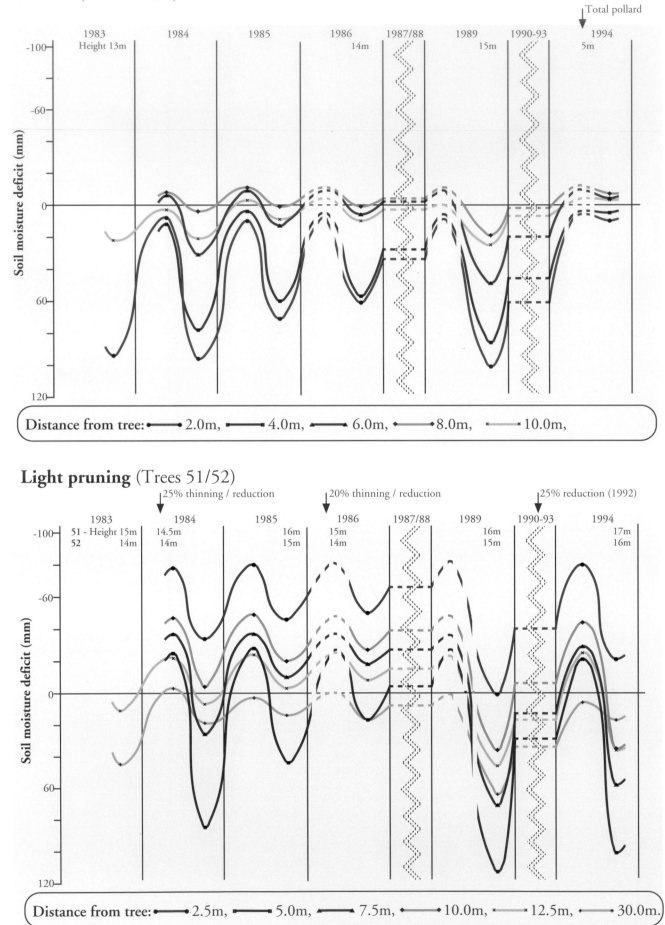

Distance from tree: 2.0m, 4.0m, 6.0m, 8.0m, 10.0m,

Light pruning (Trees 51/52)

Distance from tree: 2.5m, 5.0m, 7.5m, 10.0m, 12.5m, 30.0m.

Seasonal fluctuations in soil moisture deficit at 1.0m depth

Moderate pruning (Trees 53/54)

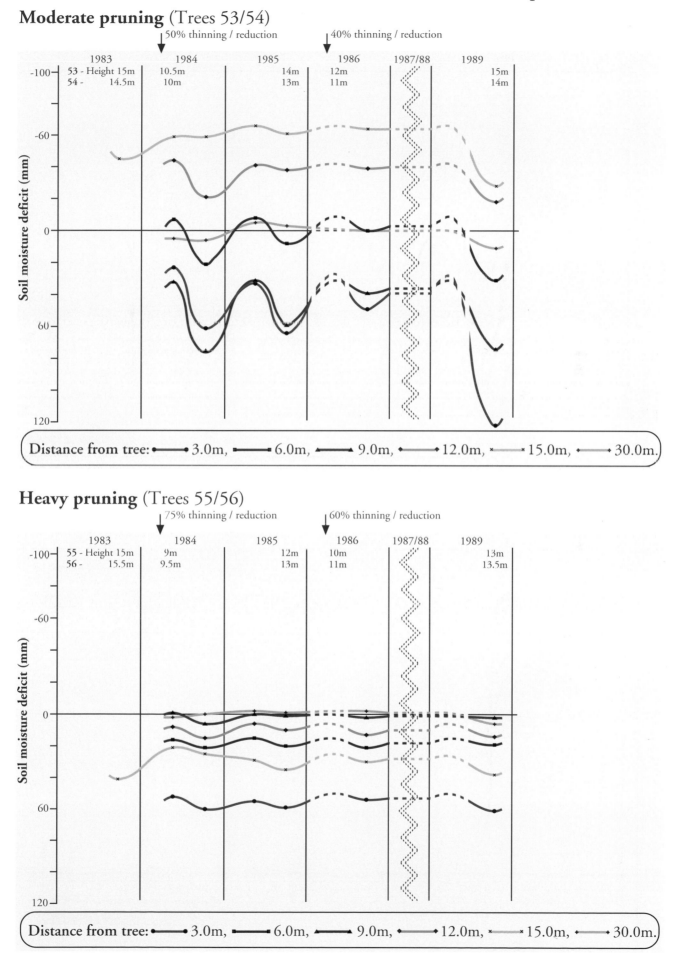

50% thinning / reduction

40% thinning / reduction

Distance from tree: ●——● 3.0m, ■——■ 6.0m, ▲——▲ 9.0m, ◆——◆ 12.0m, ×——× 15.0m, +——+ 30.0m.

Heavy pruning (Trees 55/56)

75% thinning / reduction

60% thinning / reduction

Distance from tree: ●——● 3.0m, ■——■ 6.0m, ▲——▲ 9.0m, ◆——◆ 12.0m, ×——× 15.0m, +——+ 30.0m.

Reduction in soil moisture content in September 1984 (29-30th) compared with spring average

Control (Trees 49/50)

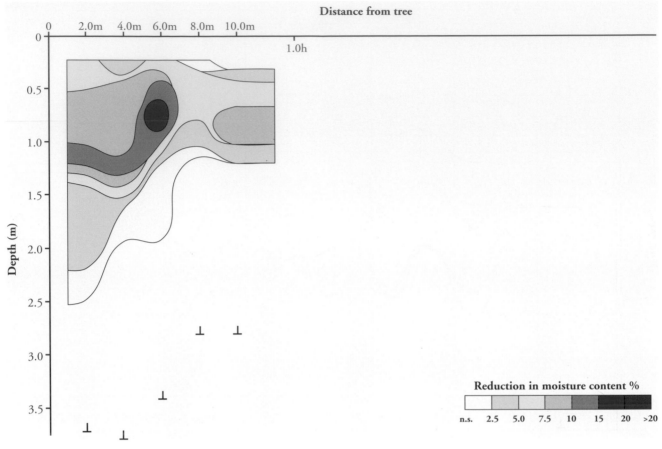

Light pruning (Trees 51/52)

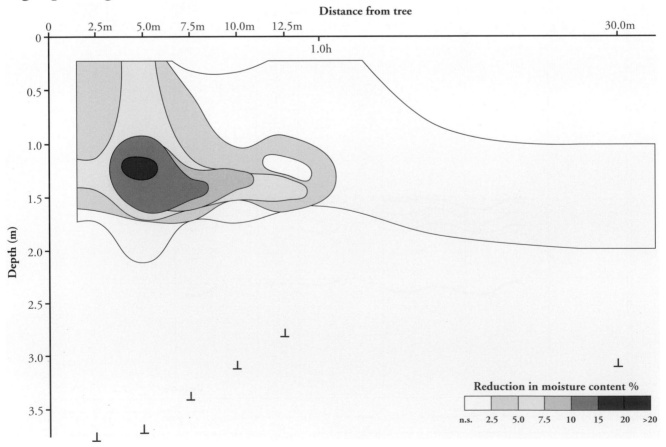

Reduction in soil moisture content in September 1984 (29-30th) compared with spring average

Moderate pruning (Trees 53/54)

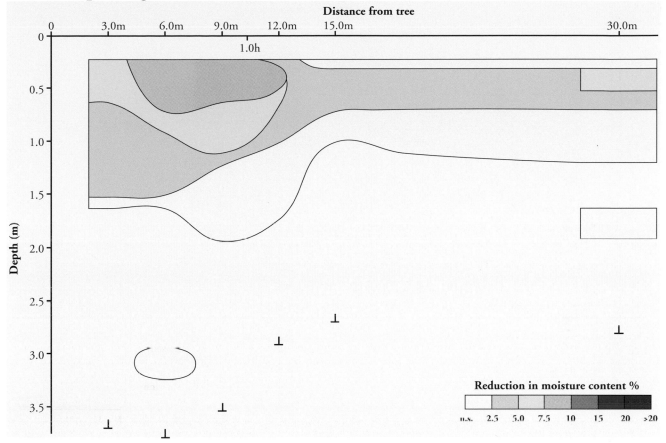

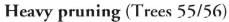

Heavy pruning (Trees 55/56)

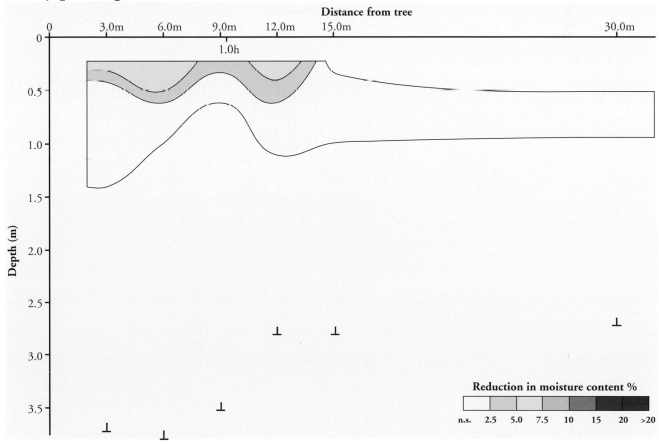

Soil moisture deficit in September 1984 (29-30th) compared with spring average

Control (Trees 49/50)

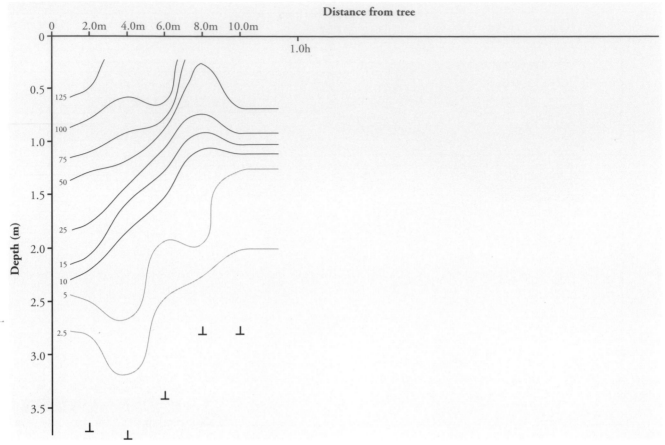

Light pruning (Trees 51/52)

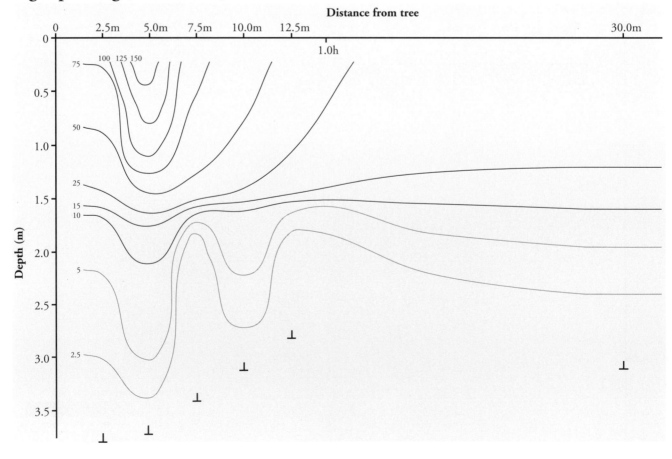

Soil moisture deficit in September 1984 (29-30th) compared with spring average

Moderate pruning (Trees 53/54)

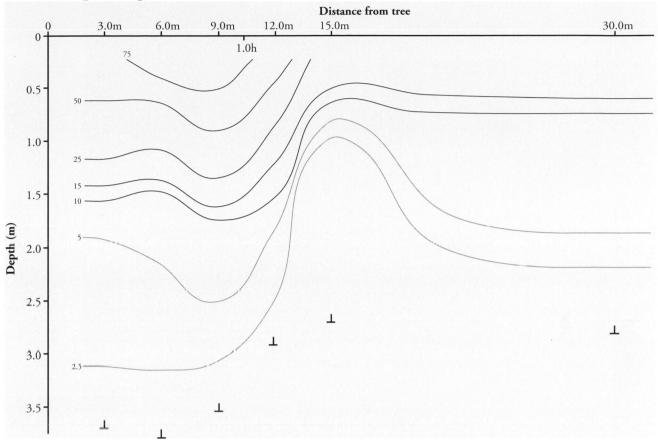

Heavy pruning (Trees 55/56)

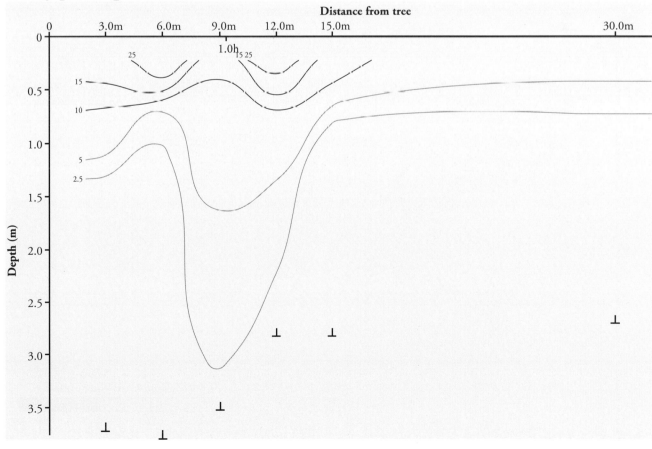

Reduction in soil moisture content in September 1986 (22-23rd) compared with spring average

Control (Trees 49/50)

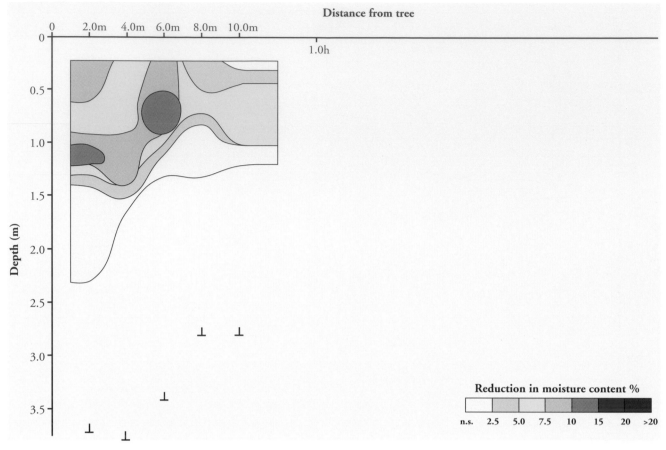

Light pruning (Trees 51/52)

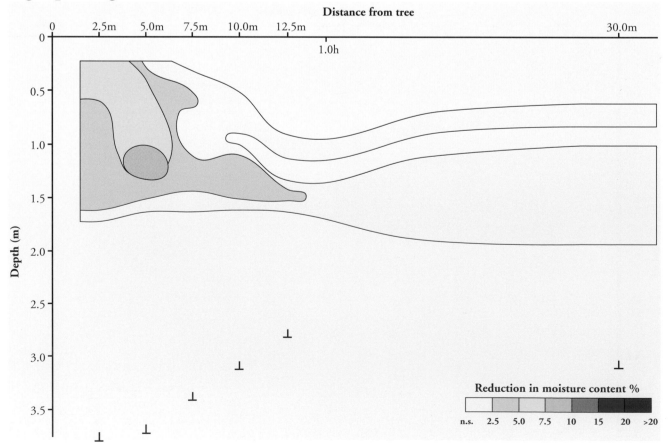

Reduction in soil moisture content in September 1986 (22-23rd) compared with spring average

Moderate pruning (Trees 53/54)

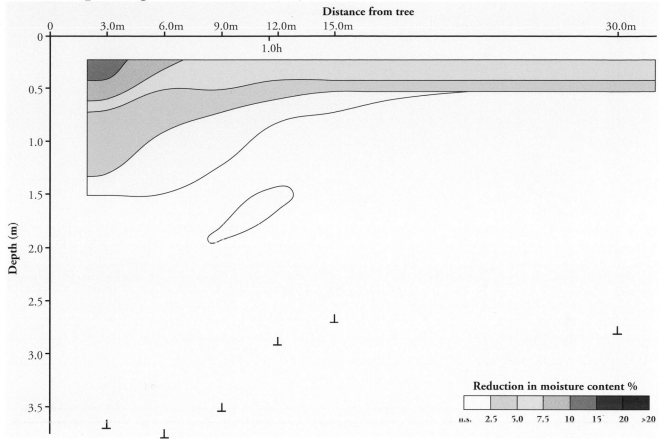

Heavy pruning (Trees 55/56)

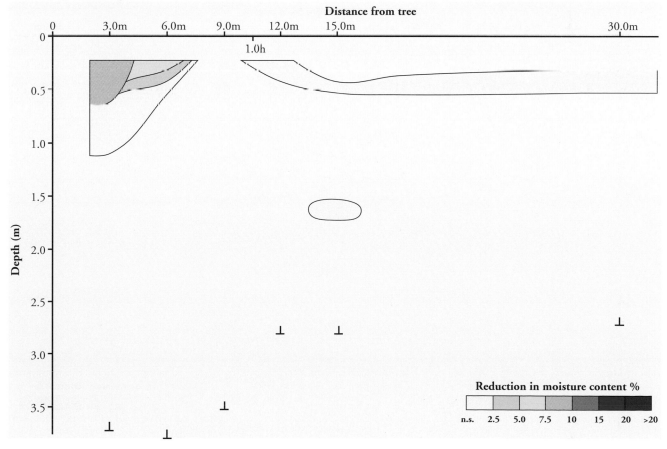

Soil moisture deficit in September 1986 (22-23rd) compared with spring average

Control (Trees 49/50)

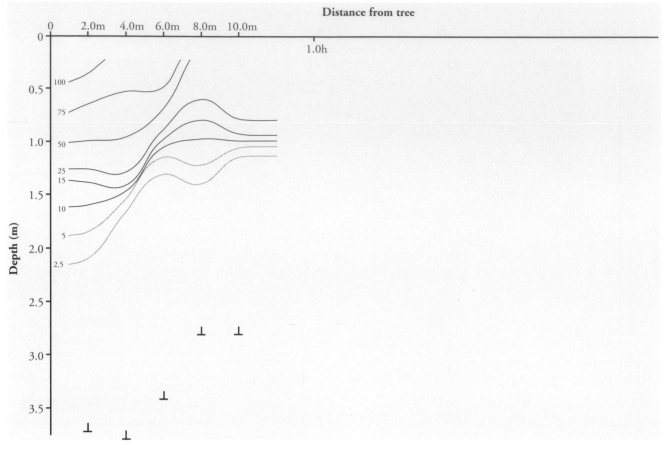

Light pruning (Trees 51/52)

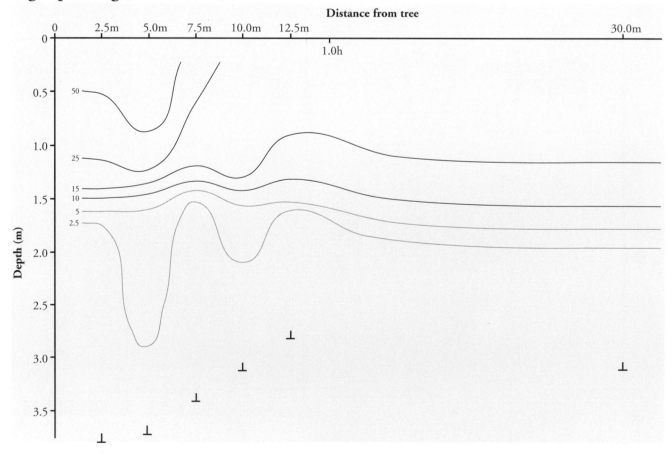

Soil moisture deficit in September 1986 (22-23rd) compared with spring average

Moderate pruning (Trees 53/54)

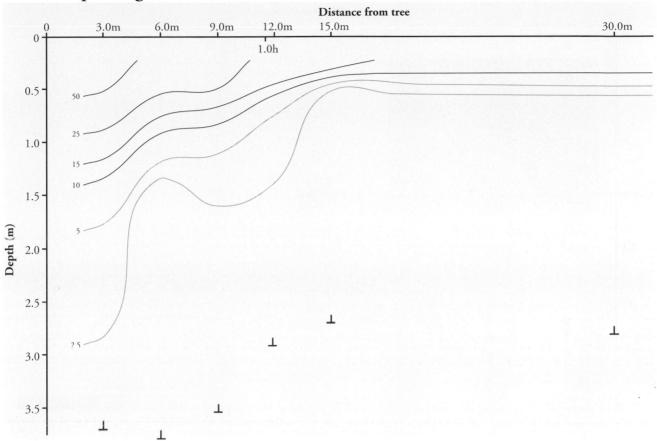

Heavy pruning (Trees 55/56)

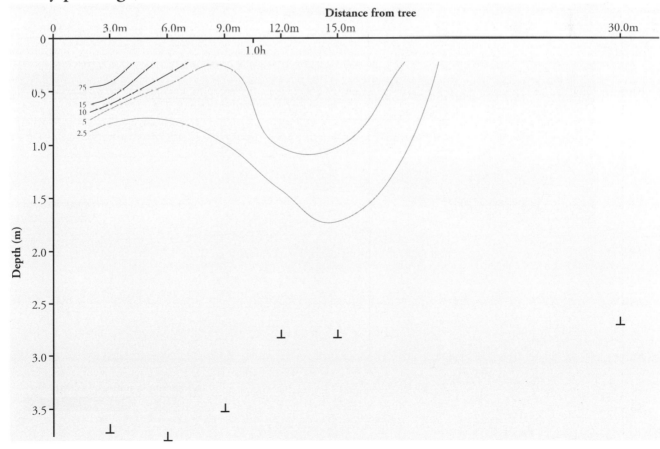

Reduction in soil moisture content in October 1989 (2-3rd) compared with spring average

Control (Trees 49/50)

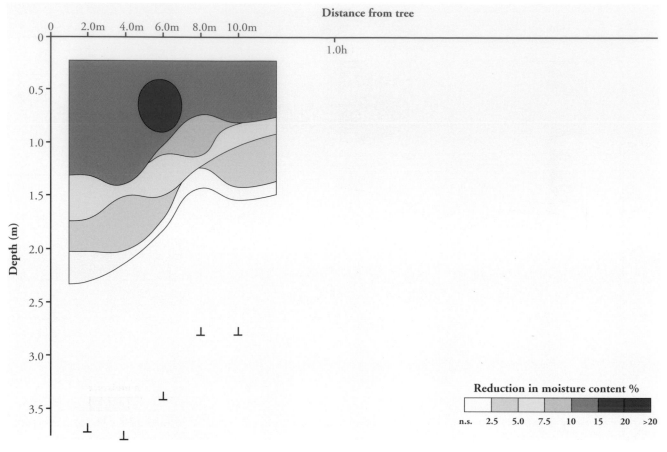

Light pruning (Trees 51/52)

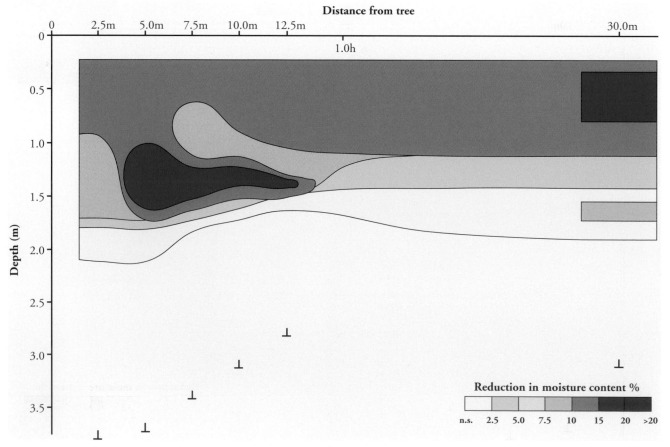

Reduction in soil moisture content in October 1989 (2-3rd) compared with spring average

Moderate pruning (Trees 53/54)

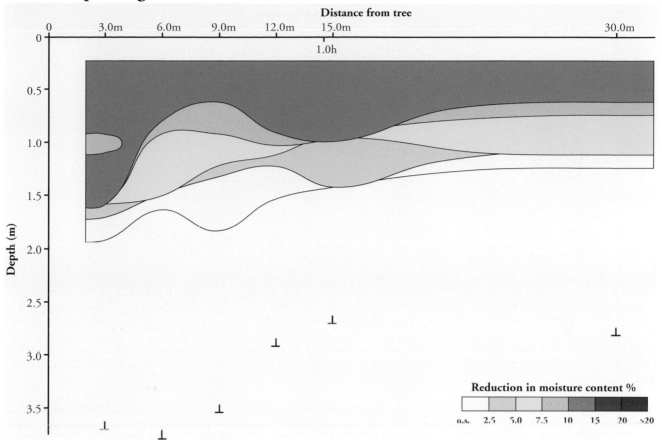

Heavy pruning (Trees 55/56)

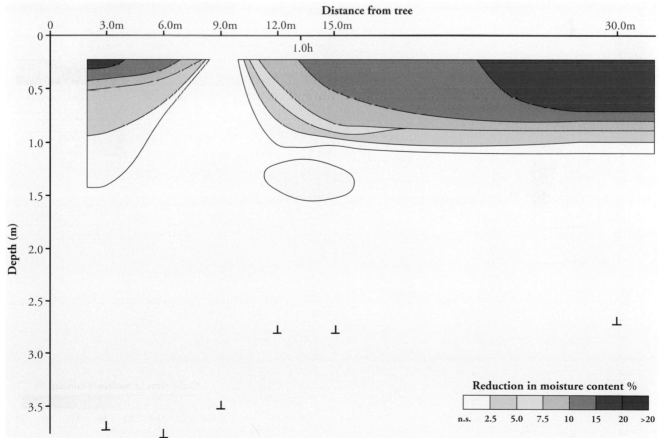

Soil moisture deficit in October 1989 (2-3rd) compared with spring average

Control (Trees 49/50)

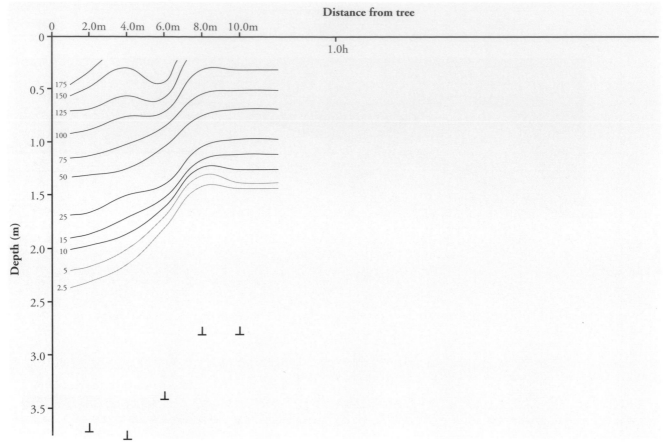

Light pruning (Trees 51/52)

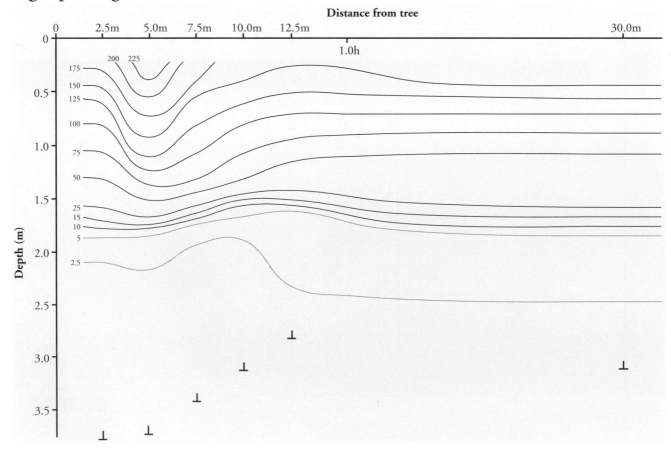

Soil moisture deficit in October 1989 (2-3rd) compared with spring average

Moderate pruning (Trees 53/54)

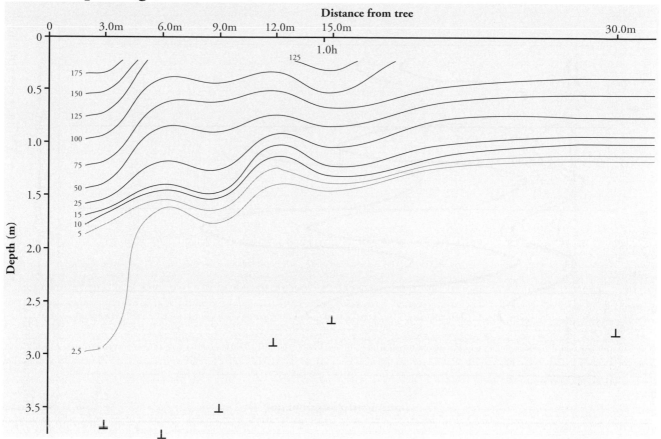

Heavy pruning (Trees 55/56)

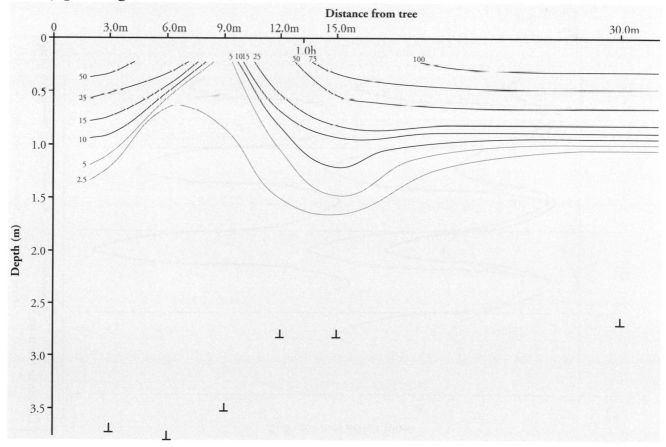

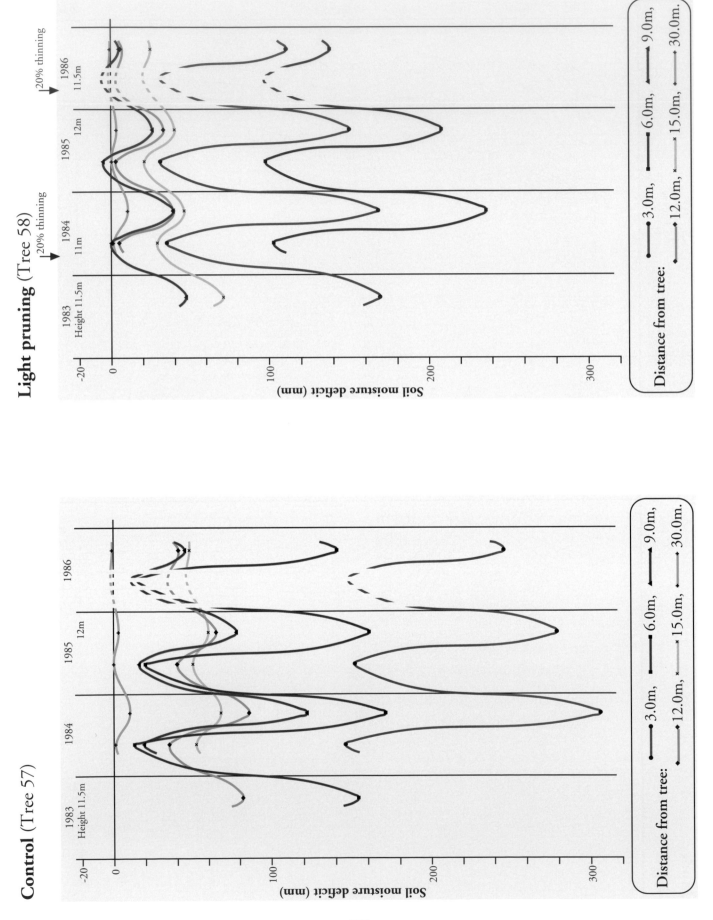

Seasonal fluctuations in soil moisture deficit at 1.0m depth

Seasonal fluctuations in soil moisture deficit at 1.0m depth

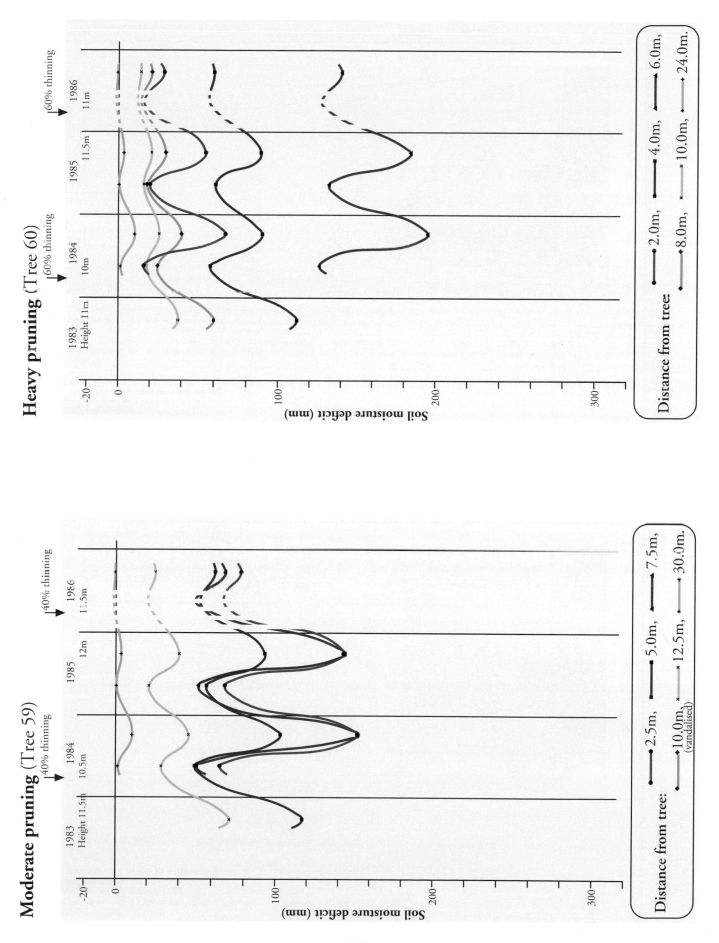

Reduction in soil moisture content in September 1984 (27-28th) compared with spring average

Control (Tree 57)

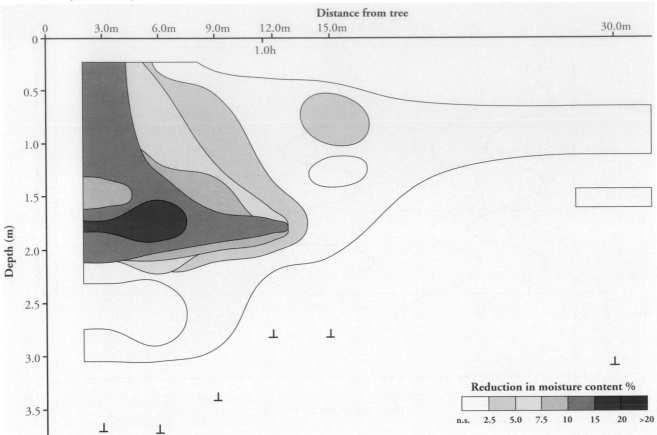

Light pruning (Tree 58)

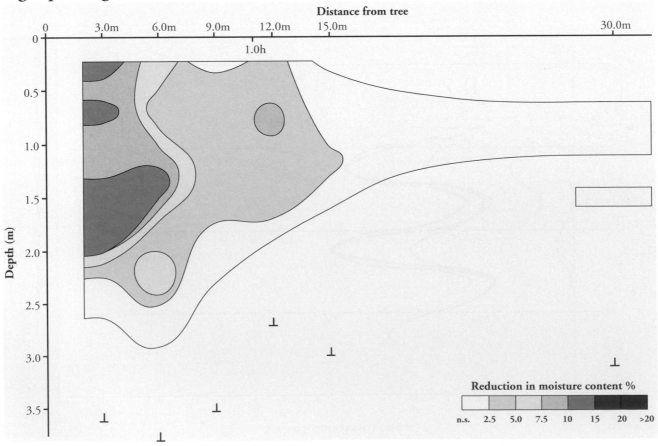

Reduction in soil moisture content in September 1984 (27-28th) compared with spring average

Moderate pruning (Tree 59)

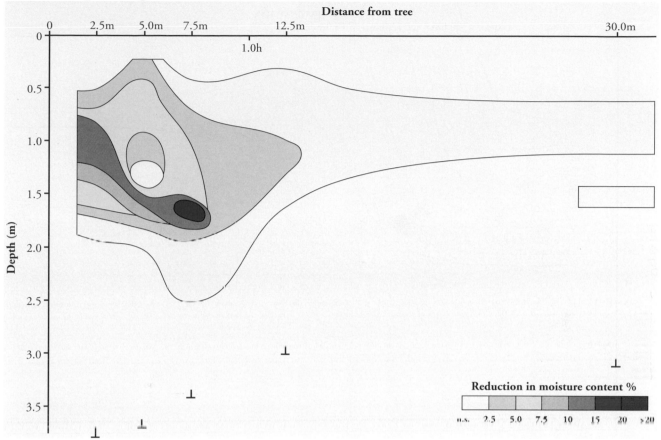

Heavy pruning (Tree 60)

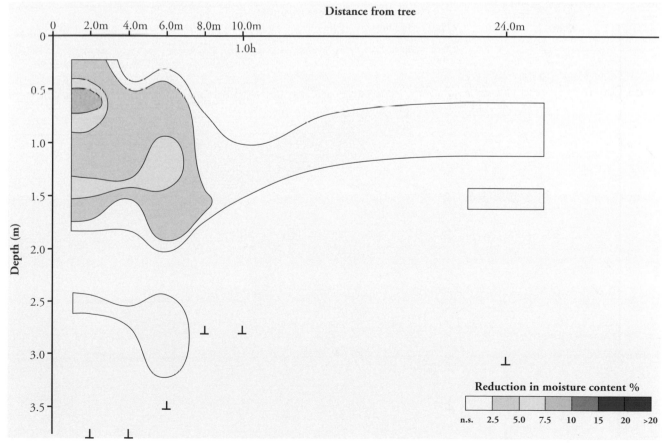

Soil moisture deficit in September 1984 (27-28th) compared with spring average

Control (Tree 58)

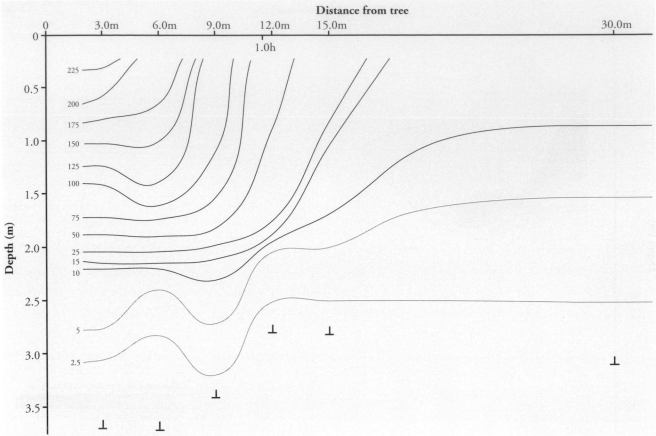

Light pruning (Tree 58)

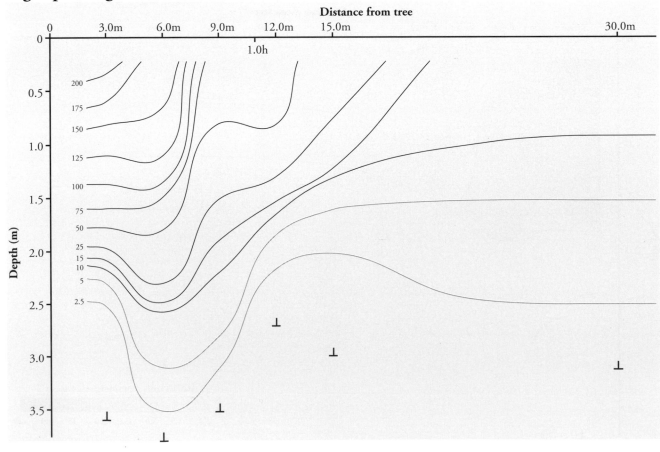

Soil moisture deficit in September 1984 (27-28th) compared with spring average

Moderate pruning (Tree 59)

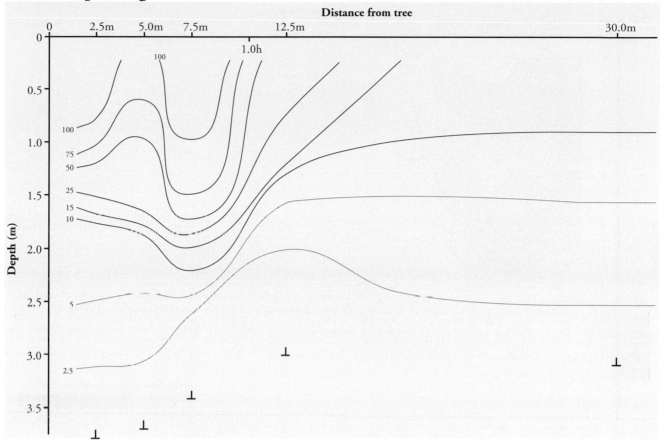

Heavy pruning (Tree 60)

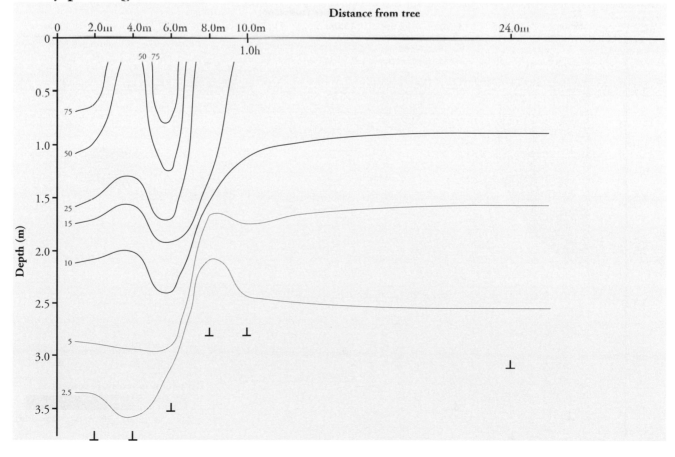

Reduction in soil moisture content in September 1986 (22-23rd) compared with spring average

Control (Tree 57)

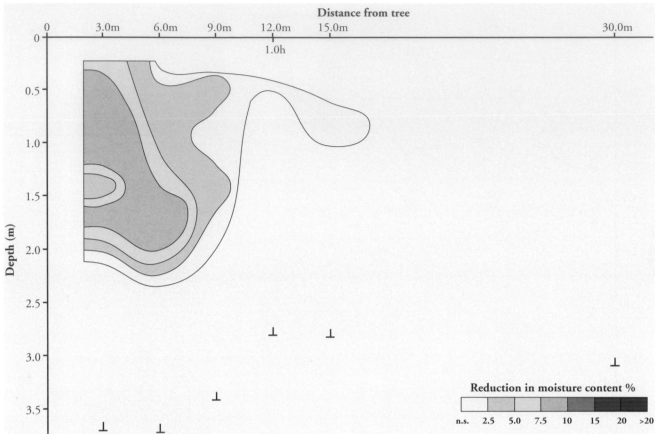

Light pruning (Tree 58)

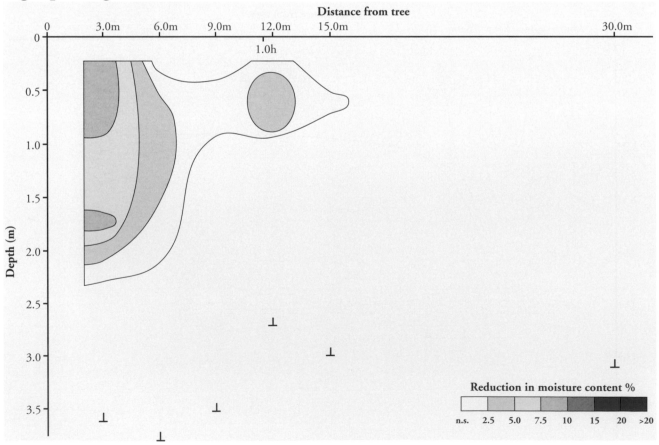

Reduction in soil moisture content in September 1986 (22-23rd) compared with spring average

Moderate pruning (Tree 59)

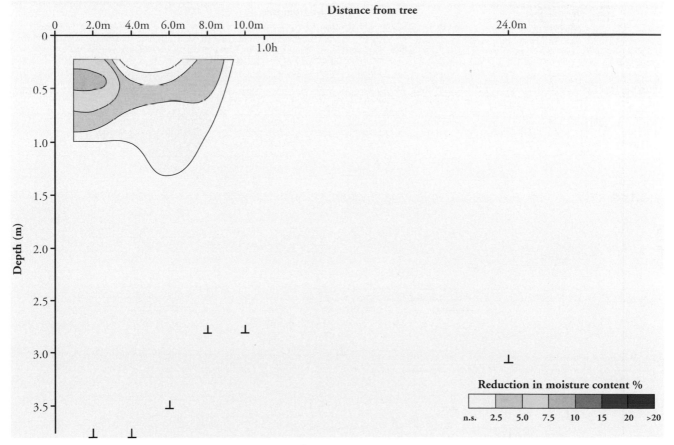

Heavy pruning (Tree 60)

Soil moisture deficit in September 1986 (22-23rd) compared with spring average

Control (Tree 57)

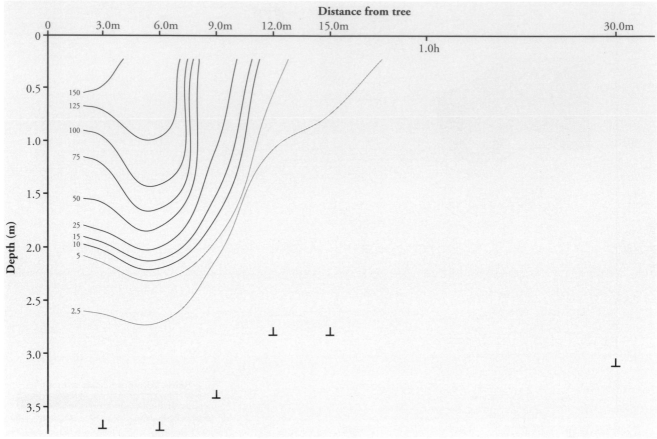

Light pruning (Tree 58)

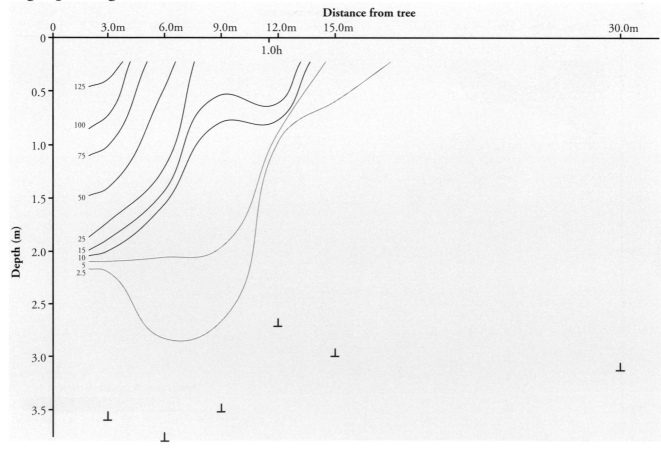

Soil moisture deficit in September 1986 (22-23rd) compared with spring average

Moderate pruning (Tree 59)

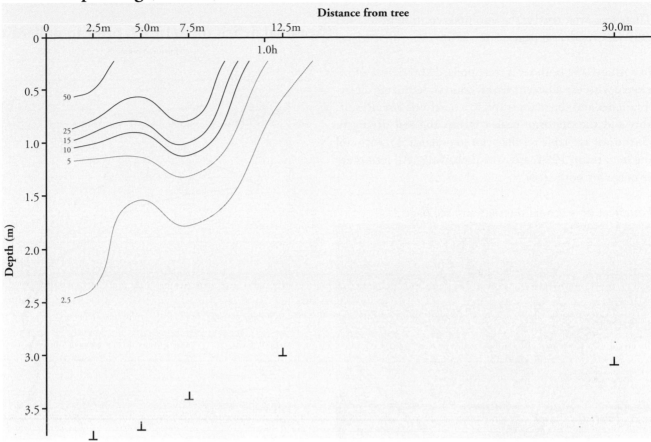

Heavy pruning (Tree 60)

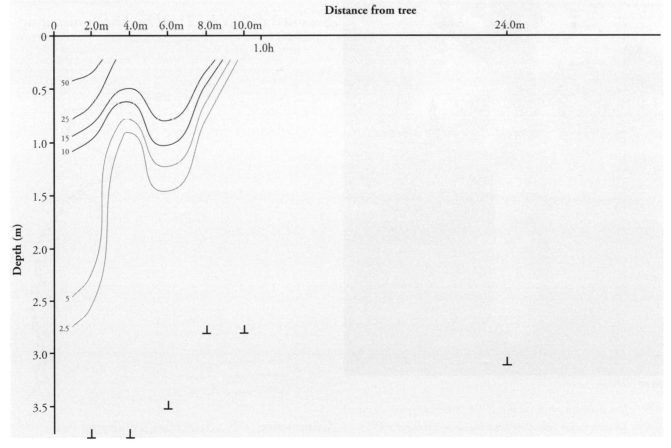

Plane (effect of pollarding) (Trees 49 - 50)
London Clay

These trees were used as the unpruned controls from 1983 to 1989 (see results on pages 274 - 286).

In spring 1994 both trees were pollarded (because of interference with the adjacent tennis courts), removing all lateral branches and the main trunk to a height of 5m. Results on this and the opposite page contrast the soil drying in 1989 (the last available results prior to pollarding), with soil drying in autumn 1994, after the pollarding. All results are the average for both trees.

For effect on seasonal fluctuations, see page 274.

Figure 20

Tree 50 after pollarding in spring 1994, and with one season of regrowth (photograph taken at bud burst in spring 1995).

Seasonal deficit on 4/10/89, prior to pollarding

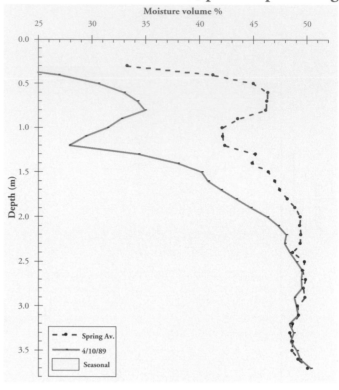

Seasonal deficit on 21/9/94, after pollarding

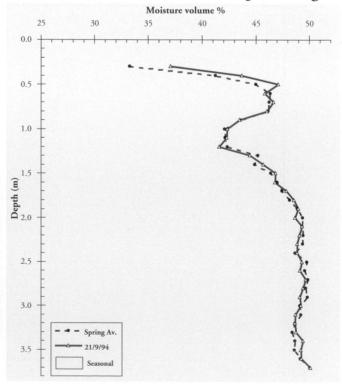

Comments: No detectable soil drying

298

Reduction in soil moisture content on 4/10/89, prior to pollarding, compared with spring average

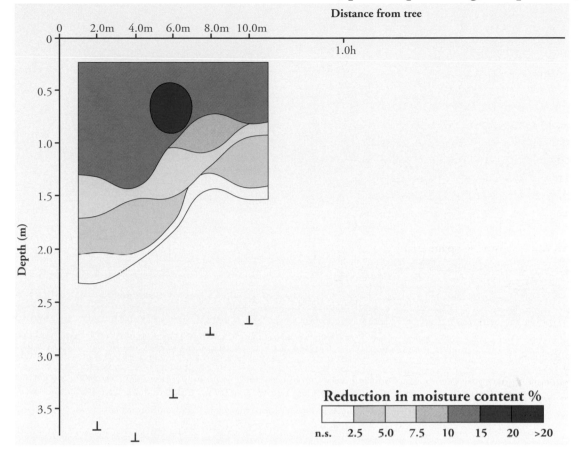

Reduction in soil moisture content on 21/9/94, after pollarding, compared with spring average

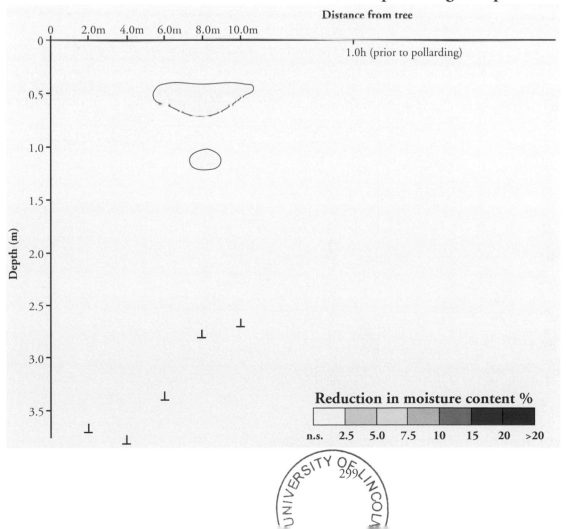